Very good

LIFE SERIES

On Eagles' Wings

Level 12
Seventh-day Adventist Readers

Patricia A. Habada

Gary B. Swanson

Sally J. McMillan

LuWana J. Kumalae

Acknowledgments

Grateful acknowledgment is made to the following:

Ginn and Company for assistance in the preparation of this book; and to Rosly Walter, Ginn staff editor, for guidance.

Reading steering committee members: George Babcock, chairman; Patricia Habada, secretary; Frances Clark, Southwestern Union; Malcolm Graham, Canadian Union; Marion Hartlein, General Conference; Erna Hauck, Columbia Union College; Sandra Herndon, Northeastern Conference; Elizabeth Hudak, Florida Conference; Erma Lee, North Pacific Union; Norwida Marshall, Southern Union; Lorraine Miller, Oregon Conference; Joyce Morse, Southern California Conference; Esther Novak, Wisconsin Conference; Phyllis Paytee, Pacific Union; Desmond Rice, Southern Missionary College; Aleene Schaeffer, Union College.

Canadian consultants: Herbert Penney-Flynn, Newfoundland; Frances Schander, Saskatchewan; George Unger, Ontario.

Special consultants: Margaret Hafner, New York; Betty McCune, Loma Linda University; Millie Youngberg, Andrews University.

Grateful acknowledgment is made to the following publishers, authors, and agents for permission to use and adapt copyrighted materials:

Dorothy Aitken for "White Wings beneath the Waves" from an article entitled "White Wings Beneath the Waves" by Dorothy Aitken. Copyright © 1968 by the Review and Herald Publishing Association. Reprinted and adapted from *The Youth's Instructor.*

The American Bible Society for Scripture text designated (TEV), which is from the *Good News Bible*—Old Testament: Copyright © 1976 by the American Bible Society.

Virginia Olsen Baron for "In My Mountains" by Jill Yokomizo from *Here I Am!* by Virginia Olsen Baron. Text copyright © 1969 by Virginia Olsen Baron. Used by permission.

Jean Bradley for "A Better Mouse Trap" by Jean Bradley.

Curtis Brown, Ltd., for "The West Wind Blew Danger" by David Savage. Copyright © 1958 by David Savage. Originally appeared in *This Week* magazine.

David Budbill for "New York in the Spring" from *Barking Dog* by David Budbill, by permission of the author.

Children's Health Publications for "The Message" by Carol Behrman from *Child Life* magazine. Copyright © 1979 by The Saturday Evening Post Company, Indianapolis, Indiana. Reprinted by permission of the publisher.

Dodd, Mead & Company for "How to Tell the Wild Animals." Reprinted by permission of Dodd, Mead & Company, Inc., from *Baubles* by Carolyn Wells. Copyright © 1917 by Dodd, Mead & Company. Copyright renewed 1945 by Bridget M. O'Connell. Also for "Those Crazy Barnstormers" from Chapter 3 of *By the Seat of Their Pants* by Phil Ault. Reprinted by permission of Dodd, Mead & Company, Inc. Copyright © 1978 by Phillip H. Ault.

E. P. Dutton for "Madrugada" by Octavio Paz and translation "Dawn" by Eliot Weinberger from *New Poetry of Mexico* by Octavio Paz, translated by Mark Strand. Copyright © 1966 by Siglo XXI Editores, S. A. English Translation Copyright © 1970 by E. P. Dutton & Co., Inc. Reprinted by permission of the publisher, E. P. Dutton. Also for "Snow Treasure" slightly adapted from the book *Snow Treasure* by Marie McSwigan. Copyright © 1942 by E. P. Dutton & Co., Inc. Renewal © 1970 by Kathryn McSwigan Laughlin. Reprinted by permission of the publisher, E. P. Dutton.

The Family Circle, Inc., for "The Great Sandwich-Eating Contest of 1938" by Leslie Peters. Reprinted from the April 1975 issue of *Family Circle Magazine.* Copyright © 1975 The Family Circle, Inc.

Harcourt Brace Jovanovich, Inc., for "To Look at Any Thing" by John Moffitt. Copyright © 1961 by John Moffitt. Reprinted from his volume *The Living Seed* by permission of Harcourt Brace Jovanovich, Inc.

Harper & Row, Publishers, Inc., for "Adventure on the Last Frontier" abridged and adapted from pp. 106-127 of *Lady with a Spear* by Eugenie

permission of Viking Penguin, Inc. Also for "The Turkey Buzzard and the Aerodrome," "Bicycles and Flying Machines," and "Not by Miracles," all from *A Bridle for Pegasus* by Katherine B. Shippen. Copyright © 1951, renewed 1959 by Katherine B. Shippen. Reprinted by permission of Viking Penguin, Inc. Also for "The Last Day" from *The Elderberry Bush* by Doris Gates. Copyright © 1967 by Doris Gates. Reprinted by permission of Viking Penguin, Inc.

Ellen G. White Publications for "Beyond the Planets" from pp. 13-20 of *Early Writings* by Ellen G. White. Copyright 1882 by Mrs. E. G. White, renewed 1945 by The Ellen G. White Publications.

Xerox Education Publications for "Mystery of the Ancient Balloons." Special permission granted by *Senior Weekly Reader,* published by Xerox Education Publications, Copyright © 1976 Xerox Corp.

Illustrations were provided by the following:

Donn Albright (48-62); Jennifer Al-Faqih (64-81); Harry Anderson (228); Matthew Annantonio (12-31); Ruth Ansel (208-217, 234-241); Stuart Armstrong (130-141); Ruth Burke (34-47, 201-207); Kevin Chadwick (82-95, 242); Guy Danella (128); Susan Foster (332-347); Taly Gaon (142-157); Wayne Hazen (96-97); Jerry Lang (295, 299, 300); Renee Gettier-Street (118-127, 168-179); June Goldsborough (100-107); Marsha Lederman (406-415); David McPhail (304-317); Pat Morrison (180-185, 418-511); Bradley O. Pomeroy (158-166, 348-366); John Romaine (384-405); Paul Salmon (188-199, 218-226, 248-257); David Street (167, 368-382).

Photographs were provided by the following:

ANIMALS ANIMALS/Roger Archibald (324); The Brooklyn Museum for "The Peaceable Kingdom" by Edward Hicks (231); Camerique (227, 303, 320, 323, 328); Jerry Cooke/Sports Illustrated © 1978 Time Inc. (383); Culver (223); Robert Erwin, National Audubon Society (273); Douglas Faulkner (275-291); Four by Five, Inc. (327); A. A. Francesconi, National Audubon Society (268); Georg Gerster/Photo Researchers, Inc. (245); Bohdan Hrynewich (108-117); Stephen P. Maka (367); David Muench (292-293); Dr. David Nathan (298); Navy Photo (247); Norman Parkinson (274); Herb Randle (416-417); Allen Roberts (260, 261, 266 bottom, 272); H. Armstrong Roberts (63, 200, 294-295, 301, 319); Rudolph Robinson (32-33); Leonard Rue Enterprises (266 top); William M. Stephens (286); Smithsonian Institution (197, 216-217); Robert Strindberg (262, 263); U.S. Air Force Museum (188).

The unit introduction pages were designed by Gregory Fossella Associates except for pages 186-187 which were designed by Tom Dunbebin. Cover design by Tom Dunbebin. Cover photograph by Camerique. Harry Knox and Associates, Inc. provided consultation services in art and design.

Every effort has been made to trace the ownership of all copyrighted material in this book and to obtain permission for its use.

Contents

6

On Eagles' Wings

10

Which Turning?

Almost anything can happen anytime, and it could happen to you. In this unit you will read about real and important problems that any girl or boy could be faced with. How the characters in the stories discover solutions to their problems is what makes each character a unique person. As you read the stories ask yourself what "turning" you would have chosen if you had been faced with similar problems. Would your "turning" have been different?

The "Empty" Wasn't Empty

THERE'S SOMETHING SCARY about an empty house. It stands with hollow eyes and stares you down. But if you must go into an "empty" for a good reason, you do. Benny and Chico think they have a good reason, but going into the "empty" leads them into a predicament.

Benny and his friend Chico had been guessing about the snow all the way home from school, along Washington Boulevard and West Park, and now down Thirty-third Street.

"Up there it looks ready to let loose," Chico observed hopefully, his face lifted to the heavy gray sky bulging low over the tall city buildings.

"But there has to be at least seven inches for no school," Benny reminded him, kicking his shoe against a piece of hard ice left from last week's snow. A new sugar sprinkling flecked the red brick sidewalk.

They reached their block, Sycamore Avenue at Thirty-third, and stopped in front of Altmann's Delicatessen at the corner, wedged hard between the narrow-angled streets. Old Mrs. Altmann, spying them from the window, tapped her bony finger against the glass, beckoning urgently.

12

"I wonder what Mrs. Altmann wants?" said Benny, looking at the frantically gesturing old woman.

"Must be something pretty important," thought Chico. "Maybe we better go see."

"Sure," agreed Benny, "come on."

Inside the warm little store, smelling pleasantly of cheese and pickles, the boys rested their school books on the counter as they listened to Mrs. Altmann's hasty explanation.

"Go quickly, boys," she was saying, holding out a ring of keys toward Benny who was the taller of the two. "I need some things from the 'empty' and my Otto is down with the flu. A bad storm is coming and I am short of these things." She handed Benny a penciled list along with the keys. "Do you think you can find them in the 'empty'?"

"I'm sure we can," Benny assured her. "We've helped Mr. Altmann lots of times."

"It's easier now," Mrs. Altmann said. "Since the cold weather, we don't keep many groceries in the 'empty.' Just stuff that won't freeze. And take this carton back." She pointed to a carton full of empty bottles over near the door. "You do this for me and I'll give you each a quarter."

"Thanks," said Benny, a happy grin on his face. This was like old times.

Chico's eyes were dancing. "We'll be careful and we won't forget a thing."

"Just be careful you don't let anything drop. I can't have broken packages," warned Mrs. Altmann.

Benny picked up the carton of empty bottles and with Chico behind him started for the "empty." The old house had been so smoke-damaged by fire which burned down the one adjoining it that it had to be abandoned. The rubble from the burned house had been trucked away, so now there was a vacant lot along side the "empty."

When the boys reached the stone steps, Benny set the carton down and ran up with the keys to unlock the door. The lock was stubborn at first, but at last he swung the door open on creaking hinges to reveal a narrow, gloomy hallway with a battered stairway going up one side. The front windows were kept shuttered so only a dim light seeped along the hall from the back of the house, past the stairs, meeting at last the square patch of daylight by the open door. Benny pushed the door wide, then ran back for the carton. He carried it into the house and to the large front room off the hall. There he set it down with a clatter of banging bottles and reached high to turn on the single light bulb hanging from a discolored cord in the very middle of the ceiling. There were several half-filled cartons scattered about the room and as Benny

14

read from the list, Chico scampered about like an enthusiastic retriever gathering what was needed. At last all the items were assembled in a neat pile near the door.

"I guess that's it," said Benny, slipping the list into a pocket of his jeans.

Chico sat back on his heels and sent a glance around the scarred old room.

"Sometimes I wish Tyrone was back living here again. We had a lot of fun in this room."

"You can have Tyrone," said Benny. "I don't want any part of him. Not since he told on us."

"Funny how he did that." Chico's face wore a puzzled frown. "He was always such a great kid."

"Might be the new neighborhood he moved to. Maybe we aren't good enough for Tyrone any more. In my book, a kid who tells just isn't good enough for me."

Until the fire, Tyrone had been a good friend of Benny and Chico. But when the landlord decided that the old house wasn't worth the repairs it would need to make it habitable after the fire in the one adjoining it, Tyrone's family had had to move away. The three boys continued going to the same school, but everything else was different. Most important, Tyrone was different. Benny and Chico had run into him several times in the neighborhood of the "empty." But each time when they had tried to be as friendly as ever, Tyrone had not responded to their friendliness. Once he turned and ran when he saw them coming.

"He looked like he was crying," Chico had then said, with concern. "What does he have to cry about?"

"Don't know," Benny had replied. "Maybe he's homesick."

They had more or less accepted this strange behavior, hopeful that in time Tyrone would be his old friendly self again.

Then something had happened which even Benny and Chico could not forgive. Tyrone had betrayed them. He had gone to Mr. Altmann and told on them. Anyway, that's what he had said he was going to do and the boys believed he had.

It had all happened the last time Chico and Benny had gone on an errand to the "empty." There they had gathered up all the

16

things that Mr. Altmann had wanted, and were ready to leave. Then Chico suggested that they have a look around.

They had explored as far as the deserted kitchen, when an angry voice behind them had demanded, "What do you think you're doing?"

Chico and Benny had whirled around to see Tyrone standing in the door to the kitchen, staring at them.

"Mr. Altmann sent us here to get some stuff for him," Benny explained. "Not that it's any of your business."

"We'll see about that," Tyrone answered. "Mr. Altmann sure doesn't want you fooling around back here with the front door wide open for anybody to walk in and help himself."

Whether Tyrone had really told or Mr. Altmann just wanted to save quarters, that was the last time he ever asked them to run an errand. They badly missed the quarters and they never forgave Tyrone.

Now, today, they began gathering into their arms the items from Mrs. Altmann's list.

"I wonder what ever happened to that old cat he used to take care of," Chico said.

"The Altmanns had it for a while," Benny reminded him.

"Not after it got into the herring," Chico said.

Benny grinned, suddenly recalling the afternoon that Mrs. Altmann had pursued the cat for half a block waving a broom, the cat running for dear life with a fish hanging out of its mouth.

Their arms full, they started out of the "empty." Benny slammed the door shut on its automatic lock. Had he happened to glance inside he might have seen a face appear over the bannister of the stairway an instant before the door closed.

Next morning the bustling, noisy city lay crippled under a deep white cover. The snowplows screeched and labored up Sycamore. It was noon before Benny, with Chico's help, had the sidewalk clear outside his father's barber shop. Here were the seven inches they had hoped for and the schools were closed. And here was the white, freshly fallen snow to play in. Stacking their snow shovels, they made for the vacant lot beside the "empty."

"Let's play forts," said Benny. "The first one to knock out the other's fort will be the winner. You make yours here by the street and I'll make mine up by the 'empty.'"

Accepting this arrangement, Chico squatted down in the snow and began scooping and piling it into a high wall facing the "empty" toward which Benny was trudging.

"Whoever gets his fort finished first can start firing," Chico called, working frantically.

Benny didn't reply, but his steps quickened and the snow spurted away from his hurrying feet. Suddenly he stopped and looked quickly toward the "empty." Then he turned and called to Chico.

"Hey, Chico, hold it. Look what I found."

Chico rose slowly, his face dubious. Was this a trick to slow him down? Already a good high heap of snow stood between him and his future target. But it wasn't like Benny to play a trick.

Benny made an impatient gesture toward his friend. "Come on, what are you waiting for?"

Chico hastened over to where Benny stood and his gaze followed Benny's pointing arm. "Look there at that upstairs window."

The window was grimy and there was darkness behind it, but even so, Chico could see at once the face of a cat close against the glass. He could even see the pink of the cat's mouth and knew that it was crying.

"What does that look like to you?" demanded Benny.

"It's Tyrone's cat," said Chico almost in a whisper.

"I see it," said Benny, "and it's shut in there and starving. It must have slipped in yesterday when we went to get the things for Mrs. Altmann."

"We can't let it starve," said Chico.

"Come on," said Benny. "We'll go get the keys from Mrs. Altmann and let the poor thing out."

20

"I wonder where it's been living," said Chico, and they trotted
through the snow, the building of forts forgotten.

"I don't know," Benny replied. "I haven't seen it since
the day she chased it with the broom."

They reached the store all out of breath only to find it was
locked.

"Old Mr. Altmann must be worse," said Benny. "Guess Mrs.
Altmann couldn't mind the store and him too."

"What do we do now?" demanded Chico.

"We bang," Benny told him, fitting action to the words.

But though he banged on the door and rattled its lock, no
Mrs. Altmann came to let them in.

"Now what?" asked Chico.

"We have to get into the 'empty,' that's what," said Benny.

"You mean break in?" Chico sounded scared.

"It's not the same as if the Altmanns hadn't let us in before," Benny reasoned. "They know us and we'll tell them about it later. Besides, there's nothing much in there but some empty bottles. Not like it was before the cold came."

This seemed to satisfy Chico and together they ran toward the "empty."

First they tested all the downstairs windows, but all of them were firmly closed and locked. Benny went around back and studied the short flight of steps and the door at the top of them. Above the door was a transom.

"You know, Chico," he said at last. "I think if you stood on my shoulders, you could reach up to that transom and if it isn't locked, you could push it open and crawl in."

22

"I won't break anything," said Chico, looking worried.

"Who asked you to? We won't break anything. Come on."

It wasn't much of a feat to climb up onto Benny's shoulders, though he complained once when Chico's foot hit his ear.

"Take it easy," Benny cautioned.

Gingerly, bracing one hand against the door, Chico reached up to give the transom a cautious shove. His hand brushed the sill and a handful of snow dropped onto his face. The transom swung in.

"Good," cried Benny, indifferent to Chico's plight. "Now get hold of the edge and I'll help boost you in."

Somehow, with a good deal of scrambling, they managed it and Benny heard the thump which signaled Chico's landing on the floor of the hallway inside. Seconds later, he had opened the door and Benny slid in.

A gray, winter light came bleakly in from the dirty window over the kitchen sink. The window in the door had been boarded over. Across the room, the door to the cellar was ajar.

Chico went on ahead toward the front hall and the stairway, calling, "Kitty, kitty." But no cat appeared.

"It's upstairs," said Benny. "Come on," and he started up.

Halfway to the top, he was flung back against the wall as a flying object descended past him.

"Open the back door, Chico. Maybe it'll run out," he cried.

Chico headed back toward the kitchen, and Benny continued up the stairs. Reaching the top, he paused for a look around. Three doors opened onto the landing, shedding their light onto it. Suddenly Benny tensed. He had heard something! The room to the left. A funny sound, almost human, yet slightly different. There it was again, almost like a cat's cry. But the cat was gone!

Slowly, Benny started into the room. Just inside the door he paused. The room was a proper mess. An old mattress was up-ended against one wall, newspapers were scattered about, and over near the mattress was a shiny pie plate, such as a bakery pie comes in. An old sofa with a broken leg leaned in one corner. On it was a carton. As Benny started toward it, he caught that sound again. This time there could be no doubt, and a smile came to Benny's lips.

Kittens! There, curled tightly on an old gray sweater on the bottom of the carton, were three tiny kittens. Two were black and one had gray stripes. The gray one had lifted his head to cry, but his eyes were shut, as were the eyes of the other two. They couldn't be more than a few days old.

"Hey, Chico," Benny called. "Come see what I found."

Chico came banging up the stairs and into the room. He approached the old sofa slowly at a signal from Benny.

"Wow," he breathed, reaching in to put a gentle hand on the crying one. Suddenly he straightened. "The mother cat ran out. Now how will she get back to them?"

"She can't," said Benny. "We'll have to take the kittens to my house."

"Will the mother cat find them there?"

"Probably not," admitted Benny. "But they'll die of starvation if we leave them here."

"They'll die anyway," said Chico, "because they're too little to lap milk. They've got to have their mother."

For a moment the boys were silent as they considered their problem. It was unthinkable that they should leave the "empty" open for the mother cat's return. It was useless to consider catching her, for she had become as wild as a bobcat.

Suddenly in the very depths of the old house, they heard a noise. It sounded as if someone had bumped into something. *Who could be in the "empty"?* The boys looked at each other quickly, their faces frightened.

"Let's get out of here," said Benny, whirling toward the door.

"But the kittens," protested Chico, his face crinkling with concern. "They'll *die.*"

"Not so loud," whispered Benny. "Are you coming, or am I going to leave you here to face whoever is down there?"

Chico gave a last despairing look at the kittens. "I'm coming," he said.

Moving as quietly as possible, they descended the stairs and headed toward the kitchen and the back exit. So far they had seen no one and had heard nothing. Now they were at the kitchen door, Chico so close at Benny's heels that when the former stopped, the smaller boy ran smack into him.

"What. . . ?" began Chico in an irritated whisper, and then he looked over Benny's shoulder.

There in the center of the kitchen, tense and staring, was Tyrone. His head was bare, his hood hanging down his back from the collar of his heavy jacket. In his mittened hands was a paper bag. His face was white and his chest heaving. Behind him the cellar door was wide open.

"What are you two doing here?" he said at last. "You have no business here."

Benny recovered from his surprise to say, "We have as much as you have."

"I came to feed my cat," said Tyrone. "Why did you come?"

"Same reason," said Benny. "We came to let her out. She was crying at the upstairs window. We let her out before we knew about the kittens."

"How did you get in?" said Tyrone. "The store isn't open."

"We found that out," said Benny. He and Chico were now standing in the kitchen and the atmosphere was getting more relaxed. "We figured somebody had to do something about the cat, so we tried that transom," nodding toward the back door, "and it wasn't locked. Chico made it in."

Tyrone looked from one to the other. "I didn't know you cared about cats," he said.

"We figured the cat was hungry, that's all," said Benny.

Tyrone nodded. "She was hungry all right. I'm late and she couldn't get out on account of the snow."

"Have you been coming here right along?" asked Benny.

Tyrone nodded again, his face troubled. "There's a broken window in one of the cellar wells and I know how to work the

bars loose and unlock it. I learned about it when I lived here. The cat kept coming back here all the time; wouldn't stay in the new place. She got in through the broken window, only today the well was full of snow and I had to clear it out. I had to sneak food in here because I didn't want Mrs. Altmann to know about the cat. She wouldn't have let it stay."

"That's why you acted so mean the day you found me and Chico back here in the kitchen," said Benny. "You didn't want us to find out about the cat."

"But you had no business squealing on us," said Chico.

"I never did," said Tyrone. "I only said that to keep you out of here. I never told anybody."

Benny and Chico exchanged glances and something like a smile passed between them.

"We aren't going to tell on you, either," said Benny.

"That's right," said Chico. Then he added, "What are you going to do with the kittens?"

"I've been thinking about that while we've been talking," Tyrone answered him. "I've been thinking that if I took the kittens home, the cat would stay home to take care of them. Only my mother wouldn't let me keep three kittens. I know she wouldn't."

There was a moment's silence, then Chico spoke. "How would it be if you kept the three till they were big enough to lap and then gave one to me and one to Benny? My mother would let me have one. How about you, Benny?"

Benny's face registered sudden interest. "I could ask her. I have a feeling she'll let me. A cat's a good thing around a shop too."

"You can have the two black ones," said Tyrone. "Now let's go upstairs and wait till the cat comes back. She can get in now that I've cleaned the snow away from the window."

Together, the three trooped back upstairs. The kittens had stopped crying and were curled against each other, sound asleep. Crouching around the carton, the boys talked in whispers. It was almost like old times again in the old house, Tyrone's old house.

All at once the kittens began to stir.

"Shh, listen," whispered Tyrone. "I think she's coming back. I have to catch her and get her home. So you two have to stay out of sight. When I get hold of her, I'll wrap her up in the sweater, then you can take the kittens and we'll head for my house."

And that's just the way it worked out. The mother cat wailed in Tyrone's arms and looked anxiously at the other two boys who had her kittens cuddled close inside their jackets. But with the sweater wrapped firmly around her, she was helpless to escape.

They descended the stairs to the front hall.

"How're we going to get out of here?" asked Benny.

"I know," said Chico, promptly. "We're going right out that front door and slam it shut behind us, and then we're going straight to the Altmann's store and make her let us in. And we're going to tell her all about everything and how the 'empty' wasn't empty. She'll understand, all right. See if she doesn't."

And Mrs. Altmann did. She even went so far as to ask for the gray kitten.

"I've always liked kittens," she explained.

—Candida Palmer

30

What Do You Think?

1. A good title excites interest and gives clues to what the story is about. Do you think "The 'Empty' Wasn't Empty" is a good title? Why or why not?

2. The boys entered the "empty" without permission. Do you think they were right or wrong in doing this? Why? Have you ever broken rules in order to help someone? Explain whether or not you think you were right in doing this.

3. Have you ever been in a frightening, "empty" place? If so, what did you do to keep yourself from being afraid?

4. Suppose Benny and Chico had left with the kittens before Tyrone returned with the food. What do you think might have happened?

Taking a Closer Look

1. Who do you think was the leader, Benny or Chico? Support your answer with evidence from the story.

2. Why do you think Tyrone didn't want Benny and Chico to know that he was keeping a cat in the "empty"?

3. An author sometimes interrupts a story and explains events that happened before the story took place. This technique is called *flashback*. Find the pages where a flashback is used and explain how you know it is a flashback.

4. Why do you think Tyrone's cat wouldn't stay in the new place? Why couldn't he keep the three kittens?

Putting Ideas to Work

Sometimes a misunderstanding can hurt a friendship. Write a paragraph telling about a time when you and a friend cleared up a misunderstanding.

New York
in
the
Spring

Sometimes when I
am walking down the street
early in May
late in the afternoon
after it's rained
on the first hot day
of the hot summer
when the sidewalk
is still wet
and the grass smells new
the way it won't soon

When the dust is mud
and the sidewalk darkens
from the water
and the sun's not out yet
and it's cool and good
to be walking outside
after the rain

Before the dust flies in my face
and the sidewalk turns
white again
and so hot
it hurts my feet
right through my shoes
and reminds me about
the hot summer
and the sweat
and no cool air to breathe
and nowhere to go
away from the heat.

Before that

Before I take
another step
into the sun

For a moment
for a second

When the city smells cool

I forget about the space
between my teeth and I
laugh with my mouth open.

—David Budbill

33

Laura Bridgman could not see, hear, or talk.
She had almost no sense of taste or smell. Her
bright mind was trapped inside her. Old Asa
Tenney had taught her to use her hands and
feet to learn about stones and birds' eggs and
the pond. But Laura needed to learn more. Dr.
Howe thought he knew of a way to teach her.

Child of the Silent Night

It was Columbus Day, October 12, 1837, just a few weeks before her eighth birthday, when Laura Bridgman started out on her great adventure. Seated in a light carriage, called a chaise, between her father and mother, Laura was tense with excitement. Where was she going? No one could tell her.

Why had she helped her mother put the best of her old clothes and many new ones in a large trunk that she knew was in the carriage with them? Why had her treasures been taken out of her boot and put in a box among her clothes?

Laura knew that something very unusual was happening. Exactly what it was she did not know, but at least her parents were with her.

The trip from Hanover to Boston was a long one in those days. Never had Laura been on such a long journey, never had she felt herself in the midst of so many strangers.

After what must have seemed to Laura an endlessly long time, the coach finally stopped. Mr. and Mrs. Bridgman and Laura were helped out. Laura clung to her mother as they went up a short flight of stairs and into a building. In another moment Laura felt her small hand once again held by the large hand that belonged to the unusually tall man who had visited her once in Mill Village. Was this his home? What was she doing here? No one could explain, of course.

36

Then Laura felt a woman's soft hand take hers. Laura could not know that this was Miss Jeannette Howe. Laura and her mother took off their coats and bonnets. Following the strange woman, they walked along — what was it? A room? A hall? Laura could somehow sense the largeness of the rooms. She was accustomed to small, low-ceilinged rooms at home. She felt very small and lost in so much space. She clung to the strange but friendly woman on one side of her and to her mother on the other.

Now they had entered a smaller room and she was allowed to feel about. There was a bed, a rocking chair, a washstand, and a little table. The furnishings here were not unlike those in her own room at the farm. She was encouraged to help her mother take her dresses and other clothes out of the trunk in which they had been placed at home. Were they perhaps going to stay here for a visit? Where was her mother's bag?

37

There, now they had come to her box of treasures. She felt her mother take it and place it on the table by the bed. Was this going to be her own room? Would her little brothers, Addison and John, be coming too? Would her treasures be safe on the table? No one can know whether questions such as these passed through Laura's mind; and no one, of course, could have made her understand the answers to them.

Now they were going back through the long hall to the large room from which they had come. Laura was led over to a low chair near her father. The tall man gave her a cup of milk and a cookie. When she had finished eating, she sat quietly in her chair.

Then she felt people getting up around her. Her father leaned down and patted her. Laura started to jump up. That pat usually meant that he was going away. His firm hand pushed her back down into the chair again. Now her mother leaned over and patted her.

Laura was terrified. This too was a good-by pat. Surely her father and mother were not going away! Surely they were not going to leave her in a strange place! Laura struggled to get out of the chair. Now the large hand of the friendly man and the gentle hand of the woman held her back.

Laura felt a door close. She was allowed to get out of the chair, and she rushed madly toward the door. It was closed. Laura let out a loud unpleasant sound. It sounded almost like a wounded animal. She began crying and pounding on the door with her little fists.

"We must let her tire herself out some with her grief and tears," said Dr. Howe to his sister. "She is already

38

tired from the long journey. The fear and sorrow of this separation will exhaust her further. In a little while we must take her to her room. Her box of treasures and her clothes at least will be familiar to her."

"Oh, Sam, it is so pathetic to see her frightened and upset," said Miss Jeannette. "If there were only some way to let her know that it is all for her own good that she has come here." Dr. Howe and his sister watched the terrified little girl crying, beating the door, feeling about the room for some familiar object or person. When she came near them, they tried to comfort her. Each time she would draw away.

At last, when they felt that Laura would allow it, they led her to her room. They left her there and locked the door. When Miss Jeanette returned in less than half an hour, she found Laura sound asleep on her bed.

"We can expect that there will be several more scenes like the one we have just witnessed before Laura will accept the fact that she must stay here," said Dr. Howe to his sister.

"Of course!" said Miss Jeannette. "Can you imagine how she must feel? Suddenly, with no warning — for how could anyone warn her — she has been taken from the familiar surroundings of the farm. She has been separated from her father, her mother, her little brothers, and her good friend Mr. Tenney. Why, it is as if she had been suddenly plunged into an even darker prison than the one she has always lived in. There is still no light, no sound, almost no smells or tastes, and now not even the familiar things and people around her to touch!"

"I had thought of having Mrs. Bridgman remain here at the school for a few days," said Dr. Howe. "But I decided that since Laura is so bright and friendly, she would recover from the shock of separation quickly. I can begin her education sooner if we do not have to wean her gradually from her mother. I hope I am not wrong about this."

"She *is* bright and friendly, Sam," said Miss Jeannette enthusiastically. "I could see that even in the little while before her parents left."

And Dr. Howe was right in thinking that Laura would quickly recover from the first shock of separation. In less than a week Laura began to be her own lively self once more. She began to reach out with her wonderful hands to learn all she could about her new home.

At the end of two weeks Laura was so happy in her new surroundings that Dr. Howe felt he could begin the

41

experiment he had planned. The night before he began, he discussed his plans with his sister.

"My goal is perfectly clear to me, Jeannette," he said. "I am going to try to bring into Laura's mind the idea that there are twenty-six different signs or letters that everyone uses. I want her to know that by combining these letters into words, we can share our thoughts with each other."

"But Sam, how in the world are you going to 'tell' Laura that?" asked Miss Jeannette, puzzled. "If she were just blind, you could have her feel the raised-up letters with her fingers and tell her their names. Or, if she were just deaf and mute, you could show her letters. But she is blind and deaf and mute, so what can you do?"

"I know just exactly how I am going to try to do it," said Dr. Howe, smiling. "You may attend the first class with Laura tomorrow morning and see for yourself."

The great day dawned. When the first lesson began, Laura was seated at a table across from Dr. Howe. Beside her sat Miss Drew, who was to be Laura's own special teacher. Miss Jeannette Howe sat watching nearby.

The doctor had arranged a row of objects on the table in front of him. There were a large key, a spoon, a knife, a fork, a book, a cup, and a few other things with which he felt sure Laura would be familiar.

First Dr. Howe put the key into Laura's hand. It was a very large key. He let her handle it and feel it all over. She knew immediately what it was. The key at home with which she locked her boot in the cupboard was very much like this one — except for one thing. Her sensitive fingers

42

paused as they felt the long key. There was something *on* this one.

Dr. Howe had fastened a paper label on the key. On the label the word KEY was written in a special kind of raised lettering or embossing that was used at that time in writing for the blind. The Braille system, now so widely used, had not yet been adopted. Dr. Howe guided Laura's fingers over the raised lines of the letters several times. She had no idea, of course, what the letters were.

Then he took the key away from Laura and handed her a spoon. She took it, felt it, and immediately recognized it as a spoon much like the ones with which she set the table at home. Again there was one important difference. Along the handle of the spoon Dr. Howe had pasted a label with the letters S-P-O-O-N written in raised type. Dr. Howe guided her fingers carefully over this word several times.

Now the doctor took away the spoon and gave the key back to Laura. He directed her fingers to the label on the key again. Then he gave her back the spoon. He directed her fingers to the label to feel that the shape of the lines on the spoon label were just as different from each other as the key and spoon themselves were different from one another.

Somewhere, thought Laura, I have felt lines like these before, but where? Was it on my plate that Uncle Asa gave me?

Now the doctor did something else. He took away the key and the spoon and gave Laura just a piece of paper with some raised letters on it. The letters were K-E-Y again. Taking the key once more, Dr. Howe directed Laura's fingers to the label on it.

An expression on Laura's face made it quite clear that she recognized that the raised letters were the same on both papers, the one on the key and the separate label. Dr. Howe went through the same process with the spoon and a separate label that read S-P-O-O-N.

The rest of that first lesson was spent letting Laura feel the remaining objects — cup, knife, book, and so forth. She also felt the labels for these, both those pasted on the object and those that were separate. From that time on, Laura had lessons every morning and afternoon. She seemed to enjoy them thoroughly and to consider them just a game, not work. It was difficult for Dr. Howe and Miss Drew to get her to stop "playing" this game.

By about the third day, Dr. Howe and Miss Drew were delighted to see that Laura had grasped the important point that the separate label for KEY somehow went with

44

the key and the label that was separate from the spoon went with the spoon. They knew she understood when she could take a separate label, such as the one spelling BOOK, and feel about until she found a book without any label. Then she would place the label on the book.

The lessons were going so well that Dr. Howe felt Laura was ready to take another important step forward. He had Miss Drew cut the labels for the words KEY, SPOON, KNIFE, and so forth, into separate letters. Up until this time, Laura had seen words as wholes. Now he wanted her to learn that they are made up of parts — letters. Laura was allowed to follow closely, with her hands, all that Miss Drew did. After the words had been cut into separate letters, her hands followed Miss Drew's as she arranged the letters back into words.

In an astonishingly short time, Laura had grasped the point of this new "game." If Miss Drew handed her the letters O, S, N, O, P, in a flash Laura could arrange them in the correct order to spell S-P-O-O-N. If Miss Drew gave her Y, K, E, Laura arranged them into the word K-E-Y. O, K, O, B and I, K, E, N, F were equally simple for her. After a few more lessons, Laura could do this with all the words in her vocabulary. Soon after that she could take from a whole pile of loose letters whatever ones she wanted and spell correctly any word she wished of those she had been taught. This would have been a great accomplishment for any eight-year-old. How much more remarkable it was for a little girl like Laura Bridgman!

And then it happened! For two months Laura had been "playing" these games with letters and words almost the way a trained dog performed certain tricks. Now, suddenly, it was different. Dr. Howe always said that he knew almost the exact moment when Laura's face showed that she at last really understood what all this meant. Suddenly it seemed to become clear to her. Every object had a name. These names could be spelled by letters, either in raised letters, metal types, or, most easily of all, by the manual alphabet.

Laura had found the rope that Dr. Howe was dangling before her. She had caught hold of it at last and could be drawn up from the dark pit in which she lived into the light of day.

— *Edith Fisher Hunter*

What Do You Think?

1. Imagine being blind, deaf, mute, and having no sense of taste or smell. How would you find out about your world?
2. How does this story teach that it is sometimes necessary to go through unpleasant experiences in order to learn? What were some of these experiences for Laura? Tell about a time when you learned something from an unpleasant experience.
3. Explain what the author meant by the rope that Dr. Howe was "dangling" before Laura. Has anyone ever "dangled" a rope before you? Explain.
4. Were Laura's parents cruel to leave her alone with the Howes? Explain your answer.
5. In your own words, explain why it would be so difficult to teach the alphabet to someone who is blind and deaf.

Taking a Closer Look

1. How old was Laura at the time of this story?
2. How did Laura know that her parents were leaving her at Dr. Howe's?
3. What was Dr. Howe's goal for Laura? What objects did he use in his first lesson with Laura?
4. After learning that certain letters made up S-P-O-O-N and K-E-Y, what important discovery did Laura make? Why was it important?
5. Was Laura intelligent? Support your answer with details from the story.

Putting Ideas to Work

Blindfold your eyes and place cotton in your ears. Then ask a classmate to guide you around the room. Stop at three places and try to tell where you are. Tell the class about your feelings.

THE SEA IS NOT A PLAYGROUND. It can be savage. It can kill. It can demand all the strength and courage a person has. Paul and Clay learn this important lesson, but only after they face a dangerous ocean storm.

SAIL, CALYPSO!

It was Clay who first found the old hulk half buried in the sands. It was he who dug it out and read the name in faded letters across her stern, *Calypso*. Every day of this summer he hastened to the beach right after breakfast to work on the old wreck, to clean the sand from her sides, and to dream of making her seaworthy again.

Then one morning on arriving at the beach, he saw a boy's head looking up at him from inside the *Calypso*. A stranger in his boat! Clay ran forward furiously to challenge the newcomer. But Paul claimed the boat as his. "I found her too," he said. Clay insisted that he had already begun work on her and hence had a better claim than the younger boy.

For a while they distrusted each other as each one tried to improve the condition of "his" *Calypso*. But gradually this gave way to a grudging tolerance as they saw that each of them had something to contribute and together they could achieve what separately would be impossible for them. Tolerance turned to friendship as the summer sped by. When the time came to practice sailing the *Calypso* in a nearby pond, each boy would have found it hard to imagine sailing her alone.

49

After that practice sail they were ready for the open sea. Their objective was an island opposite their shore. It had been beckoning them for weeks. So on this particular morning they set forth, reaching the island without mishap. But before they had had time to explore it thoroughly, they noticed that the sky had become overcast and a wind was rising.

"I smell rain," Clay said. The wind blew gusty and damp, cold against his body. He shivered. "C'mon!"

Together he and Paul ran to where the *Calypso* awaited them on the sand.

They launched the boat and worked it through the shallows, Clay at the tiller and Paul at the bow on the lookout for rocks. Free of them at last, Clay brought her about and now they were running before the wind, headed for the mainland.

Paul turned an anxious face to Clay who grinned and shouted over the wind, "She'll take us back safe, Paul! Don't you worry."

"She'd better!" Paul, catching some of Clay's spirit, laughed and the shakiness of the sound was covered by the wind. "I don't swim very well. That's an awfully long way to land!"

Then Clay remembered the orange life jackets he had found so long ago, remembered he had thrust them back into the locker and forgotten them. Until now.

"Hey!" he called. "Get those orange things out of the locker. Now's when we need 'em. Just in case . . ."

So Paul found the jackets and hauled them out. He slipped into one, awkward for a moment with the two ties that cinched in front.

50

"You'd float 'most forever in that!" Clay assured him. "Take the tiller now, and I'll get into the other one."

So finally they were both secure in the jackets and the bright color was somehow reassuring and cheerful in the dark vastness of sea and clouds.

They could still see the mainland far ahead as the swells swept under and past them, hurrying to that low shore, alternately raising them to the dizzy crests, then plunging them with stomach-clutching suddenness into the troughs.

The rain had begun to fall. At first there were only wind-driven spits of stinging drops. Then it came more steadily. Lightning slashed across the black sky. Thunder crashed above them. And the rain increased.

Clay struggled with tiller and sheet. Paul bailed furiously. The water from the downpour mingled with the seawater that the *Calypso* had already shipped. Slowly it rose until it was up as high as the boys' ankles, a small sea of itself, dashing and sloshing about as the boat pitched and yawed in the running swells.

"I can't see land any more!" Paul yelled.

"Me neither!" And for only a second Clay took his eyes from the sail, the mast, and the danger of the swinging boom. "I'm trying to keep the wind behind us! And the swells are running toward the beach! Maybe we ought to try to take the sail in. The water's bound to push us into shore!"

He didn't like to think of the size of the breakers that would be pounding the beach. How would they ever get the *Calypso* in with the waves breaking over her stern! But there was no time to worry about that.

"Shall I lower the sail?" Paul called.

"Yeah. Be careful! Don't go overboard! You'd never get back in! Not the way the *Calypso's* rolling!"

Paul stowed the bailing can. He moved cautiously forward, gripping the rail. When he was opposite the mast, he reached for it, stretching to keep the safety of the rail until he had grasped the spar with one hand. Then wary of the boom, he pulled himself over, squatted there with a tight hold on the mast, and began to work with the halyard. It was wet and his fingers were icy. With the wind behind them the sail jerked and bucked and pulled so tight that he could not manage the soaked line.

Clay close-hauled the sheet, as much as his strength would allow. He managed to pull the boom in almost parallel to the *Calypso's* length. Thus the wind, driving over the stern, had less surface to batter. He knew now they should have lowered the sail long ago. Anxiously he glanced at Paul who still clung to the mast trying to loosen the jammed halyard. Once the other turned and Clay could see him shake his head, but then Paul once more bent doggedly to the task.

"If those clouds would only rise up a little," he muttered to himself, to the *Calypso.* "If I was just sure we're sailing for the beach instead of China . . . "

Then presently, as though the clouds had plucked his wish from the swirling air, they lifted a little above the water's surface and thinned a bit.

Clay was sorry he had uttered the words!

For before the clouds closed in once more, the *Calypso* had topped a white-ridged swell and Clay had

52

his view of the mainland. It was nearer, much nearer, than he had thought it would be! Even from this seaward side he could see the breakers pounding the beach, making a foaming terror of the surf. In that brief view before the clouds closed in once more, the boiling stretch of sea looked like certain death for the *Calypso*.

"Paul!" Clay shouted. "Paul . . ."

The other did not hear him, but seemed welded to the mast as though intending to work through eternity at the task of the jammed line.

Desperate, Clay screamed, "Paul! Paul! We gotta turn her! Watch the boom! We gotta turn! Paul! Watch out. . . ."

Though the wind seemed to smother his cry before it had left his lips, it could not mask another sound—the wild clash of surf along the shore; the thundering, pounding force that would break the *Calypso* into a thousand pieces, that would grind Paul and himself into the sand along the ocean floor.

Once more he screamed, "Paul!"

And as though the desperation reached the other when the sound could not, Paul raised his head and looked back at Clay.

"I'm gonna come around!" Clay shouted. "Keep your head down! Hold on!"

Now Paul shrank against the mast, holding tightly, watching Clay struggle with the yanking sheet. His blue eyes were wide but he seemed calm enough and even managed an encouraging nod, though by now he could hear the roar of the surf and understood their danger. Their eyes held for an instant, then Clay was putting the tiller over just as the *Calypso* started her slide down the steep backslope into a trough.

The valiant little craft managed half the turn before she hit the bottom of the slant. The dark water seemed to pile above her on all sides. Clay forced the tiller as far as it would go. Just as the bow began to finish the arc of its turn, the rising slope of the next wave began to lift her. All might have gone well, but a malignant lash of wind caught the sail from a new angle, yanked it against the *Calypso's* natural roll. She plunged to one side. Her starboard rail raked beneath the water. Clay was thrown violently to the bottom of the boat. In that instant he lost his hold on the tiller, and the sheet whipped free, lashing this way and that.

He wallowed, helpless, in the sloshing water that the *Calypso* had shipped. He clung to one bench, pulled himself about facing the stern, almost reached the tiller, then slipped again. He felt the flailing boom graze his skull. He ducked low as he struggled to regain his feet. The plunging of the boat now whirled him about again and he had a glimpse of Paul. The other had released his hold on the mast and was clutching the rail, trying to work himself back to help his friend.

"Watch out for the boom!" Clay shouted but again he floundered in the shipped water. This time he fell against the bench, gashing one cheek. Blood spread down the wet dark skin along his jaw.

"Clay!" Paul cried. And then forgetting the danger of the boom he half stood, reaching to help the other.

"Look out! Paul . . ." Clay shouted, unaware of his own hurt.

But the vicious swipe of the boom caught Paul along the side of his head. He slumped across the rail, a limp bright orange pillow. As Clay watched in horror, unable to help, Paul teetered there, then slowly rolled over, disappeared from sight.

Fear for his friend lifted Clay from the boat's floor. He flung himself at the tiller, managed to head the *Calypso* directly into the westerly, squarely into the shoreward-rolling swells. All the while he wildly scanned the waters for the bright life jacket. Twice he glimpsed it off the *Calypso's* port rail. At first it was close to the boat. The second time the gap had widened. And Paul appeared to be face down, though it was difficult to see in the gloom. Frantically Clay secured the sheet

55

so that the sail was set at a proper angle for sailing into the wind. He lashed the tiller in place with a quick turn of line to try and keep the *Calypso* heading straight seaward. Maybe he'd have a chance of bringing Paul back to the boat. Maybe—if the surge of the sea offset the *Calypso's* effort to make way—she might stay almost in the same place. Maybe—

Awkward in the bulky jacket, he worked his way along the rail. He kept looking for Paul in the roll of black water. The orange splotch had disappeared. Careful of the boom, he reached the mast. Clinging to the spar he stepped on the bench. Balanced there. Searching. Searching.

And strangely he remembered how Paul had looked that first day. He remembered Paul peering over the rail of the little derelict boat. An owl. A pale owl. He had disliked the Owl for taking his new love. For taking the *Calypso*. When had the friendship truly begun? He couldn't remember! Now it was not the *Calypso's* fate that caused the sick panic in his middle.

Paul!

The *Calypso* climbed up the next long slope. As she rose the view broadened.

"Paul!" Clay cried aloud.

There! There, a splash of orange! Closer than Clay could possibly have hoped!

And Paul was not face down. Instead he floundered dizzily. He seemed unable to keep his head clear of the water for more than a few seconds at a time. He'd never make it to shore!

"Paul! Hold on . . ." Clay screamed.

With all of his strength he thrust himself away from the mast, kicked with all of the power of his sinewy legs away from the rail. He arched through the air. Then he was in the water, striking out for the spot he had fixed upon.

His life jacket made swimming difficult, but each time one of the white-topped swells thrust him under, the buoyant jacket popped him back to the surface again.

If he couldn't find Paul soon, it would be too late! Then just as he was sure that the search had failed, he saw a flash of orange. The bright color had shown just at the crest of the swell ahead. He himself floundered in the trough. Now he strained to keep his head clear of the water. Up he rose on the rush of the next wave.

There it was again—the orange jacket. Catching the forward thrust of the swell just below its crest, Clay swam with all of his strength. The orange jacket had settled in the trough and now it began to rise. Furiously Clay pumped with arms, legs, managing to ride just in front of the white crest. He could see Paul's face now, the gaping mouth struggling for breath, the eyes nearly closed against the stinging spray.

Once more Clay thrust forward, snatched at the orange blob. Had it! Shifted his grasp! Now his grip was firm! He slipped one hand under Paul's chin, cupping his fingers over the open mouth, shielding it partly from the dashing brine.

"You're all right!" Clay managed to say close to his friend's ear. "Take it easy, you old Paul."

He was gasping himself from the effort of the swim. For the first time he was grateful for the awkward life jacket. Now it buoyed him and he saved his strength by resting in the harness with his mouth scarcely above the water.

"Go ahead—Breathe—I got you—That's it—See, we're okay—Breathe again—The jackets make us safe —safe as a bathtub—Breathe—That's it—"

Apparently it had been the blow from the boom that had made Paul so helpless, for now, slowly, he began to revive a little. Finally he was able to breathe when he should, hold his breath when the water swept over them. But Clay kept his grip on the other's jacket. Now he remembered the *Calypso*. Their little *Calypso*! Where was she? Was there any hope they could reach her?

Just as he was thinking that she must already have gone down, or maybe was dashing to splinters on the beach, he saw her.

"Hey . . ." he cried despite the wind and the roll of the sea—"there, she's sailing. . . ."

Weakly, Paul twisted his head, but when the wind-driven water slashed into his face, he turned away.

"She's sailing straight out to sea. . . ." Clay gasped, straining to see, blinking the stinging spray from his eyes. "She's leaving us!"

When Clay glanced again at the *Calypso*, he saw that the distance between them had widened. He had secured the sheet and lashed the tiller, and the little boat had picked up the westerly. It was as though her own spirit had taken command. With the weight of

58

the boys gone, the shipped water only acted as ballast and she rode well across the running swells. Now she had managed to free herself of the shoreward-sweeping currents. She was heeling over to leeward, racing gaily across her sea, heading straight away from the land that had too long held her captive. She would not die upon the shore!

"The surf . . ." Clay heard Paul's voice.

He wrenched his gaze from the flying *Calypso*. At this moment they rode high on the crest of a mountain of dark water. The sea had swept them closer to shore. There was the beach, no more than two hundred yards away. But the surf! They had one terrible view of it before they dropped down the back of the swell.

"Next swell's gonna put us in it!" cried Clay.

Now from the trough the water rushed them upward again. It seemed as though this time they shot straight to the sky. They both gasped. For only an instant they looked down on all that surrounded them. The roar and thunder of tons of water crashed on the flat shore. Clay saw that the crest they rode was passing beneath them. He knew it would drop them for the next huge comber to bury. He glanced back. The sea was gathering itself, rising behind them.

But beyond the piling water he caught his last glimpse of the *Calypso*. She was growing small with the distance. She still flew straight away to sea. Her sail stretched jaunty and tight in the gale. Her blue hull gleamed clean and bold.

"Hey, sail, you *Calypso*. . . ." he shouted, but his voice was lost.

59

The swell dropped them in the trough. The comber behind piled higher. Rising. Rising. Up. Up. Now the crest seemed to climb upon itself, thin at the top until a pale green light filtered through its arch. It curved over above them. Suddenly they felt themselves sucked upward. For an instant as they swept up the smooth reaching wall of water, they saw they were inside a curving liquid tunnel.

Together they yelled! Then they were whirled up and over into the foaming top. From this height it crashed them down with its own tons of brine. Down, down. Tumbling. Whirling. Then they were scoured for an eternity along the sand of the bottom. At last they shot to the surface. But they had become separated.

Clay gagged, with the salt water strangling him. Then he managed a gasp of air. There was a churning foam all around and before he could truly catch his breath, he was snatched up into another giant, curving wave. Hurled to the bottom. Up to the top again. Gasping, choking. A little air for the lungs. Then up and over and down again. And again. And again, until he was sure each next one would truly finish him. The nightmare of the whirling sea was endless.

One particular thrust of water, more vicious than the rest, crashed him against the sand with such force he blacked out for a moment and then was conscious only enough to be aware that he lay on his back looking up from the pale depths as the water sheeted away, slipping back to the sea. Thus miraculously he found he could breathe air instead of gulping salt water. With gigantic effort he turned over, found himself on

60

his hands and knees in the thin surf of the shore. Before he could struggle to his feet another wave rushed upon him. But it was gone in a moment and Clay found himself standing, staggering, slipping, falling, standing again, moving up the flat of the beach. There he collapsed.

He thought of Paul, but he could not move. He felt himself gag, and salt water poured from his mouth and his nose. He began to shiver, but he still could not force himself to rise.

"Are you all right, Clay?"

The voice was close to him and he felt a hand on his shoulder. He nodded weakly and sat up. There was Paul squatting beside him, his round eyes full of concern.

"You'll feel better in a while, Clay. I guess you just about swallowed the whole ocean." Then after a bit, "You're shaking all over."

After a bit Clay stopped his shivering. He raised his head and looked around. It wasn't raining and he saw that the clouds to the west were beginning to thin. To the south there were a few streaks of pale blue showing. The ocean remained cold and gray and the waves still pounded the shore. But the island was free of the overcast. There it stood, out toward the horizon, and it seemed impossible that they had sailed there and landed on that far, strange shore.

There was not a sign of the *Calypso*. She was gone. Back to her beloved sea.

—*Adrienne Jones*

What Do You Think?

1. What do you think was the most exciting moment of the story? Why?
2. How did the boys seem to feel as they watched their *Calypso* "racing gaily across her sea"? How would you have felt?
3. Have you ever been in a situation where you had to pit your courage against the forces of nature? If so, tell about your experience.

Taking a Closer Look

1. How did Clay and Paul feel toward each other in the beginning? How did they feel at the end? What do you think caused these changes?
2. Both Paul and Clay showed that they had courage, a quick wit, and strength. Find examples to prove this.
3. Where do you think the story reached a high point of action or climax? Was there more than one climax? If so, where did each occur?
4. The action of this story can be described as "exciting." What are some other words that describe the story's action?
5. The reader is not told where the story took place. Find clues that tell you if the story took place on the East or the West Coast of North America.
6. The author used verbs very effectively. For instance, "Paul *shrank* against the mast." Look for at least five more good examples.
7. *Personification* is a device used to make an object seem human. How did the author make the *Calypso* seem human? Find some examples in the story.

The grey winds. the cold winds

The grey winds, the cold winds are blowing
   Where I go.
I hear the noise of many waters
   Far below.
All day, all night, I hear them flowing
   To and fro.

—James Joyce

Henry was James and Ellen White's eldest son. He had a dream of achieving greatness on the battlefields of the American Civil War. But at a very early age, Henry achieved a special kind of greatness. Read to discover what it was.

Henry White, Drummer Boy

"Look, Willie, there's a new company of soldiers drilling. They must be straight from their farms. They don't have uniforms yet, and they haven't even learned how to march." Henry copied their slouching walk, and Willie laughed.

Edson, the third of the White brothers, joined in. "Let's show them how to keep step." The boys lined up. Henry, 14, Edson, 12, and 7-year-old Willie formed a three-man squad and paraded up and down.

After trying in vain to keep up with his older brothers, Willie protested. "Say, Henry, how do you expect us to keep step without a drum? We have to have a drum if we want to look like soldiers." Wiping his sweating face, he sat down on the grass.

Henry answered, "That's a great idea, Willie. Of course we have to have a drum."

But Edson questioned that idea. "Just where do you think we'll get one? Remember how long and hard we had to work at the Review printing office to earn a hundred dollars for our harmonium?[1] I'm not going to spend any of *my* hard-earned cash on a drum."

"I wasn't thinking of buying one," said Henry. "We'll make one." His brothers laughed, but Henry wasn't joking. He put his plan into action at once. It cost only a few dollars to buy two round cheese boxes and a

[1] harmonium (hahr-MOH-NEE-m)

sheepskin. Willie was set to work scraping all the wool off the old sheepskin, and Edson knocked out the ends of the cheese boxes. Then Henry cut the sheepskin in two, stretched it tightly over the open ends of one box, and slid the rims over each end. Next he strengthened it with wires and slats from the second box, and they had a drum. After painting it they whittled a pair of drumsticks.

"Now, let's really march!" commanded Henry. Again the three boys lined up. To the beat of the drum they moved up and down the fairground. The drum was so noisy that Theodore and Ogden Lewis, teenage friends, hurried to join the little army. Soon the five boys were drilling in a manner that put the new Civil War recruits to shame.

Then Willie had another idea. "When real soldiers drill," he said, "they have other music. They play fifes, not just the bang, bang of a drum. It would be more fun if we had a tune to march by."

Henry agreed. He had spent hours watching the fife and drum corps practice on the race track. Seeing only the glamorous side of war, he had dreamed of enlisting as a drummer boy in the army. He had memorized the different drum rolls and knew how they acted as commands in marching and even in camp life. Since drum calls were obeyed by soldiers, Henry thought, I could be like a leader in the army. Working at the Review isn't as exciting as going to war would be.

But for the moment he kept such thoughts to himself. He answered Willie, "Well, we can whistle. Come on, let's try, 'Tramp, Tramp, Tramp, the Boys Are Marching.' I'll beat the drum and we'll whistle in time. Come on. One-two-three, go."

The five boys all began whistling, but their first attempt wasn't too successful. After they had practiced for an hour, Willie was sorry he had introduced the idea. But Henry gave them no rest, and soon the boys were responding to the drum beat in the best military fashion and whistling army songs in perfect tune.

One day Edson came running into the house calling, "Willie! Willie! Come see something you won't believe. But be quiet or you'll spoil everything." Curious, Willie followed his brother to the fence that divided their home from the fairground. And there he saw a sight he truly couldn't believe.

The fife and drum corps was marching round and round the race track. Henry was marching right along with them, beating his noisy drum and whistling his shrillest. In his concentration Henry didn't realize that the commander of the army group had signaled for his drummers and fifers to be silent. With only the music of Henry's whistling and the beat of Henry's drum, the entire corps stepped smartly around the track. Every man wore a broad smile on his face!

Edson and Willie watched until the men stopped marching and proceeded to cheer their new drummer boy. Red-faced and embarrassed, Henry ducked for home, only to meet his two brothers, who teased him until his threats kept them quiet.

It seemed there was no end to what Henry could do. After watching some soldiers on horseback he took a close look at the two White family horses, Jim and Jack, and decided to train Jack as a performer. Before long he was entertaining the soldiers and the whole neighborhood. He stood barefoot on Jack's bare back and played his small accordion while Jack pranced to the music!

The Whites worried about their sons' great interest in the war. Knowing this, the boys tried to keep some of their activities a secret from their father and mother. They loved to sit on the fence and sing such war songs as, "Tramp, Tramp" and "We Are Coming, Father Abraham, a Hundred Thousand Strong." They did this on Saturday evenings after sunset, when both parents had gone to the office. Henry and Edson also played these Civil War songs on the harmonium, with Willie and the neighbor boys singing along.

When the Whites' nearest neighbor, Jonah Lewis, complained to Elder White, he had a talk with his boys. "You know," he explained, "your noisy drum is disturbing the neighbors. Brother Lewis is complaining about your war spirit. He feels it isn't having a good influence on his own boys."

"But, Father," Henry replied, "Brother Lewis is noisy too. He prays out by his haymow three times a day, and you know the whole neighborhood can hear his shouting. Why does he think that the louder he yells the sooner God will answer his prayers? Our drum doesn't bother the neighbors as much as his shouting." James White didn't attempt any answer, but smiled to himself at this reply. A few days later Henry's mother suggested to Brother Lewis that God can hear even a whisper, and Jonah Lewis's shouting ended.

Complaints continued. James White, being a noncombatant and a leader in helping to keep young Adventist men out of the war, finally ordered his boys to get rid of their drum. Regretfully, they stored it away in the attic. But they continued to be absorbed in the war activities going on at the fairground next to their home.

James and Ellen White grieved about the change in their surroundings. When they had first moved to Wood Street in Battle Creek, their home had been surrounded by forest. A little grove on their property had been made into an outdoor chapel where they could go for prayer and quiet meditation. But what had been called Manchester's Woods was now a fairground with a mile-long racetrack. Horse trotting was carried on every Sunday, and when the Civil War began, the racetrack became a training ground for young recruits.

The fence around the White home proved no barrier to three lively boys who played battle when their parents were busy.

Months passed and the drum was almost forgotten. Then one day Henry and Edson went to the attic to find something. Suddenly Henry said, "Look, Edson. Remember the fun we had with that old drum?"

Edson, delighted, crawled over a pile of old furniture and pulled out the drum, and the two boys took it outside. "Let's beat it like we used to," they said. "Come on, Willie, march with us." And the noise began.

After a little while sharp-eyed Willie said, "Here comes Father. We'd better get the drum out of sight." They tossed it behind a pile of logs in the woodshed and ran into the house.

But James White had heard the drum, and he felt sad. He thought of his efforts to help young Adventist men try to keep out of the struggle. He thought of the thousands of dead and of the sorrow of a suffering nation. And he was upset because his own sons had disobeyed him. He hurried to Henry, Edson, and Willie and asked, "Where is that drum?"

A little frightened, Henry answered, "In the woodshed, Father."

Without another word the man strode to the woodshed. He seized the big ax, and the boys heard crashing sounds as James White quickly hacked that symbol of war to splinters.

Henry, Edson, and Willie were upset also. To them the war had meant glamour and excitement, and now their father had smashed their drum. Finally Henry spoke. "I tell you, that settles it. I've been thinking about it for a long time, and now I am going to do it."

"Do what?" asked Edson.

"I'm going to run away from home. And nothing will stop me. Since Father has destroyed my drum, I'm going

to get a better one — a real one. I'm going to enlist as a drummer boy in the army."

However, being a member of such a close and loving family, he found it easier to consider than to actually *do* something that he knew would break their hearts. The ties of home tugged strongly, and his brothers begged him not to enlist.

Meanwhile, Ellen and James White were wondering how they could draw their boys away from the nearby drill field and its military atmosphere. They made a plan, and one evening after worship James announced, "Boys, we are going on a trip."

"Who will be in charge of us this time, Father?" asked Willie. His parents had to be away so much of the time that he was used to having Jennie Frazer or some other kind Adventist woman move into the home and "mother" him and his brothers. During their parents' trips, the boys received loving letters from all sorts of distant places where their parents were busily working, doing the Lord's business. These letters counseled the boys, reminded them of their parents' love and concern, and kept them from getting too lonesome. So Willie expected that another such trip was now being planned.

"Who will be in charge of you?" his father answered. "Your mother and I, for all three of you are going right along with us!"

Great excitement followed this announcement. Questions were asked and answered. The boys learned that they would be visiting New England, and that while their parents went on shorter trips, they would stay with old friends, the Howlands, at Topsham, Maine.

74

"My old home, where I stayed from the time I was a tiny baby until around my fifth birthday," laughed Henry. "I know I'll remember it. I wonder if anyone will remember me?"

"Well, they'll have a time remembering, for you're a little taller than you were when they last saw you," replied James, looking proudly at his nearly grown son.

Edson or Willie must have whispered to their parents of Henry's anger over the smashed drum and his vow to run away. At any rate, this trip came just at the right time to prevent him from carrying out his plan. It was an excited trio of boys who boarded an eastbound train at Battle Creek on August 19, 1863. Suitcases, bedrolls, and loaded lunch baskets went with them. As the train rolled out of the station, the White boys put out of their minds the marching, drum-beating, fife-playing soldiers on the fairground in Battle Creek.

At Olcott, New York, the family got off the train and spent four days visiting friends. Determined to make this trip really enjoyable for their sons, James and Ellen rented two large rowboats. The little group of Adventists spent pleasant hours rowing along the shore of Lake Ontario.

James White, enjoying the recreation as much as anybody, called out to his boys, "Come on, sing! Keep time with your oars!" And he led out, singing, "On

Jordan's Stormy Banks I Stand." Different ones thought of songs mentioning water. Strangers were charmed by the sight of two large boats filled with happy people, stroking in perfect rhythm and singing hymns.

At the time the three boys didn't realize what their father was trying to do, but many years later Willie wrote, "In nearly every home where we visited during this Eastern tour, we three boys were lined up to sing gospel hymns. I could not then understand the reason why, but later I understood that it was an attempt by our parents to bind our hearts to the work in which they were engaged, and to help us forget the worldly songs that had filled our minds in Battle Creek."

So they traveled and sang their way to Topsham, where they were greeted warmly by the Howland family. As soon as Father Howland learned of Henry's musical ability, he got a melodeon[1] for him to practice on. Edson and Henry

---

[1] melodeon (mə-LOD-e-ən)

took turns pumping. They played and sang hymns whenever they could find the time. The Civil War and its marching music seemed far away.

When Adventists in other parts of New England heard that the Whites were nearby, they insisted on personal visits and meetings with God's messenger and her husband. One day James announced to his boys that they would be left for a while in the care of the Howlands. "You will be kept busy," he said. "Father Howland is pasting prophetic charts on cloth so they will be durable. You must help him while we are away."

The boys went with their parents to the depot. It was later written in *Appeal to Youth* that "before the family parted, Henry, Edson, and Willie, by request, sang 'The Evergreen Shore,' much to the gratification of the crowd waiting for another train. The whistle was heard, the 'good by' and 'farewell' were said, and away sped the train, bearing the parents on their mission of love, and leaving the children again without their watchcare."

One day Mr. Howland said, "Boys, we've run out of charts. We have to wait for more to get here from Boston. You've worked hard, so now you can have a little vacation."

"Not sorry to hear that," Henry said. "Now we can go exploring."

"Where?" asked Edson.

"Down along the Androscoggin[1] River," answered his brother. "Rivermen are rolling logs there, I heard. A lot of logs broke loose from their rafts during a heavy flood, and they're trying to get them together again."

[1] Androscoggin (an-drə-SKAH-gən)

So the two brothers headed for the river. Caught up in the excitement of the shouting rivermen, they waded and tramped for miles, watching and wishing they could help with the log rolling.

One afternoon, especially tired from one of these long hikes, Henry went back to the shop and lay down in his damp clothes. He went to sleep, not realizing that a chilly wind had come up and was blowing directly on him through an open window. He slept hard, and when he woke up he felt stiff and thoroughly chilled. As could be expected, he developed a bad cold.

Meanwhile, in Brookfield, New York, Henry's father awoke one morning and said to his wife, "Ellen, I've had a dream that makes me think all is not well with our boys. Perhaps we should hurry to Topsham to find out if they are sick or in some kind of trouble."

Ellen became alarmed. Her mind went back to the fall of 1860. James had gone to Wisconsin on a preaching tour, leaving her at home with a very young, perfectly well baby boy. One night in a dream he had seen little John Herbert, but the baby wasn't healthy — he was very sick. The worried father hurried home to find that his worst fears were true. Not long after his return John Herbert had died.

But now the boys were older. Surely in the good care of the Howlands nothing could go wrong. Instead of hurrying home they wrote a letter, asking if everything was all right. News from Topsham reported that all was well. But this didn't satisfy their minds, and they returned to their children. When their cars stopped at the depot, Henry bounded through the crowd and hugged his mother. At Brother Howland's house he played and sang one of his favorite pieces, "Home Again."

Four days later Henry's cold turned into pneumonia. "We must get help," said Elder White. The Howlands recommended their kindly old family doctor, who did his best for the sick boy. But the medicines used in those days were useless in his case, and Henry rapidly became very ill.

From the first day of his sickness, Henry felt that he would not get well. His bed was moved to a large downstairs room. There the family group talked earnestly and prayed together. At first Henry was restless. He felt that he had not been a good example to Edson and Willie, had neglected prayer, and had failed to make his parents happy at all times. But as they talked and prayed together, the peace of God entered his heart and he was able to rest quietly.

One morning the sick boy said, "Promise me, Mother, that if I die I may be taken to Battle Creek. Lay me beside my little brother, John Herbert, that we may come up together in the morning of the resurrection." His mother promised. Then he confessed that he had sometimes thought his parents were too strict with their boys. "But," he added, "you have not been any too strict. I now realize that I was in danger, and am glad you said as much as you did. I wish I had heeded your advice more faithfully."

A few days later he dictated a special message to his many young friends. "I consider it a privilege before I sleep," he said, "to say a few words to my young friends. My age is sixteen years. I was baptized and united with the church last winter. I have a good hope of coming up with the saints in the first resurrection. I would appeal to all my young friends to not let the pleasures . . . of the world eclipse the loveliness of Christ . . . . Spend the best of your days in serving the Lord."

While lying there, Henry remembered his adventures on the fairground at Battle Creek. Now he understood why his father had destroyed the drum. It had been a symbol of the terrible war between the States, still raging, and perhaps a symbol of that greater war between Christ and the powers of evil. Now he said thankfully, "If I don't get well, at least I'll escape being drafted into the army!"

He often asked Edson to go into the parlor and play the melodeon for him. Once when Edson finished playing, Henry thanked him and told him how well he had played. "Music in heaven will be sweeter than that," Henry said.

Henry did not recover. He was laid to rest beside his brother as he wished. Edson and Willie treasured the memory of the brother who had been so talented and such a leader. Henry's parents ever afterward referred to him as their "sweet singer." And they were comforted, knowing that when Jesus comes, they will be reunited with their firstborn son, Henry Nichols White.

— *Alta Robinson*

What Do You Think?

1. If you had been James White, would you have destroyed Henry's drum? Explain your answer.
2. What single word would you choose to describe Henry White? Explain the reasons for your answer.
3. Why did the White boys want to be like the soldiers?

Taking a Closer Look

1. Why did Henry want to run away from home?
2. What was the main idea of Henry's last letter to his friends?
3. Why did the Whites take Henry, Edson, and Willie with them to New England?
4. What embarrassing experience occurred with Henry and his drum? If this had happened to you, what would you have done?
5. Why did Henry say Brother Jonah Lewis had no right to complain?
6. Why did James White so strongly disapprove of war? Why did he encourage his sons to sing hymns instead of play soldiers?

What goes through the mind of a native child when a missionary first arrives in her village? In what ways does the "bird with no feathers" help the child and others in this village? Draw a picture in your mind of the "bird-without-feathers." Read the story to see if your picture was correct.

A Bird with No Feathers

Somehow I knew it was going to be a special day that morning weeks ago when I woke up and saw little brother's mat was empty. The fingers of the sun had already crept in between the cracks in the wall behind me. I didn't know why I felt so much alive that day, why my heart seemed to sing with the songbird in the bamboo grove down by the river. It was as if I knew that something special was going to happen.

After I rolled off my mat, I took some rice from the big bowl in the corner and went out on the veranda. Mother was already down below, weaving the palm fronds for the new roof they are making for our longhouse. Two days ago when the big rain came and the river climbed out from between its banks, the water splashed down and in on us fiercely. She said we must make a new roof. All the women will help, except Grandmother. Grandmother is sick. She lies all day on her mat and coughs. Sometimes blood comes out. It is an old sickness, but it makes me afraid.

I crept slowly down the notched log, as quiet as a snake. If Mother heard me, I would have to carry up the daily water from the river, and that day I did not wish for anything to delay me. I was still quiet when I passed the big tree behind the longhouse, for I did not wish to anger the spirit that lives there. Our Pastor Maung says there is no truth to the stories of the spirits in the trees, but Grandmother says it is best to be careful in any case.

First I stopped near the bamboo grove by the river. Little brother and I once found a vine hanging there from an old tree that is bent like Grandmother's back. The vine is long and thick, and we pull it back up on the bank and swing out over the water. Little brother can swing farther than I, although he is younger.

I soon tired of our vine, though, for I do not like to be alone in my games. It was so quiet. I wondered where little brother was and where my friends had gone. Some of the women I could see down by the river at the rocks, washing their sarongs. Others were up with my mother now, helping to weave the palm fronds. But nowhere could I see my cousins or little brother. I looked up the trail to the mountain where we sometimes play "hunters," but the path was as empty as a deserted spirit-house. It was then I heard the sound — the sound like the rumble of faraway thunder, but not so deep. I knew then where they all were. It was coming — the strange bird with no feathers that carries the foreign man inside.

Running as quickly as I could, I felt I could race with the deer that morning and not fall behind. I knew that the bird-without-feathers would stop down by the small shelter where the men have cleared a long strip of land. There I knew I would find my friends.

It was true, what I had thought. Little brother and our cousins all crouched behind the bushes along the edge of the cleared land. The bird-without-feathers soon dropped down out of the sky and ran along the ground, louder and louder; then, as suddenly, quiet as the end of a storm when only the rainwater drips in the jungle.

I had seen the bird-without-feathers before. Also the foreign man who rides in it, for he comes sometimes to talk to our Teacher Maung. But that day when the sides of the bird opened, I almost cried out in surprise. Two foreign women also stepped out, and they all talked together in strange words that have no meaning. Maybe it wasn't safe, or maybe not in the good manners of their land for us to listen to them, but we were so curious we forgot to be afraid. We came out and stood close to the strangers, waiting to see what would come next.

The foreign women were taller than my mother, and their skin was a strange pale color as though the sun had not shone on it for many years and it had faded. Their hair was not black and long and straight like mine, but bent into many shapes, short, and the color of a deer's skin. They wore cloth of many colors and shapes so that I could hardly take my eyes off the women. In my mind I searched for words to describe them to my mother. Maybe she would like to see such cloth.

Then a strange thing happened. The man bent low by the bird and opened a little door in its belly. From inside he began to pull out boxes — many boxes — and carry them over to the side of the cleared strip. When the bird was empty, they all looked at the sky. I looked, too, but could see only the gray clouds of approaching rain. That must have been what they searched for, because they took a large piece of clear skin and covered the boxes. I went up, then, and touched the skin, for it looked as if the water would splash right through it, but it was heavy and stiff.

After the man spoke some more words, he got back into his bird. The bird began to sing as though happy to have the man in him again. The women raised their hands. Then the man and the bird flew away, only they forgot and left the women here with us. One of the women, the taller one with the red and blue cloth, turned and smiled at me. Suddenly I knew what was happening that day. The foreigners had come to stay with us — in our village.

For a while I waited for them to take the path to the longhouse, but they only stood there looking either at the sky or at their pile of boxes under the stiff, clear skin. I

86

spoke to little brother, and together we said to them, "Come with us."

They did not answer but took some of the smaller boxes with handles; so we all picked up what we could carry. Across the rice fields I could see some of the village men, but they only watched us.

Halfway to the village, the path crosses a river in a small swampy area. A tree serves as a bridge. We went on ahead, but the women halted there with their boxes. They would put one foot up, then another, but the box would slip in their hands, and they would almost lose their balance. From the way they acted, I decided it must be the first time in their lives they had walked a tree lying across a river. As I ran back to them and took the big box, I wondered how they crossed rivers in their country. Perhaps it has no rivers. Anyway, without the box they crossed soon enough, and we came to Teacher Maung's house.

Since Teacher Maung was not at home, we left the boxes under his house. One of the neighbors came out to invite the strangers to her house. It is the best in our village, next to Teacher Maung's, for it has clear glass windows and large rooms.

It was raining then, but even through the rain we could see the men and boys from the rice fields bringing up the big boxes, carrying them easily on their heads. My uncle took a log, walked up to a window, and pushed it open. Soon all the boxes sat in Maung's house, and the foreign women went over there.

By now the news had spread to everyone, and even Mother had come to see the new guests. When she spotted me, she frowned with surprise. Among those who came were some of the older children who have been to Teacher Maung's school and who know some foreign words. They asked many questions, then said the foreigners wanted to bathe. We took them to the pool by the swamp, but it did not please our guests. They said the water was not clean. I looked carefully, and it was true. The water was not clear and bubbling like it is in the streams that run into the river. I said, "There is a clear running stream close to the bamboos. Let us take them there."

We waited outside the house. Soon the women came out, but now they wore sarongs like our women do. They did not look so old, maybe not so much more than my sister who is away at the Christian school.

It was an exciting night for all of us. My mother helped them to start a fire, and when she left, she did not close the door at the back. I watched from under the house where Mother could not see me and take me home with her. Soon chickens filled the house, and I could hear the foreigners running after them. Creeping out as soon as Mother left, I laughed loudly as the chickens came flying out of the house, scattering feathers behind them. When the foreigners laughed, too, I walked up the log into the house. There I helped them learn to talk the way we do. They would point to something, and I would tell them the name of it. They would repeat it again and again until they said the name right, then they would motion to something else.

When I finally went home, Mother scolded me, of course, but I told her that the foreigners had needed my help. I explained how I had carried their boxes, showed them the stream, and finally, how I had begun to teach them to talk. Though she scolded me still, her words were not sharp.

Life was different after that. The next day the foreigners opened up their boxes and began to take out the things inside. They contained many bottles and medicines, and soon we understood that the women knew how to use them. People began coming from all around, though it was difficult to get the right medicines sometimes, since they did not understand the meaning of our words. One woman came in to say her stomach hurt. After much talking, the foreigner — the tall one — told the woman she would have a baby, and everyone laughed and laughed. Even her husband laughed, but I didn't see what was funny. It is good news to have a baby coming.

That evening my mother invited the strangers to our house. When I heard about it, I raced home with my heart singing again like the songbird in the bamboo grove. It was not easy for Mother to talk to them, but already I had learned to read the meaning of their hand motions, of their looks, and of the laughter that comes to them as quickly as it does to me. When the tall one laughs, it is like the sound of the stream jumping over the rocks on its way to the river. Already I began to call her my sister, for I am lonely for my big sister. Little brother says it is foolish for me to call her so, for she is not one of us, but that is not true. I have heard Teacher Maung say that all men are of one family and that God is the Father of all, so why should she not be my sister?

Teacher Maung came back before the next sunset, and soon he helped them give out medicines. Milton, his son, talked to them in their own words, and often he helped with the medicines. Each day I would watch all that went on. I discovered that my foreign sister went to the river each day to bathe. At first I thought maybe that was why her skin was so pale, but now that she has been here so long, the sun has browned hers almost to the color of mine. No, the bathing was to keep her as clean as the stream whose voice she imitates when she laughs. Wanting to be like her, I went each evening to the stream also. She showed me how to wash the dirt and smoke away, even behind my ears and in my hair. I learned to keep the inside of my mouth clean, too, by washing it with a stick after each time I eat.

On the seventh day she taught me songs to make my heart sing with words, not only the notes the songbird sings. She told me it is true what Pastor Maung says about God who is our Father — hers and mine. On some seventh days she goes with her friend and with Teacher Maung to other villages, and then I am lonely. Sometimes they stay for several days.

During one of her trips, I had a bad experience with a stick. I was lonely and restless, and I fought so loudly with little brother that Mother sent us away so we wouldn't bother her. I went down to the swinging vine where I hadn't gone since the day "my sister" first came. Although I could swing farther than ever before, my heart was not there with me, and my eyes were blind to what I was doing. The vine twisted and jerked suddenly as I came back high above the bank, and I lost my grip. It was nothing new for me to fall. Since I am like a monkey and can always land on my feet, I was not afraid. But when my feet hit the ground, I felt a sharp pain like nothing I had ever known before. Blood streamed from my foot, and I could see where the stick had broken inside the wound. Crying with the pain, I crawled to my mother.

Mother could do nothing, and neither could Grandmother. Pastor Maung was gone with "my sister" and her friend. Four days passed before they returned.

"What have you done to yourself?" she cried when she saw my foot. She carried me to the medicine room and laid me down on a bench. "I am sorry I must hurt you," she warned me gently, and it was true that she had tears in her eyes.

92

Taking a piece of shiny metal, she reached into the wound with it. I shut my teeth tight together and tried not to cry. After a while she stopped and shook her head. "I can't reach it," she said. And then I forgot all the pain, for she put her arms around me and held me tight for a moment. It was only two days later that she had my uncle carry me down to the place where I had first met her. There she told me, "I am sending you to the hospital with Pastor Hall."

"You mean I will ride in the bird-without-feathers?" I cried.

She laughed at me. "Yes, little sister."

"But I must go alone?"

"No, others from the village must go too, so you will not be alone."

So I rode in the bird-without-feathers that is not a bird at all but a machine with many eyes inside. And at the hospital, which is like a big white longhouse, only not high off the ground, they took the stick out of my foot. It did not hurt, for they first put a needle in it to take the pain away, but I was glad to return home, for I missed *her*.

Now that I have been to school, I am putting this down in words on paper because I don't want to forget any part of all that happened during those weeks. My life has changed — I learned to sing, to be clean. I learned to play strange foreign games. I learned about the machine that flies and how to say the foreigners' words with meaning. I learned all about the great Father, God, who loves me so much that He sent this foreign sister especially for me from so far away. And I learned what it means to love without wanting something for yourself, because now that she is gone, I speak to my Father and ask Him for things that are not for me, but for her.

— Donna June Evans

What Do You Think?

1. The girl in this story felt that "something special was going to happen." Have you ever had a feeling like that? Tell about it.
2. Teacher Maung taught that "all men are of one family." What does this mean? Did the missionaries believe this? Support your answer with details from the story.
3. Describe the friendship that developed between the child and missionary. How did it develop? How did the child's mother feel about it?

Taking a Closer Look

1. What clue did the girl have that the foreign women had come to live in her village?
2. In your own words, tell about the girl's accident.
3. How did the girl say she had helped the newcomers?
4. What kind of work did the newcomers come to do?
5. What things did the girl learn from the newcomers?
6. In this story the girl explains things in words she can understand. For example, she calls the airplane a bird-without-feathers. Find and explain three other things that she describes in this way.

Putting Ideas to Work

Imagine you are the missionary. In words the child will understand, describe a snowstorm, an automobile, a train, an apartment building, and a bicycle.

When i see what has been accomplished, i am filled with confidence in Christ as a leader. We have nothing to fear from the future except as we forget the way the Lord has led us and His teachings in our past history.

E. G. White

Nothing to Fear

Remembering our spiritual roots can take away our fears for the future. This thought is shown in the sculpture at the left, a paraphrase from the writings of Ellen G. White. The sculpture below depicts six pioneers whose courageous lives led to the founding of the Seventh-day Adventist Church.

The illustrations on these pages are photographs of two bas-relief wood sculptures hanging in Founders' Hall at Atlantic Union College in Massachusetts.

Pictured above are (from left to right): J. N. Andrews, S. N. Haskell, Hetty H. Haskell, Joseph Bates, James White, and Ellen G. White.

On the Light Side

What's so funny? You may keep a stony silence as someone else laughs aloud. Or you may smile broadly and chuckle over something that is not funny to another person. Not everyone thinks the same things are funny. That's what "on the light side" is all about.

UNEXPECTED BENEFITS

SOMETIMES GOOD THINGS happen when we don't expect them. What unexpected benefits did a composition assignment bring to Ramona and her sister?

Clank! Clank!

One afternoon Ramona was on her knees on the kitchen floor working on a picture when Beezus came home from school, dropped her books on the kitchen table, and said, "Well, it's come."

Ramona looked up from the picture of Glenwood School she was drawing on the roll of shelf paper taped to the floor. Mr. Quimby, who had a dish towel tucked into his belt for an apron, turned from the kitchen sink. "What's come?" he asked. Although it was late in the afternoon, he was washing the breakfast dishes. He had been interviewed for two different jobs that morning.

"Creative writing." Beezus's voice was filled with gloom.

"You make it sound like a calamity," said her father.

Beezus sighed. "Well — maybe it won't be so bad this time. We aren't supposed to write stories or poems after all."

"Then what does Mrs. Mester mean by creative?"

"Oh, you know. . . ." Beezus twirled around on one toe to define creative.

"What are you supposed to write if you don't write a story or a poem?" asked Ramona. "Arithmetic problems?"

Beezus continued to twirl as if spinning might inspire her. "She said we should interview some old person and ask questions about something they did when they were our age. She said she would run off what we wrote on the ditto machine, and we could make a book." She stopped twirling to catch the dish towel her father tossed to her. "Do we know anyone who helped build a log cabin or something like that?"

"I'm afraid not," said Mr. Quimby. "We don't know anybody who skinned buffalo either. How old is old?"

"The older the better," said Beezus.

"Mrs. Swink is pretty old," volunteered Ramona. Mrs. Swink was a widow who lived in the house on the corner and drove an old sedan that Mr. Quimby admiringly called a real collector's item.

"Yes, but she wears polyester pant suits," said Beezus, who had grown critical of clothing lately. She did not approve of polyester pant suits, white shoes, or Ramona's T-shirt with Rockaway Beach printed on the front.

"Mrs. Swink is old inside the pant suits," Ramona pointed out.

Beezus made a face. "I can't go barging in on her all by myself and ask her a bunch of questions." Beezus was the kind of girl who never wanted to go next door to borrow an egg.

"I'll come," said Ramona, who was always eager to go next door to borrow an egg.

"You don't barge in," said Mr. Quimby, wringing out the dishcloth. "You phone and make an appointment. Go on. Phone her now and get it over."

Beezus put her hand on the telephone book. "But what'll I say?" she asked.

"Just explain what you want and see what she says," said Mr. Quimby. "She can't bite you over the telephone."

Beezus appeared to be thinking hard. "OK," she said with some reluctance, "but you don't have to listen."

Ramona and her father went into the living room and turned on the television so they couldn't overhear Beezus.

In a moment Beezus appeared, looking flustered. "I meant sometime in a day or so, but she said to come right now because in a little while she has to take a molded salad to her lodge for a potluck supper. Dad, what'll I *say*? I haven't had time to think."

"Just play it by ear," he advised. "Something will come to you."

"I'm going too," Ramona said, and Beezus did not object.

Mrs. Swink saw the sisters coming and opened the door for them as they climbed the front steps. "Come on in, girls, and sit down," she said briskly. "Now what is it you want to interview me about?"

103

Beezus seemed unable to say anything, and Ramona could understand how it might be hard to ask someone wearing a polyester pant suit questions about building a log cabin. Someone had to say something so Ramona spoke up. "My sister wants to know what you used to do when you were a little girl."

Beezus found her tongue. "Like I said over the phone. It's for creative writing."

Mrs. Swink looked thoughtful. "Let's see. Nothing very exciting, I'm afraid. I helped with the dishes and read a lot of books from the library."

Beezus looked worried, and Ramona could see that she was trying to figure out what she could write about dishes and library books. Ramona ended another awkward silence by asking, "Didn't you make anything?" She had noticed that Mrs. Swink's living room was decorated with mosaics made of dried peas and beans and with owls made out of pinecones. The dining-room table was strewn with old Christmas cards, scissors, and paste, a sure sign of a craft project.

"Let's see now. . . ." Mrs. Swink looked thoughtful. "We made fudge, and—oh, I know—tin-can stilts." She smiled to herself. "I had forgotten all about tin-can stilts until this very minute."

At last Beezus could ask a question. "How did you make tin-can stilts?"

Mrs. Swink laughed, remembering. "We took two tall cans. Two-pound coffee cans were best. We turned them upside down and punched two holes near what had once been the bottom of each. The holes had to be opposite one another on each can. Then we poked about four feet of heavy twine through each pair of holes and knotted the ends to make a loop. We set one foot on each can, took hold of a loop of twine in each hand, and began to walk. We had to remember to lift each can by the loop of twine as we raised a foot or we fell off — my knees were always skinned. Little girls wore dresses instead of slacks in those days, and I always had dreadful scabs on my knees."

Maybe this was why Mrs. Swink always wore pant suits now, thought Ramona. She didn't want scabs on her knees in case she fell down.

"And the noise those hollow tin cans made on the sidewalk!" continued Mrs. Swink, enjoying the memory. "All the kids in the neighborhood went clanking up and down. Sometimes the cans would cut through the twine, and we would go sprawling on the sidewalk. I became expert at walking on tin-can stilts and used to go clanking around the block yelling, 'Pieface!' at all the younger children."

105

Ramona and Beezus both giggled. They were surprised that someone as old as Mrs. Swink had once called younger children by a name they sometimes called one another.

"There." Mrs. Swink ended the interview. "Does that help?"

"Yes, thank you." Beezus stood up, and so did Ramona, although she wanted to ask Mrs. Swink about the craft project on the dining-room table.

"Good." Mrs. Swink opened the front door. "I hope you get an *A* on your composition."

"Tin-can stilts weren't exactly what I expected," said Beezus, as the girls started home. "But I guess I can make them do."

Do! Ramona couldn't wait to get to Howie's house to tell him about the tin-can stilts. And so, as Beezus went home to labor over her creative writing, Ramona ran over to the Kemps' house. Just as she thought, Howie listened to her excited description and said, "I could make some of those." Good old Howie. Ramona and Howie spent the rest of the afternoon finding four two-pound coffee cans. The search involved persuading Howie's mother to empty out her coffee into mayonnaise jars and calling on neighbors to see if they had any empty cans.

The next day after school Howie arrived on the Quimby doorstep with two sets of tin-can stilts. "I made them!" he announced, proud of his work. "And Willa Jean wanted some, so I made her a pair out of tuna cans so she wouldn't have far to fall."

"I knew you could do it!" Ramona, who had already changed to her playclothes, stepped onto two of the cans and pulled the twine loops up tight before she took a cautious step, lifting a can as she lifted her foot. First the left foot, then the right foot. *Clank, clank*. They worked! Howie clanked along beside her. They clanked carefully down the driveway to the sidewalk, where Ramona tried to pick up speed, forgot to lift a can at the same time she lifted her foot, and, as Mrs. Swink had recalled, fell off her stilts. She caught herself before she tumbled to the sidewalk and climbed back on.

Clank, clank! Clank, clank!

—*Beverly Cleary*

107

MAGGIE DECIDED to run against Thad for class president. Noah, the shy class scholar, guided her campaign. Thad selected Henry as his manager. After a trying campaign, the voting began.

Your Next President Is...

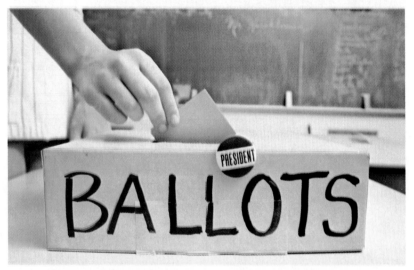

Maggie made a small x in the space beside the name *Maggie Marmelstein* on the ballot. She had always planned to make a huge X, but now she didn't feel like it.

Maggie put her ballot through the slot in the ballot box. The box was closely guarded by Mr. Krickleman in his social studies classroom. As each member of the sixth grade voted, Mr. Krickleman crossed a name off his long list. The ballots had the names *Maggie Marmelstein* and *Thad Smith* printed on

108

them, and a third name: *Other.* "Other," Mr. Krickleman had said, "is anyone else in the sixth grade you wish to vote for. Simply write in the name. Please refrain from voting for your dog, your favorite television program, various fruits and vegetables, detergents, musical groups, sports heroes, assorted rodents or any other idea that you think is funny. It might *be* funny, but it will be a wasted vote. Anyone can vote for herself or himself, as Maggie and Thad of course know. There are forty-nine students in the sixth grade. Four are absent today. So we should have forty-five votes." The name of the winner was to be announced in the lunchroom after school.

109

Maggie wished the election were over. She tried not to look at Thad during the day. She tried not to look at the campaign posters. She tried to pretend to herself that she wasn't a candidate. "I'm silly," she told herself. "I should be eager, but instead I'm silly."

Ellen and Noah were waiting to walk to the lunchroom with her after school.

"I must tell you," said Noah, "that I think the election will be very close. Nobody won the debate yesterday, because there was, in fact, no debate."

"Well, whatever it was, Tamara lost it," said Ellen.

Maggie smiled. She felt good when Ellen said that. Very good.

"Where should we sit?" asked Maggie when they reached the lunchroom.

"Anywhere the president wishes," said Noah.

"That table by the window," said Maggie.

"Excellent," said Noah. "A kind of natural spotlight on the winner."

"You think of everything, Noah," said Maggie.

"Well, I've tried to help you win," said Noah. "And in these last few moments before the winner is announced, I want you to know that it's made me thoroughly happy to be your campaign manager."

"We've enjoyed having you, haven't we, Maggie?" said Ellen.

"You're the best, Noah," said Maggie.

Maggie saw Thad and Henry come into the lunchroom. They sat down at the next table. Maggie thought they looked terrific together, just the two of them.

110

Mr. Krickleman entered the room. He was carrying the ballot box. He placed the box on a special table that had been set up at the far end of the room. Then he took the cover, with the slot in it, off the box. He emptied the ballots on the table. He started counting the ballots, and writing on a piece of paper. Maggie tried to figure out how he was doing what he was doing. She strained to see if there were a big pile of ballots and a little pile of ballots, but the box was in the way. Mr. Krickleman was talking to himself. Whatever he was doing with the ballots, he was doing twice or three times or even four times. He put his fingers through his hair, he wiped his nose, he loosened his necktie and he kept counting and writing. At last he looked up and announced, "I have counted and recounted the ballots to make certain there was no error. And now, members of the sixth grade, we have a winner! You have a president." Mr. Krickleman tightened the tie he had just loosened. He said, "When I announce the winner's name, will that person please come forward and say a few words to the class."

Maggie felt she couldn't wait another second. She couldn't breathe. She longed for the ordinary, plain moments of her life.

"Your new president," said Mr. Krickleman, "is NOAH MOORE!!!"

"Noah?" said Maggie. "Noah?"

"I don't believe it. I don't believe it!" said Noah.

Most of the sixth grade was cheering wildly.

Maggie looked over to the next table. Thad and Henry appeared to be in deep shock.

"Come, Noah, speech! Speech!" called Mr. Krickleman.

Noah got up. Slowly, as if his legs had been given a new job that they had no previous experience for, he walked toward Mr. Krickleman.

"Poor Noah," said Ellen to Maggie. "Down deep he's still a scared person. And I think I know what he's going to say to the class. He'll say, 'Thank you. I quit.'"

"No, he won't," said Maggie. "Noah will say, 'Thank you for the great honor you have bestowed upon me. Unfortunately, I am unable to fulfill the functions of the presidency of this class. I therefore resign.'"

Noah was now standing beside Mr. Krickleman, who shook his hand.

Noah turned and faced the class. He said, "Thank you. I accept."

Another great cheer went up for Noah. Maggie couldn't believe it. She couldn't believe anything. Noah elected as president! Noah saying, "I accept." I *accept*. How could he accept? He was her campaign manager. More than that, he was her friend.

"I can't believe it," Maggie said to Ellen.

"Go up and tell Noah you can't believe it," said Ellen. "See what he says. And if it's any help, tell him I can't believe it either."

Maggie walked up to Noah, who was still standing facing the class. Everyone was looking at Maggie as she walked up to Noah. But Maggie didn't even notice.

"Noah," she whispered when she got beside him, "I don't believe this. Neither does Ellen."

Noah whispered back, "Count me in. I don't believe it, either. But Maggie, I want to tell you something immediately. I'm not really accepting. I'm too frightened *not* to accept right now. I can't get up in front of everybody here and tell them that the object of their enthusiasm does not want to be president."

"You mean you don't *want* to be president?"

"It never crossed my mind. I enjoyed being your manager. I wanted *you* to win."

Mr. Krickleman and the class were staring at Maggie and Noah. Why would they be standing in the middle of the room whispering to each other?

"Louder, louder," shouted Ronald. "We want to hear."

"Be quiet, Ronald," said Maggie. "This is private."

"Private in the middle of the lunchroom?" said Ronald. "Ridiculous. Everybody who wants to hear, raise your hand."

Hands shot up all over the room. Even Ellen raised hers.

Noah whispered to Maggie. "I failed as a manager when I wanted to succeed and I succeeded as a presidential candidate when I wasn't even running. And I messed up your campaign."

"You didn't mess it up," Maggie whispered. "I know why you got elected."

"Tell me," said Noah.

"Louder," shouted Ronald.

Maggie turned toward Mr. Krickleman. "May I speak to the class?" she asked.

"Anything," said Mr. Krickleman, "that would quiet Ronald would be greatly appreciated."

"Class," said Maggie, "I wanted to be president. And Thad Smith, who was a fair and honest opponent, also wanted to be president. But Noah should be president. He knows the most about what the sixth grade needs. And you know it. And that's why you voted for him."

Ronald yelled, "You're hogging the show, Maggie. Let Thad talk, too."

Henry pulled Thad up from his seat and gave him a slight push toward the center of the room.

Then Thad, Maggie and Noah were standing together in the middle of the room.

Thad spoke to the class. "I have three things to say. If you want Noah for president, it's okay with me. That's the first thing. The second thing is that I am still fair and honest. The third thing is that Maggie Marmelstein is sometimes great. The reason I said the third thing is because the second thing is true."

114

Maggie felt wonderful. She also felt victorious. But not victorious over anyone. How could that be? Maybe there were different kinds of victories, and you couldn't campaign for some of them. They weren't won. They were earned.

Noah whispered to her and Thad. "It is definitely better to lose together than to win separately."

"What do you mean?" asked Maggie.

"I mean I didn't want to be president," said Noah. "That's what I've already told you. But now both of you have told the sixth grade that you support me. Now I can't resign simply. I'll have to resign complicatedly."

"How do you do that?" asked Thad.

"I don't know," said Noah. "It's going to be hard work. It's going to be the most difficult work I've ever done."

Noah shook Maggie's hand and Thad's hand. Then he left the lunchroom before anyone could catch up with him.

The class slowly left after him.

Maggie and Thad walked home together. "Well, Noah is president," said Maggie. "For weeks and weeks and weeks. It will take him all that time to do an absolutely first-rate job of resigning. He'll search for all kinds of information, he'll go to every library in the area, he'll send for booklets from the government, he'll rehearse and he'll rehearse again.

"Then what happens?" asked Thad. "If he finally resigns?"

"A new election, I guess," said Maggie.

"Would you run again?" asked Thad.

"Maybe," said Maggie. "Would you?"

"Maybe," said Thad.

Maggie and Thad reached their apartment house.

"Want some victory cake?" asked Maggie.

"Why not?" said Thad.

—*Marjorie Weinman Sharmat*

116

What Do You Think?

1. In what ways did the adventures of Ramona and Maggie bring "unexpected benefits"?

2. How are Ramona and Maggie alike? How are they different?

3. Suppose that "Clank! Clank!" had a different ending. What ending would you suggest? What different ending would you give to Maggie's story?

Taking a Closer Look

1. The author describes Beezus as the kind of girl who "never wanted to go next door to borrow an egg." What is she saying about Beezus?

2. Describe how Mrs. Swink once made tin-can stilts.

3. What were some of the ways that Mrs. Swink surprised Ramona and Beezus?

4. In what ways did Maggie show her excitement as the voting progressed?

5. Why did Mr. Krickleman count the ballots more than once?

6. How did Noah's statement to the class surprise Maggie?

7. The author states that: "Maggie felt wonderful. She also felt victorious. But not victorious over anyone. How could that be?" How did Maggie answer this question?

Sometimes even an Investment project goes wrong. Willy believed that he had the idea for a better mousetrap. He just hadn't counted on the side effects. This is the story of a really exciting idea that didn't work at all. But something much more important happened.

A Better Mousetrap

"My Investment project will bring in a hundred dollars, at least," I boasted.

The whole Sabbath school class gasped. Annabelle's eyes glassed over. It was just the effect I'd hoped for. She had single-handedly received two Jasper Wayne Awards only a month before. That wouldn't have bothered me so much if the adults hadn't treated her like Jasper Wayne himself. Even the conference president came to shake her hand, and she got her picture in the *Messenger*.

"How are you going to raise a hundred dollars?" asked Annabelle.

I smiled. "You'll have to wait and see. But I can tell you one thing for sure; this is a project that this church will remember for a long time. As my Grandmother always says, 'If you build a better mousetrap, the world will beat a path to your door.'"

The Sabbath school class didn't know that I had a secret weapon. They were picturing some unique contraption that would lure and kill mice by the dozens, but my mousetrap was no mechanical contraption. Zap, my pet ferret, was my secret weapon.

118

Before he came to our house, mice got into everything. They were already in the house when we moved in, and they seemed to resent our being there.

My mother carried a broom for self-defense. Whenever she saw a mouse, she swung the broom like a near-sighted hockey player. She broke a window, four brooms, and a plate of her favorite china, but she never came close to a mouse. They were just too fast for her.

After I got Zap from the pet shop, the mice disappeared. Mom really wasn't too sure about having a ferret around the house. "Isn't it related to a weasel?" she had asked. We did have to make a few adjustments for the new member of the family, but Mom even accepts him now. She hasn't had to buy a new broom in nearly two years.

On Sunday morning I sat down at my desk to write an announcement for the church bulletin. This turned out to be tougher than I had expected. After an hour, wadded up papers covered the floor. Finally I came up with the perfect announcement: "An Investment project: Have mice in your house? I can Zap them for you. Satisfaction guaranteed. Call Willy Ilchuk at 555-9756."

I read the announcement in the bulletin the following Sabbath. It looked pretty good except that my first name was spelled *Milly*.

My first call came Sunday afternoon. "May I speak to Milly Ilchuk please."

"This is *Willy* Ilchuk. They misspelled my name in the bulletin. May I help you."

"This is Mrs. Hyde-White. Can you really get rid of mice?"

"Sure can! Satisfaction guaranteed."

"How much do you charge?"

"Well, remember it's an Investment project. It will cost five dollars."

"When can you start?"

"I can come over tomorrow before you go to work."

I showed up at the Hyde-White's house at 7:30 Monday morning. Mrs. Hyde-White was in an awful hurry. "Come in," she said as she put on her coat. She looked me over. "Where are the traps?"

"I have something better than traps," I grinned, unzipping my coat. Zap popped his head out, and Mrs. Hyde-White leaped onto a chair.

"What is that," she shrieked.

"It's a ferret. He won't hurt you. I'll just leave him in the house while you're at work. He's a better mouser than any cat you ever saw. I'll come back and pick him up tonight and bring him back tomorrow. A couple days ought to do it."

"Get that animal out of the house," she shuddered.

"But this is my Investment project."

Mrs. Hyde-White thought a moment. "Is that thing housebroken?"

"He'll be fine until tonight."

"All right, but you be sure to pick him up by 5:30 when I get home. Don't let him loose till I get out the door."

I set Zap down on the entryway floor. "OK, Zap, go get 'em," I said.

The day went quickly, and I was back at the Hyde-White's ten minutes early. I expected Zap to be waiting for me at the door, but he wasn't there. That was only the first surprise. Mrs. Hyde-White followed me through the house as I looked for Zap. One of the pillows on the bed was torn. Feathers covered the bedroom like snow. In the bathroom we found a vase in a million pieces on the floor.

The kitchen was last and worst. The bird cage lay broken and twisted on the floor, and all that was left of the canary was a pile of feathers. Zap slept peacefully in the sink.

"Get that animal out of here, and don't bother coming back tomorrow," Mrs. Hyde-White wailed.

"Does this mean I don't get five dollars?"

Mrs. Hyde-White's scornful glare gave me her answer. I quickly stuffed Zap into my coat and left.

The news must have got around to other members of the church. Nobody else called. I knew it was just a matter of time before the kids at school would find out about it too. It didn't take long.

"Hey, Milly," they laughed, "have you zapped any mice lately?" Even the older kids gave me a hard time, but Annabelle surprised me a little.

"I'm sorry your Investment project didn't work out," she said one day at recess. "It sounded like a good idea to me."

"Yeah, but I don't know what I'm going to do now. Zap's a great pet, but nobody appreciates him."

"Well, I've been thinking. I don't have a project yet, and people do like pets. They just don't like to have their houses torn up."

"That's for sure," I groaned.

"Maybe we should have a pet fair. You and I could organize it and make it a class Investment project."

I hesitated. I had never thought about working with Annabelle on anything. "Do you think we could make much money that way?"

She was warming to the idea. "I think most of the kids in this school would pay to see Zap."

I grinned. "Yeah, I suppose so."

"But we'll have to have more than just Zap. I have an ant farm. Rodney has a rabbit. Andy has three hamsters. Keith has a garter snake. Priscilla has mice."

"After what has happened, do you think you'll be able to talk Priscilla into bringing her mice?"

Annabelle laughed. "They're in cages. Zap won't hurt them."

124

"The canary was in a cage too," I reminded her.

"Well, maybe you'll have to put Zap in a cage for the day."

"He won't like that, but he owes me a favor."

We asked our teacher, Mrs. Forbes, if we could have a pet fair, and she liked the idea. She asked the other kids in the class if they would like to bring their pets to school, and the idea caught fire. "Annabelle and Willy think this would make a good Investment project for the whole class."

"Why don't we have it on a Sunday. Then our parents can come." Andy suggested.

"We could sell popcorn and apple juice," Priscilla added.

Before too long, we had it all planned. Mrs. Forbes helped us write an announcement for the church bulletin. This time they got the spelling right.

When the day came, people jammed into the school gymnasium. Zap didn't seem to mind that he had to stay in the cage for most of the day. Somebody put a sign on his cage that read: "Milly's Mouse Trap."

It was interesting to see all the different kinds of pets. Even some of the parents brought some. The father of one of the third graders brought three Malamute sled dogs. He gave rides around the frozen playing field for fifty cents. Pastor Webb brought his talking mynah bird, but he kept it on the other side of the gym. He'd heard about Zap too. Even Mrs. Hyde-White came, but if she had any other pets, she left them home.

The fair was pretty successful. It was lots of fun, and we raised $137 for Investment.

"We ought to do this every year," declared Annabelle.

"It was sure a better idea than my mousetrap," I added.

— Jean Bradley

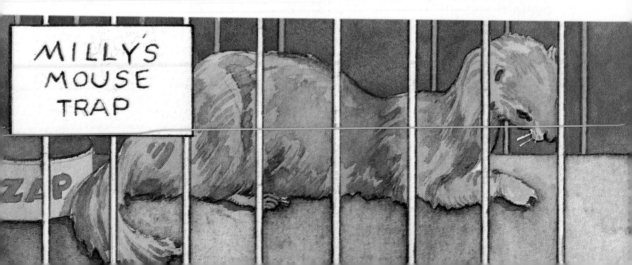

What Do You Think?

1. Which Investment idea would you prefer to be involved in: the mousetrap or the pet fair? Why?
2. Do you think that Willy's first interest was Investment? Support your answer with details from the story.
3. What did Willy learn about cooperation from this experience?
4. Have you ever had a project of yours fail? Why did it fail? How did you feel? What did you learn?

Taking a Closer Look

1. How did Willy know that Zap could catch mice?
2. Willy said, "This is a project that this church will remember for a long time." Was he right? Support your answer with details from the story.
3. Why was Annabelle's reaction to the disaster at Mrs. Hyde-White's unexpected?
4. Describe in your own words the damage Zap did at Mrs. Hyde-White's home.

Putting Ideas to Work

What other unusual Investment ideas have you heard of? Share them with the class. If you don't already have an Investment project of your own, think of one. You may want to talk to some other students and decide on a group project.

Limericks

There was a young lady of Niger
Who smiled as she rode on a tiger;
  They returned from the ride
  With the lady inside,
And the smile on the face of the tiger.

— *Unknown*

One day I went out to the Zoo,
For I wanted to see the old Gnu,
  But the old Gnu was dead
  And the new Gnu they said
Was too new a new Gnu to view.

— *Anonymous*

128

There was an Old Man with a beard
Who said, "It is just as I feared!
    Two Owls and a Hen,
    Four Larks and a Wren,
Have all built their nests in my beard!"

— *Edward Lear*

I wish that my room had a floor;
I don't so much care for a door,
    But this walking around
    Without touching the ground
Is getting to be quite a bore!

— *Gelett Burgess*

The Lomax boys didn't have much. But they had something that drew the neighbors together.

The Great Sandwich-Eating Contest of 1938

All the kids liked them, but it was forever a mystery to us how the two Lomax boys could be fat. We never saw them eat much. The thing was, of course, they didn't have much to eat.

They were as poor as anyone I knew as a boy. We all had a soft spot for them and tried to be extra considerate when we had our wits about us.

130

They had a hard time of it. We never called them by their first names. In volume they looked about the same, but the older and taller was called Big Lomax; the younger, Little Lomax. They called each other simply, Brother.

The Lomaxes had just this one old bicycle between them. The way they managed was a system the like of which I haven't seen since. One would ride the thing for a block, or, if they were on the highway, the distance between two telegraph poles. Then that one would lay it down and start walking. The other, who had done the same thing a-ways back, would walk up, mount the bike and ride on past. They would keep trading off and on until they got to where they were going.

You might think that with the bike being laid down all over the place, someone might try to take it. Nobody ever did. In fact once, when Little Lomax laid down the bicycle in a strange neighborhood, a man called after him, demanding that he not be leaving junk on the street corner. Little Lomax tried ignoring him, and the man ran after him half way up the block. By then, of course, Big Lomax went pedaling by. Little Lomax explained to the man, who told him he still shouldn't be doing it, no matter what.

That bike of theirs was the most pitiful thing you would ever want to see going down the street. It had black friction tape flapping from around the hard tires more places than not, rags tied on for seat padding, and the frame all speckled with sand that had blown when they painted it with some awful orange paint they had found somewhere.

I remember it was a Monday that the posters went up and everyone was talking about the contest. That coming Sunday there was going to be a sandwich-eating contest in each of the local parks, sponsored by the biggest and newest bakery in town.

The rules were simple. A line would be started at three o'clock. At four they would pass out sandwiches and have the contest. They planned to have enough sandwiches for everyone who showed up. But if they didn't, the rules stated, those first in line would be the ones to be in the contest. A gun would be fired to start the eating. The first girl and the first boy through eating who stepped forward and whistled would be the winners. These two, one boy and one girl, would compete in the finals at the high school auditorium for the city championships.

Prizes in the local parks, to be awarded to each of the winners, were $1 bills. The grand prizes at the high school were balloon-tire bicycles with chrome trim, speedometers, wheel-generator lights, rear racks, and even horns.

As you might guess, there wasn't a kid amongst us who didn't think almost immediately of the Lomaxes — right after, of course, he had thought for a while about how he would like to win that slick new bike for himself. The Lomaxes were certain to come to mind. We all knew how great it would be for them to get that bike. We knew, too, that they might have the special talent to win.

That Sunday we came together at Prindle Park no later than three. We were thunderstruck to find a line a half block long already there ahead of us. Running for the best places left, we shuffled around to make sure that the

Lomaxes were in the front. We worked Little Lomax up forward. But Big Lomax sensed what we were doing and fell in behind me, making him the very last of our bunch.

"Wonder what's going to be in them," George said, meaning the sandwiches.

"Hope cheese," said Big Lomax, talking more to himself.

"My cousin," added Steve, "heard from some guy who actually works for the bakery that they bought 20 cases of persimmon jam, special-made, with hardly any sugar."

"Dirty," said someone else.

"What's persimmon?"

"Some kind of fruit that makes your mouth all wrinkle up."

"Nahhh. They wouldn't do that. Wouldn't be good for business."

"They got to do something to make it hard, don't they?"

"Yeah. Just eating a sandwich ain't nothing."

Then the cheers started going up; the trucks had arrived.

One of the bread trucks had speakers. After the traditional crackle and clunk, a loud voice blared, "Well, kids, you really turned out, didn't you? And we can see there won't be enough of everything."

The groan that followed was louder from behind us in the line. I leaned out and saw about as many back there as there were in front of us.

"We had planned to have ice cream for everybody after the contest."

Some kids groaned. Some cheered.

"Tell you what we're going to do. We'll pass out the sandwiches now as far as they will go. And then we'll give the rest of you ice cream. That way I think everyone will get something. That's the best we can do, OK?" Again — cheers, groans, and boos.

"Don't unwrap your sandwiches," the voice instructed as they started handing them out from big cartons. "Not yet. We're going to pass out the ice cream before the contest."

Peanut butter, the word spread down the line ahead of the sandwiches.

I could see that they were reaching deep as they neared us. "Good luck, son," the man said, handing me the very last sandwich. He turned the carton upside down for effect.

"Sorry," he said to Big Lomax. "Now, we want you to lead the rest of the young people over to where those ladies are setting up under that elm tree."

I sort of held out my sandwich to Big Lomax, saying, "You do it. You know I'm a slow eater," which I was.

"I like ice cream anyway," he told me, a big smile on

134

top of his disappointment. He followed the man toward the table with the ice cream containers.

For half an hour I held that paper-wrapped sandwich, watching them endlessly dip cones. Then, suddenly, the speaker shouted, "Everybody — ready! Start when you hear the gun. The first boy and the first girl to step forward and whistle will be our winners. Those people with the red armbands are the judges.

"Ready, set," he warned.

"*Bwammm!*" The gun went off just the other side of the broad lilac bush behind us and scared me half to death. George Wilson dropped his sandwich on the ground.

On my first bite I leaned out to look at Little Lomax. He was starting on his second.

I never ate so fast before or since. But when I was only half done, there was Little Lomax, shuffling out of the line and whistling away. And we were cheering our heads off. The judge jogged over and raised Little Lomax's hand in the air.

The next Sunday, the day of the second contest, I changed to my good clothes right after supper. I remember sitting on the back steps for just a few minutes before riding the bike down to the high school auditorium where the contest would be held. And I prayed some. It wasn't that I was asking or pleading, as I recall, but just kind of calling attention to how great it would be if the Lomaxes could have that new bike.

The kids came together at the bike racks in front of the auditorium. Big Lomax and one of his sisters was with us. Little Lomax was supposed to meet with the other contestants at the side door.

I vividly remember a well-dressed man coming on the stage. Then a big, heavy cardboard carton — like the ones we had seen in the park. Sandwiches were passed out up and down the line.

"Cheese this time," one of the kids informed the audience, and everyone laughed.

The wax paper was discarded and quickly picked up by an assistant. The kids waited, bare sandwiches in hand.

The starting gun was fired, this time a small blank pistol, and, with ease Little Lomax took his first bite.

Some of the kids were cramming it in at a frantic rate that was hard to believe possible. The tallest boy in the line rolled his into a ball and put it all into his mouth at one time.

Little Lomax, I thought to myself, doesn't stand a chance. He was just munching along, the same comfortable way I had seen him eat a dozen times.

A girl with one long red braid over her shoulder jumped forward trying to whistle. The attendant shook his head at her. He tapped the side of his face to show that her one cheek was still puffed wide with food.

One boy choked. He had to be slapped on the back, dropped part of his sandwich, and was disqualified.

Another, with close-cut black hair, was working his jaws up and down with his hands, trying to chew as fast as possible.

When my eyes came back to Little Lomax, I couldn't believe it. He was carefully licking the ends of his fingers.

"Whistle! Whistle!" I screamed and was joined by everyone around me. "*Whistle!*"

He did, about one second before the tall kid. We yelled and jumped up and down and pounded each other on the shoulders.

I grabbed Steve Henderson's arm next to me as we moved toward the aisle. "We got to do something," I told him. "Maybe have a party to celebrate. Let's try to get those leftover sandwiches." Against the solid mass of people leaving, I started squirming through the crowd toward the stage, pulling Henderson's arm along with me.

The man up front told us we could have them as far as he was concerned. And not waiting for someone to say different, Steve and I took the big box down the aisle and out. From the weight there had to be another 50 sandwiches in there, I figured.

When the kids outside saw the box, they were ready to empty it on the spot. Steve declared that it was for a party at the Lomaxes'. The three who had already taken sandwiches put them back.

"Okay?" I aimed the question at the Lomaxes' sister, not looking at Big Lomax. "About the party?"

"Sure," she said, all smiles. "I've got some punch mix we can make to drink."

"I'll get ice," said George Wilson. "Count on me for that. Okay?" His grandfather ran the ice house three blocks from the Lomaxes'.

And off we went, Lomaxes' sister riding my bike so she could get there ahead of us and make the punch. Steve hadn't brought his bike. He and I carried the box between us, holding onto holes that we had poked in the flaps for handles.

By the time the party in Lomaxes' front yard started, it was dark, but they lived on a corner, and there was a bright street light on the electric pole. And it was a warm night.

138

Someone brought over lemons and sugar to stretch the tub of punch, and George came through with most of the 25-pound block of ice he had carried three blocks in a gunny sack.

Of course, everybody was excited about Little Lomax's bike. Neighbors, even grownups, came over to admire it. He had it up on that broken-down front porch, with him just sitting there cross-legged looking at it as if he couldn't believe it was real.

"Hey, Little Lomax," George shouted at him. "You're going to ride it sometime, aren't you?" And everybody quieted down to see what Little Lomax was going to say.

"I rode it all the way home," he answered with a tight smile.

"Yeah, Little Lomax, give it a try," said someone else.

He pushed up from the porch to his feet. All eyes on him, he flipped the stand back into place with his toe and eased the bicycle down the rickety steps.

But halfway to the street he stopped short, as though he had only then remembered the very best thing of all. The smile held — there in the dimness of the street light — but it was a different smile.

"Brother?" he called out.

Big Lomax ambled closer.

"Your turn," declared Little Lomax.

"No, thank you," said Big Lomax. "Go on," he encouraged. "It's your bike."

"Half yours, Brother."

"How do you figure? You won it. It's yours."

"You could have beat me."

Big Lomax didn't answer.

"You know it," said Little Lomax. "You could've."

Big Lomax pursed his lips and thought about it — maybe six, seven seconds. He didn't disagree either. He gave Little Lomax a one-armed hug and then rode the bike off down the street with 30 kids running alongside.

Big Lomax's following was larger as he came back into view from up the street. And I was worried about the food holding out.

But then neighbors began bringing over more things. The man from the corner store brought down a whole case of grape juice. A big crock half-full of caraway-seed cookies came from across the street. The old lady next door, who we had always thought was so crabby, brought over a breadboard piled high with slices of fresh-baked bread and set it on the corner of the porch along with a saucer of butter. The food kept coming.

There was so much good stuff to eat that, when it was finally time to leave, at least a dozen sandwiches were still left in the bottom of the big carton. I remember the warm feeling I had when we set it inside the Lomaxes' screen door.

There never was a better party.

And during the months to follow, it was a joy each time we saw one of the Lomaxes on that new bicycle.

Funny, we had thought they didn't have much. But we were wrong. Even before they had the bike, they had a lot. They had each other.

— *Leslie Peters*

What Do You Think?

1. What might have happened if Big Lomax had won the contest? Give reasons from the story for your answer.
2. Why did Little Lomax win the contest even though other kids seemed to be trying harder than he was?
3. What examples of unselfishness can you find in this story?
4. What does the author mean by this statement: "Even before they had the bike, they had a lot. They had each other"?

Taking a Closer Look

1. Describe some of the methods the children used to try to eat sandwiches faster.
2. Why did Little Lomax think that the bike could belong half to his brother?
3. What bothered the author and the rest of the kids about the way Little Lomax ate his sandwich in the contest?
4. Where did the food come from for the party after the contest?

Putting Ideas to Work

Plan a class project involving the neighborhood around your school that will show the neighbors you care about them.

Rufus isn't the kind of person to accept things as they are. Even little things, like the price of toothpaste. What is it about Rufus that makes him this way?

The Toothpaste Millionaire

This is the story of my friend Rufus Mayflower and how he got to be a millionaire. With a little help from me. With a lot of help from me, as a matter of fact. But the idea was Rufus's.

Two years ago the company my father works for moved from Connecticut to Cleveland, Ohio. I didn't meet Rufus until several weeks after school started. Sometimes it's hard making friends in a new neighborhood, and the kids on my block weren't too friendly at first. It was okay at school, but after school and on weekends, it was lonely.

142

With Rufus I didn't even have to try to make friends. It was as if we always had been, from the first day I met him. I was riding my bike to school, and the strap that I use to hold my books on the back of the bike broke. I heard my books go thunking all over the street.

Well, I pulled up to the curb and was trying to figure out how to rescue the books. Papers from my notebook were blowing all over the place. Every time I ducked into the street to grab a paper, cars started honking their horns. It was rush hour and nobody wanted to stop.

Suddenly this kid on a bike pulls up behind me. He jumps off his bike and runs into the middle of the street and puts up his hands like a traffic policeman.

"Take your time," he says to me. Then when he gets the traffic under control, he helps me pick up all my stuff.

Some kids who lived on my street were standing on the sidewalk laughing at the two of us crawling under cars. One of them yelled, "Hey, Rufus, you'll be late for school."

Rufus didn't pay any attention, except to explain to me, "That's my name — Rufus."

He was in my math class. I hadn't noticed him before the day he picked up my books. So I was surprised when he walked into the math class later the same day.

I remember the morning Rufus got the idea for toothpaste. He had to do some shopping for his mother, and I went along with him. We were in the Cut-Rate Drugstore, because toothpaste was one of the things on Rufus's list.

"Seventy-nine cents!" Rufus muttered. "Seventy-nine cents for a six-inch tube of toothpaste. That's crazy!"

"It's better than eighty-nine cents," I said. I pointed to some eighty-nine-cent tubes farther down the shelf.

"That's even crazier," Rufus said. "What can be in those tubes anyway? Just some peppermint flavoring and some paste."

"Maybe the paste is expensive to make," I said.

"Paste!" Rufus said. "You don't need powdered gold to make paste. Paste is made out of everyday ordinary stuff. Didn't you ever make paste?"

"Toothpaste?" I said.

"I mean just plain paste for pasting things together," Rufus said. "My Grandma Mayflower showed me how to make paste when I was four years old."

"How do you do it?" I asked.

"Simple," Rufus said. "You just take a little flour and starch and cook them with a little water till the mixture has a nice pasty feel. Then you can use it to paste pictures in a scrapbook. Or paste up wallpaper."

"But you couldn't brush your teeth with *that*," I said.

"Well, I don't know," Rufus said. "I never tried. But I bet toothpaste isn't any harder to make. Anyway, I'm not paying any seventy-nine cents for a tube of toothpaste."

Rufus crossed toothpaste off his shopping list.

144

"But your mother said to get toothpaste," I said. "You can't help it if it's expensive."

"I'll make her some," Rufus said. "I bet I can make a gallon of it for seventy-nine cents."

The next afternoon when I stopped by Rufus's house to borrow his bike pump, he had about fifty bowls and pans scattered around the kitchen.

"What are you making?" I asked.

"I already made it," Rufus said.

He handed me a spoon and a bowl with some white stuff in it. I took a spoonful.

"Don't eat it," Rufus said. "Just taste it. Rub a little on your teeth. It's toothpaste."

I tried a little.

"How does it taste?" Rufus asked.

"Not bad," I said. "Better than the kind my mother buys in the pink-and-white striped tube. How'd you get it to taste so good?"

"A drop of peppermint oil," Rufus said. "But I've got other flavors too."

He pushed three other pots of paste across the table. The first one had a spicy taste.

"Clove-flavored," Rufus said. "You like it?"

"I don't know," I said. "It's interesting."

"Try this one."

The next sample had a sweet taste. "Vanilla," I guessed.

"Right," Rufus said.

"I like vanilla," I said. "In milkshakes. Or ice cream. But it doesn't seem quite right in toothpaste. Too sweet."

"This one won't be too sweet," Rufus said, handing me another sample.

"*Eeegh*," I said and ran to the sink to wash out my mouth. "What did you put in *that*?"

"Curry powder," Rufus said. "You don't like it? I thought it tasted like a good rice curry."

"Maybe it does," I said, "but I don't like curry."

Rufus looked disappointed. "I don't suppose you'd like it almond-flavored, either," he said. "I made some of that, too, but I decided not too many people would take to almond."

"What flavor is in that big plastic pan?" I asked. "You've got enough of that kind to frost twenty-seven cakes."

"That's no kind yet," Rufus said. "That's just seventy-nine cents worth of the stuff that goes in the paste. I didn't want to flavor it till I figured out the best taste."

"What does it taste like plain?" I asked.

"Well," Rufus said, "mostly you taste the bicarb."

"Bicarb!" I said. "You mean all this stuff I've been tasting has got bicarbonate of soda in it?"

Rufus grinned. "Yeah," he said. "It's probably good for your stomach as well as your teeth."

"You must have enough for ten tubes in that plastic bowl," I guessed.

"More, I bet," Rufus said.

"Why don't you squeeze the toothpaste in the tube into a measuring cup and then measure the stuff in the bowl," I suggested.

"That would be a waste of toothpaste," Rufus said. "We couldn't get it back in the tube." Rufus hates to waste anything.

147

"I have a better idea," he said. "I'll pack into a square pan the toothpaste I made. Then I can figure out how many cubic inches of toothpaste we have. And you can figure out how many cubic inches of toothpaste are in the tube."

"But the tube is round, Rufus," I said. "I can't measure cubic inches unless something is cube-shaped."

Rufus thought a minute. "Maybe we can squeeze the tube into a cube shape," he said.

I thought that was brilliant. But then I had another idea.

"Rufus," I said. "It says on the tube that it contains 3.25 ounces of toothpaste. Why couldn't we just weigh your paste and divide by 3.25 to see how many tubes it would make?"

"Hey — we could!" Rufus said. "You are *smart*, Kate. I'm always doing things the hard way."

That's what is really so nice about Rufus. It's not just that he gets great ideas like making toothpaste. But if *you* have a good idea, he says so.

I was pleased that I had thought of a simpler way of measuring the toothpaste, but I told Rufus, "I wish I was smart enough even to *think* of a hard way of doing something."

I *never* would have thought of measuring toothpaste in cubic inches. Partly because I never can remember exactly how to figure cubic inches. And I certainly wouldn't have thought of making a round tube cube-shaped. Would you?

148

Anyway it turned out Rufus had made about forty tubes of toothpaste for seventy-nine cents.

Before I finished breakfast the next morning, there was a knock on the door. It was Rufus. He was very excited.

"Kate!" he said. "Do you know what the population of the United States is?"

"No," I said. I never know things like that.

My father looked up from his paper. "According to the most recent census — over 200,000,000," he said to Rufus. My father always knows things like that.

"You're right," Rufus said. "And by now, it must be even bigger."

"Probably," my father said. "The growing population is a very serious matter. Have you thought much about that problem, Rufus?"

"Not yet, Mr. MacKinstrey," Rufus said. "At the moment I was thinking mainly about toothpaste. I was thinking that everybody in the United States probably uses about one tube of toothpaste a month."

"Probably," my father said.

"And if they do," Rufus said, "how many tubes of toothpaste are sold in a year?"

My father thought for a second. "Roughly two-and-a-half billion tubes."

"Right!" Rufus said.

I don't understand people who can multiply in their heads. Except that my father and Rufus are two of the people I like best in the world. How do you explain that?

I really don't like math at all, even when I have a paper and pencil and all the time in the world to figure something out.

150

And at the same time I look forward every day to Mr. Conti's math class. And how do you explain that, since that's the class where I'm always getting in trouble?

For example, the same day my father brought up the population explosion, there's Mr. Conti in math class saying:

"Kate MacKinstrey, would you please bring me that note."

"Well, it isn't exactly a note, Mr. Conti."

"I see," says Mr. Conti. "I suppose it's another math problem."

"It looks like a math problem, Mr. Conti."

The message from Rufus that Mr. Conti got to read that day said:

If there are 2½ billion tubes of toothpaste
sold in the U.S. in one year, and 1 out of 10
people switched to a new brand, how many
tubes of the new brand would they be buying?

The right answer is 250 million. It took the class a while to figure that out. Some people have trouble remembering how many zeros there are in a billion.

Then there was a second part to the note:

If the inventor of the new toothpaste made a profit of 1¢ a tube on his toothpaste, what would his profit be at the end of the year?

And it turns out that the inventor of this new toothpaste would make a two-and-a-half million dollar profit!

Well, that's how Rufus's toothpaste business started. With Rufus figuring out that if he sold the toothpaste for only a penny more than it cost him to make — it cost him about two cents a tube — that he'd soon have millions of customers.

He had to start in a small way, of course. When he started his business, Rufus packed the toothpaste in baby-food jars. A baby-food jar holds about as much as a big tube, and the jars didn't cost him anything.

People with babies were glad to save jars for Rufus, as nobody had thought of a way of instantly recycling baby-food jars before. When Rufus put a sign on the bulletin board at school saying that he could use the jars, kids brought us hundreds of them.

We sterilized and filled the jars. When we had about five hundred jars, Rufus and I stuffed our saddlebags with as many as they would hold and rode our bikes around the neighborhood selling the toothpaste.

We sold quite a few jars. At only three cents a jar, most people felt they could afford to give it a try, and most of the customers said it was good toothpaste.

Still, I could not see how Rufus was going to get rich on

three-cent toothpaste unless millions of people knew about it. Then I had this idea about how he could get some free advertising.

Everybody in Cleveland watches a program called "The Joe Smiley Show." On the show, Joe interviews people who have interesting hobbies.

I wrote Joe Smiley a letter telling him I had this friend who had a hobby of making toothpaste and could make about two years' supply for the price of one tube. And Joe Smiley called up Rufus to ask if he would be on the show.

Rufus was very good on the show, though I was afraid that he never would get around to talking about the toothpaste. I was worried because when Joe Smiley asked Rufus how he had learned to make toothpaste, Rufus started telling about his Grandmother Mayflower.

He not only told about the scrapbook paste, but about how his Grandma Mayflower had made her own furnace out of two 100-gallon oil barrels. Joe Smiley was so interested in that furnace that it was hard to get him off the subject of Rufus's grandmother.

Rufus told about his grandmother taming raccoons, woodchucks, mice, chipmunks, and catbirds. And, of course, about her brushing her teeth with plain baking soda.

You wouldn't think all that stuff about Rufus's grandmother would sell toothpaste. But then, as my father pointed out, you wouldn't think Rufus's way of advertising the toothpaste would sell toothpaste, either.

Joe Smiley is the kind of guy who is always saying things are the "greatest" thing he ever heard of. Or the most "fantastic." If a girl comes on his show in a pink coat that Joe thinks is attractive, he'll say, "That's the most fantastic coat!" There's nothing that special about the coat. He just means it's nice.

What I mean is, he exaggerates. And everybody Joe has on his show is one of the greatest people he ever met or has done the most fantastic thing.

So when Joe does get to Rufus's toothpaste, he naturally gives it this big build-up. Which is what I was counting on. And what does Rufus do?

The conversation went something like this:

JOE: Now, Rufus, this fantastic toothpaste you make — I suppose it has a special, secret formula.

RUFUS: No. It's made out of stuff anybody can buy for a few cents and mix up at home in a few minutes.

JOE: Fantastic! And, of course, it's much better than the kind you buy at the store.

RUFUS: I don't know about that. But it tastes pretty good. And for about two cents you can make as much as you get in a seventy-nine cent tube.

154

JOE: Fantastic! And where can people get some of this great toothpaste?

RUFUS: If they live in East Cleveland, I'll deliver it to them on my bike. Three ounces cost three cents — it costs me two cents to make and I make one cent profit. If anyone outside East Cleveland wants some, I'll have to charge three cents plus postage.

JOE: Fantastic! And what do you call this marvelous new product?

RUFUS: TOOTHPASTE.

JOE: Just toothpaste? It doesn't have a name like **SPARKLE** or **SHINE** or **SENSATION** or **PERSONALITY PLUS**?

RUFUS: No, it's just plain **TOOTHPASTE**. It doesn't do anything sensational such as improve your smile or your personality. It just keeps your teeth clean.

Who would have thought that telling people toothpaste wouldn't do one thing for their personality would sell toothpaste?

But three days after Rufus was on "The Joe Smiley Show," he got 689 orders for **TOOTHPASTE**. One came all the way from Venice, California, from a man who happened to be telephoning his daughter while she was watching the show in Cleveland. The daughter said, "There's a kid here who's selling toothpaste for three cents a jar." And her father ordered three dozen jars.

Fantastic!

—Jean Merrill

What Do You Think?

1. What single word would you choose to describe Rufus Mayflower? Explain your choice.
2. Compare Rufus's toothpaste project with Willy Ilchuk's mousetrap project. How were they the same? How were they different?
3. Did you ever meet someone with whom you didn't have to make friends — it just came naturally? Tell how it happened.
4. What kind of person is Joe Smiley? Have you ever seen anyone on television like him? Describe that person.
5. Did Rufus become a toothpaste millionaire? Why or why not?

Taking a Closer Look

1. Kate suggested a way to figure out how many tubes of toothpaste Rufus could make for 79¢. Was her way better than Rufus's? Why or why not?
2. What bothered Kate about the television interview?
3. Who first suggested that Rufus should appear on the "Joe Smiley Show"?
4. How much did Rufus charge for a jar of toothpaste?

Putting Ideas to Work

Write an advertising jingle that Rufus might use to sell his toothpaste.

What can a new missionary do when the people he has come to help do not trust him? This is the story of a man who found an unusual way to tell others about Jesus. First he had to get their attention. Then he had to change his name.

A Rabbit and a Hare

Eric B. Hare, a twinkling-eyed Australian, started his missionary work among the Karen[1] people deep in the interior of Burma. Elder Hare had received some medical training and went to help the jungle people physically as well as spiritually. He wanted to cure and prevent such tropical ailments as malaria and tuberculosis, eye disease, malnutrition, and ringworm for the sheer pleasure of serving mankind. But he also wanted to treat disease as a practical means to performing his lifework. If he could restore a suffering person to health and happiness, then surely that person would listen to his message of the eternal health and happiness that comes only from salvation.

Elder Hare and his wife set up their dispensary in a beautiful spot called Ohn Daw[2] on the Salween River. There they prepared to care for the wants of the shy, gentle Karens. But days, weeks, and months went by, and they had few customers. The people were suspicious and afraid. One day, entering a new village, Elder Hare saw the people look up and heard them shout, "*Daw taka!*[3] *Daw taka!*" Then he saw nothing but the backs of fleeing men, women, and children. He later learned that a *daw taka* was a half-breed between the devil and a ghost. A *daw taka* steals babies, fattens them up, and then eats them. No wonder the natives were afraid of lively little Eric Hare; they thought he was a *daw taka*.

---

[1] Karen (kə-RIN) [2] Ohn Daw (OHN-daw) [3] Daw taka (daw-TAH-kə)

One of the Karens had been down the river to Rangoon[1] and knew some English. He overcame his fears and tutored Elder Hare in the Karen language and customs. One day the teacher told his pupil a popular Karen campfire story, part folklore, which still influenced many Karens.

A baby elephant and a baby tiger were born about the same time, the story goes, became fast friends, and grew up together. One day, however, the tiger announced that he was fully grown and intended to put an end to the friendship. As a matter of fact, he had decided to have his friend for breakfast the following morning. The elephant pleaded. Finally because of their friendship, the tiger gave the elephant six weeks to reap his rice, repair his house, and say good-by to his family. Then he would have elephant for breakfast.

The elephant reaped his rice and repaired his house, and said good-by to his loved ones. But he was unhappy. He did not want to be a tiger's breakfast, not even if the tiger was a childhood friend. On the day before the six weeks were up, he went to the river, sat down on the bank, and cried. He cried so much that he made the river salty.

Along came Grandfather Rabbit, hopping down to the river for a drink. He took a big mouthful of water, then spit it out in surprise. He promptly began to scold the poor elephant for making the water so salty. The elephant told his sad story. Grandfather Rabbit, kind and sympathetic, offered his services as a lawyer, and the elephant eagerly

[1] Rangoon (rang-GOON)

accepted. Grandfather Rabbit then whispered a plan in the elephant's ear.

Next morning the tiger came trotting up, licking his lips, eager for a hearty elephant breakfast. But a strange sight met his eyes. The big elephant was down on the ground, and the rabbit was jumping up on top of him in a wild dance. Sometimes he would hop off and lift up one of the elephant's mighty legs. Then he would grab hold of the elephant's trunk or tail and turn him this way or that. The tiger didn't notice that the elephant was cooperating. He was impressed by the strength of Grandfather Rabbit.

"Good morning, Mr. Rabbit," he said, admiration in his voice. "I'm glad you're having fun playing with my elephant, but when you get through just leave him there. I'm going to eat him for breakfast."

"Says who?" asked the rabbit. "Look, Cheeky-face, I've had six elephants already for breakfast this morning, and this will be my seventh. And if you're still around here when I finish, I might even start on you."

The tiger backed down hastily and galloped off through the jungle to find himself a lawyer. All of the animals in the jungle had more sense than to argue with Grandfather Rabbit. They all turned the tiger down — all except one, a monkey. The tiger tied the monkey on his back and hurried back to the river. But before the monkey could even get started pleading the tiger's case, the rabbit started talking.

"Well!" he said, heartily. "If it isn't Mr. Monkey with one of my father's tigers at last! I've been wondering when you were going to start paying back those seven tigers my father loaned your father. Just tie that one to the tree there and then go get the other six."

Oh, ho, thought the tiger. *So this smart monkey thought he'd trap me and use me to pay off his father's debt, eh? Well, we'll see about that!* He turned and charged off through the jungle. Dragging the poor monkey through the bushes, he stretched him out so much that monkeys have been slender-waisted ever since. And so Grandfather Rabbit's cleverness saved the elephant.

Eric Hare heard the story through and thought a bit. "Tell me," he said, "in these stories about Grandfather Rabbit does he always win his cases?"

"Of course," said the teacher. "The rabbit is the cleverest creature in all the jungle."

Now it didn't take long for an alert Adventist with a name like Hare to figure out what to do next. From that time on his name was *Thara Pa Deh* — Doctor Rabbit. He

162

had new labels printed up for every one of his medicines, with his new name and a large picture of a rabbit on each. And it wasn't long before his dispensary was doing a whopping business in Bunny Brand medicines.

But that wasn't all. Doctor Rabbit had a trumpet, which he liked to play in the evening, frequently with an audience of Karen children. And if they would come to hear one trumpet, Doctor Rabbit thought, what wouldn't they do to hear a whole brass band?

And so he called on his friends in Australia to ship all the band instruments they could get their hands on. When the instruments came, he passed them out to the local boys. The tuba went to the biggest, trombones and French horns to the medium-sized, and trumpets to the smallest.

For days the noise around Ohn Daw was awful. Finally Doctor Rabbit found it impossible to teach his young would-be bandsmen to play whole scales. So he began concentrating on teaching each boy to play just two or three notes. With these few notes, played at the proper time, the band could play a harmonic background while Doctor Rabbit himself carried the melody on his solo trumpet. This they learned to do, and the band began giving concerts.

One day they set out for a village which Doctor Rabbit had never visited before. They walked single file through the jungle trail, each player carrying his own instrument. It was necessary to stop and rest occasionally for the benefit of the tuba player. Finally they reached their destination, only to find the village deserted. The huts were dilapidated and falling down. Everyone was most disappointed.

To cheer up the band, as well as himself, Doctor Rabbit began the concert anyway, with a few monkeys for an audience. But midway through the first number a most remarkable thing happened. The village was growing arms and legs! From around this hut, from behind that tree, heads, arms, legs, and finally bodies began to appear.

The people of the village, as per Karen custom when their houses rot away, had simply moved out. They were in the process of building a brand-new village just a few hundred yards away through the forest. Hearing the soft strains of the mighty brass as filtered through the jungle, they had dropped everything to come to see what was going on. Before long they were out from behind the trees, out in the clearing, listening to Doctor Rabbit's brass band.

When the people stopped coming, the crowd numbered two or three hundred. One of the boys stepped forward and told, in native language, some of the early episodes in the life of Christ. The band played another hymn, and another boy continued the story. Finally the whole story had been told. Then Doctor Rabbit put away his trumpet and brought out his Bunny Brand medicines. He began caring for the sick, especially those suffering from the eye sores so common in the jungle.

With a few hymns, a little ingenuity, and a great deal of devotion, Doctor Rabbit brought healing and the word of God to the jungles of Burma. No longer do the Karens shout, *Daw taka*! *Daw taka*! when a Seventh-day Adventist missionary visits their village.

— *Booton Herndon*

What Do You Think?

1. Why do various cultures often use folklore to explain things?
2. What do you think would have happened if Elder Hare had not changed his name?
3. Why were the Karens so fascinated with music?
4. Do you agree that Elder Hare was an alert person? Why or why not?
5. Would Elder Hare have eventually won the confidence of the people without his "Bunny Brand" medicine? Support your answer.
6. If you could be a young missionary, to what country would you want to go? Why?

Taking a Closer Look

1. Why did Elder Hare want to go to Burma? What did he hope to do there?
2. Instead of teaching all the boys to play complete scales, what did Dr. Rabbit do? Why?
3. Why were the Karen people afraid and suspicious of Elder Hare?
4. Why did the Karens think the rabbit was an especially intelligent animal?

Putting Ideas to Work

Make a vocal band with your class members. Someone can sing the melody while others hum or sing only a few notes each. You may also want to have some people clapping the rhythm.
Read Eric B. Hare's own account of his life as a missionary. Look for his book, *Treasure from the Haunted Pagoda,* in your library.

166

She Called Him Mr.

She frowned and called him Mr.
Because in sport he kr.
   And so in spite
   That very night
That Mr. kr. sr.

— *Anonymous*

OIC

I'm in a 10der mood today
   & feel poetic, 2;
4 fun I'll just — off a line
   & send it off 2 U.

I'm sorry you've been 6 o long;
   Don't B disconsol8;
But bear your ills with 42de,
   & they won't seem so gr8.

— *Anonymous*

Linda gets a mysterious message that she just can't ignore. As you read about the way she solves the mystery, think about what you would have done.

The Message

It was the first morning of vacation. Linda strolled down the street, free as a bird. She felt as if she had wings. Suddenly there was a gust of wind. Something struck Linda's face and then landed on the ground in front of her. She looked down. It was a small piece of paper. She picked it up and examined it.

On the paper was written one word: **HELP**.

Linda looked all around. It was quiet this time of morning. There was no one nearby except Tommy Sesto, who was coming out of Cheever's Pharmacy.

"Hey, Tommy!" Linda called.

Tommy sauntered over. "Hi, Linda."

"Did you throw this at me?" She handed him the paper.

"I didn't throw anything! I didn't even notice you. I was thinking about my job."

"Your job?"

168

"I was just talking to Mr. Cheever, and he gave me a summer job working behind the soda fountain. I start next week." Tommy still held the paper in his hand. He hadn't looked at it yet.

"That's great, Tommy, but if you didn't throw that paper at me, who did?"

Tommy looked at the paper. "This is really weird!" he exclaimed. He stared at the message repeating it softly to himself, "Help."

"What do you think it means?"

Tommy shrugged. "I don't know."

"We can't just ignore it," said Linda. "Someone might be in terrible trouble."

"Well," Tommy pointed out, "it must have come from somewhere near here."

They looked around. On the side of the street where they stood were three stores: Sal's Pizza Place, Cheever's Pharmacy, and Village Farm Produce. Jerry's Gas Station was on the corner. Across the street there were only three houses.

"I just came out of Cheever's," Tommy said, "so it couldn't have come from there."

"Let's start with the pizza place," suggested Linda. They walked over to Sal's Pizza and tried the door. It was locked.

"It's too early," said Tommy. "I don't think it opens till noon." He looked up at the windows of the apartment above the store. "That's where Sal lives."

Linda glanced at her watch. It was 9:30.

"He's probably still sleeping," she said. "I think he keeps the pizza store open until really late — maybe 2:00 or 3:00 in the morning. I'd hate to awaken him."

"Let's leave Sal's place for last," suggested Tommy. "How about Village Farm Produce?"

Village Farm Produce was a fruit and vegetable store. Mr. Fickett, the owner, was arranging ripe, red tomatoes on a table when they came in.

TOMATOES

171

Linda showed him the message.

Mr. Fickett's bushy, white eyebrows rose. "Where did you kids get this?"

"Somebody tossed it to me while I was walking down this street," Linda told him. "We think it might be important."

Mr. Fickett grinned. "I think your friends are just playing a joke on you."

"Our friends aren't around. We're the only ones on the street," Linda pointed out.

Mr. Fickett returned the paper to Linda. "It's got to be a joke," he insisted. "You'll see." He went back to arranging the tomatoes.

Out on the street again, Linda and Tommy looked at each other. "Mr. Fickett was alone," Tommy said. "There's no place for anyone to hide in there."

"I don't think it came from Fickett's," said Linda. "Let's walk over to the gas station."

Things were quiet at the gas station too. There was only one car outside — a large, shiny black car. They could see Jerry talking to a large man who was wearing a black coat and hat.

172

"I've never seen him around here," said Tommy.

"I've never seen a car like that around here, either," added Linda.

"Maybe he's a kidnapper, and there's someone locked in the car," said Tommy.

"Oh, do you think so?" Linda began to tremble. Her skin felt goose pimply all over. Suddenly, the man turned around and looked straight at them. His face was mean and threatening — a red scar ran down one cheek. They quickly moved out of sight.

"Maybe we should call the police," said Tommy.

"What could we tell them?" Linda pointed out. "We don't really know anything. There might not be anyone in the car."

"I wonder if there is someone on the floor of the back seat," said Tommy.

"We have to be sure first," insisted Linda. "One of us has to sneak up there and look in that car. If we both do, we'd be too conspicuous."

"OK, I'll go," offered Tommy.

Linda thought for a minute. "Maybe it would be better if I did it," she said. "I'm smaller and thinner, and less likely to be seen."

"OK," Tommy agreed (a little too eagerly, Linda thought). "I'll wait here and watch. If I see the man coming out, I'll warn you with a whistle."

Linda's heart pounded as she slowly made her way toward the black car. Once she thought she heard a whistle and started back, but it was only a bird in a tree across the street. Closer and closer she crept. At last she was there. She crouched on the other side of the car so she couldn't be seen from the office where Jerry and the man were still talking. She raised her head slowly and peered into the car.

No one was inside. Nothing was inside! The car looked brand-new and immaculate, with shiny red leather seats, a soft rug on the floor, and a lot of knobs and gadgets on the dashboard. Was that a whistle Linda heard?

"What do you want?"

Linda gasped. Jerry and the stranger had come up behind her. They were scowling.

Linda thought fast. "I was just looking at the car. I've never seen one like it."

Jerry and the stranger exchanged looks. Their expressions had changed. They were smiling.

"I told you that car would be a hit around here," said Jerry. He turned to Linda again. "It's a custom-made Mercedes,"[1] he said. "Isn't it the greatest? And this is my brother Joe. He's visiting me from Florida. He owns a string of gas stations down there."

Linda swallowed hard. "Thanks for letting me look at the car," she said as she moved away.

"Hey," called Jerry's brother, "you can look at it more if you want. It's custom-made. Cost me a lotta' bucks."

"Thanks," answered Linda weakly, "but I've got to go now. Someone's waiting for me." She dashed down the street to where Tommy had moved back to a safe position in front of Cheever's Pharmacy.

"Didn't you hear me whistle?"

Linda nodded. "But it was too late for me to get away. Anyway, it doesn't matter. There's no one in the car. We were wrong. The message must have come from somewhere else."

[1] Mercedes (mer-SAY-deez)

They looked at the three houses across the street.

"Maybe it came from one of those houses," said Tommy.

They crossed the street. A neat, white shingle hung outside the first house.

"Is Dr. Davis your dentist too?" asked Linda.

Tommy nodded. "I don't think this paper came from Dr. Davis's house," Tommy said. "His patients aren't *that* desperate."

Linda made a face. She wasn't in the mood for jokes. Her legs were still trembling from the scare she had in Jerry's gas station. "My friend Melissa lives in the second house," she said. "Let's go ring the bell."

They did. Melissa herself opened the door. She was still in her pajamas. "It's the first day of vacation," she explained, yawning. "I slept late."

They told Melissa about the message and showed her the note. She shook her head. "It didn't come from here," she assured them. "Daddy went to work, Mom's out shopping, and all the other kids are still asleep."

"Thanks, anyway," said Linda. She and Tommy turned away and headed toward the last house.

"Don't bother going there," Melissa called after them. "No one's home. The Clarks left last night for their cottage at the shore."

Tommy and Linda looked at each other. "Are you thinking what I'm thinking?" asked Linda.

"I'm thinking that an empty house, where the owners are away for the summer, is a perfect place to hide someone," Tommy said. He was echoing Linda's own thoughts.

176

They were at the Clarks's house now. A great silence and a feeling of emptiness seemed to come from it. They slowly walked around the house peering in all the windows. The furniture was covered with white sheets. Nobody was there.

"I'm stumped," exclaimed Linda. She moodily stared at the message. The big, hand-scrawled letters stared back at her. "Where did this come from?"

"Let's show the note to Mr. Cheever, my new boss," suggested Tommy.

They crossed the street again and entered Cheever's Pharmacy. Mr. Cheever, a mild, elderly man with thinning gray hair and gold-rimmed glasses, looked up from a prescription he was mixing.

"Coming to work already?" he asked Tommy. "I thought you weren't supposed to start until next week."

"Someone's in trouble," Tommy explained. "And we're trying to help." He showed Mr. Cheever the note.

Mr. Cheever came out from behind the prescription counter. He looked at the paper and frowned. The frown changed to a smile. Then he began to laugh harder and harder, until his eyes were teary and he was holding his sides. "Oh, dear!" he gasped between spasms of laughter. "This is too much!" He laughed on and on, uncontrollably.

Linda and Tommy stared at him in silent astonishment. Finally, Mr. Cheever seemed to gain control of himself. He took out a handkerchief and wiped his eyes. "Let me show you something," he said, as he led them to a wastebasket near the front door. He rummaged in the basket for a moment and finally dug out a piece of white paper. He put it next to the message Linda had received.

The two papers fit together perfectly. Mr. Cheever turned them around so Linda and Tommy could see what was written. It said **HELP WANTED**.

"That's the sign I tore up when I gave you the summer job, Tommy," Mr. Cheever explained. "I threw it in the basket, but one piece must have blown outside when you opened the door to leave."

"Oh!" cried Linda. "The things that I thought!"

"And the things that we did!" added Tommy.

"The things you did?" repeated Mr. Cheever. "I think I'd like to hear about that. Why don't you tell me the details over a couple of free sodas?"

— *Carol H. Behrman*

What Do You Think?

1. How would you have reacted if you had seen the note that said "Help"? In what ways would you have acted like Linda and Tommy? What things would you have done differently?

2. "Jumping to conclusions" means deciding something without enough evidence. How does jumping to conclusions fit in this story?

3. What kind of person is Mr. Cheever? Would you want to work for him? Why or why not?

Taking a Closer Look

1. Why didn't Linda and Tommy begin asking about the message in Cheever's Pharmacy?

2. Why did Linda and Tommy decide to go to Sal's Pizza Parlor last?

3. Who thought someone was playing a trick on Linda and Tommy?

4. Why were Linda and Tommy suspicious of the man with the black car?

5. What did Tommy and Linda both think when they found out that the Clarks were on vacation?

Putting Ideas to Work

Tell about a time when you made a mistake by jumping to a conclusion. How did it end? Was it funny or serious?

How to Tell the Wild Animals

If ever you should go by chance
  To jungles in the East;
And if there should to you advance
  A large and tawny beast,
If he roars at you as you're dyin'
You'll know it is the Asian Lion.

Or if sometime when roaming round,
A noble wild beast greets you,
With black stripes on a yellow ground,
Just notice if he eats you.
This simple rule may help you learn
The Bengal Tiger to discern.

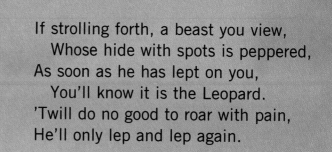

If strolling forth, a beast you view,
　　Whose hide with spots is peppered,
As soon as he has lept on you,
　　You'll know it is the Leopard.
'Twill do no good to roar with pain,
He'll only lep and lep again.

182

If when you're walking round your yard,
    You meet a creature there
Who hugs you very, very hard,
    Be sure it is the Bear.
If you have any doubt, I guess
He'll give you just one more caress.

Though to distinguish beasts of prey
    A novice might nonplus,
The Crocodiles you always may
    Tell from Hyenas thus:
Hyenas come with merry smiles;
But if they weep, they're Crocodiles.

The true Chameleon is small,
 A lizard sort of thing;
He hasn't any ears at all,
 And not a single wing.
If there is nothing on the tree,
'Tis the Chameleon you see.

— *Carolyn Wells*

To Fly

For centuries man dreamed of flying. Finally the dream has become reality. Now we know what it is like to soar like a great, silent bird. And we know what the earth looks like from 30,000 feet up. Flight has given us a new view of our planet and of ourselves.

In this unit you will read about many kinds of flying. What can you learn that will help you take wing against challenges you face?

187

When old-timer aviators tell stories about their adventures, the yarn spinning is called "hangar flying." After their planes are parked safely in the hangar, they get to talking. Soon they are recounting tales of daring in the air.

Some of their memories about the early days of flying are so vivid that they may seem hard to believe: of men without parachutes hanging by their toes from rope ladders under planes . . . a woman dropping from a low-flying plane onto a moving train . . . a wingwalker jumping from a plane without a parachute and landing safely. Hangar flying does tend to make stories grow bigger as they are repeated. But the truth about aviation in the "barnstorming" days is so fascinating that it doesn't need exaggeration.

Those Crazy Barnstormers

Many young men had their first taste of flying during World War I. The United States and Canada sent some aviators to the battlefields of France and were training more when the war ended on November 11, 1918. Airplanes had been improved during the war and began to look more like those with which we are familiar today — at least the small planes we see around private airports. Quite a few of the men who had a taste of flying during the war didn't want to quit after the Armistice. So they went into barnstorming.

Barnstorming meant buying a second-hand military plane for about $300 and touring around the country with it. The owner stopped in each town for a few days to take passengers for rides — usually the first time the customers had been in the air.

Stunt flying built up the townspeople's interest. The more the barnstorming pilots could make 'em gasp, the more the crowds admired their skill and felt safe enough to risk their own lives on fifteen-minute flights. Usually the fee for a passenger was $15.00 for a quarter-hour ride, a dollar a minute. If the pilot tossed in a few maneuvers like a spin or even a loop the price went up to $25.00.

These barnstorming days in the 1920s provided the introduction of thousands of people, especially those who lived in small towns, to airplanes. From the cow-pasture barnstormers, ready to land their planes anywhere and fly them under all sorts of conditions, came many of the later leaders of the aircraft industry, airline pilots, and World War II military heroes.

Mostly the barnstormers flew Curtiss Jennies. The Jenny was known officially during World War I as the JN-4D, but everyone knew it by the nickname. It was a biplane whose top wing was forty-three feet wide and lower wing considerably shorter. The two open seats in the fuselage were one behind the other, behind the engine. Usually the pilot sat in the rear cockpit, the passenger up front. The Jenny was rugged, and today it seems very slow. On a calm day a Jenny could fly at seventy-five miles an hour. It could land at forty-five miles an hour. Many times when the motor failed in flight, the pilot brought his Jenny to a safe dead-stick landing, coasting into the smoothest-looking field available with no power at all.

A Jenny could land or take off from almost any pasture that wasn't cluttered with trees or fences. The cows in the field usually trotted out of the way when they heard the noise of the engine and the *whirr* of the wooden propeller. Occasionally one didn't move fast enough, resulting in disaster for the cow or the plane, or both.

Once a Jenny got into the air, climbing took a long time, five minutes to rise to an altitude of one thousand feet. This meant that most barnstorming was done at low altitude. The Jenny's fuel tank held only twenty-one gallons. So when barnstormers set up shop in a field outside a town and their passenger-ride business was brisk, they had to keep an errand boy running into town for more fuel.

Often the barnstormers carried blanket rolls in their cockpits. Using these, they slept on the ground under the wing of the plane, to protect it and to save money on hotel bills. Few flyers got rich from barnstorming, although they had fun and felt delightfully carefree.

What was it like, taking your first flight in one of these open cockpit planes? Two barnstormers went to South Bend, Indiana, in the summer of 1919, giving residents of that city their first opportunity to fly. Early during their visit they invited a newspaper reporter up for a ride. They figured that his story would whet his readers' desire to try the sky. It did too. And the daily newspapers dutifully published the names of all the townspeople who had the nerve and the $15.00 to take a ride.

Outfitted in leather helmet and goggles, the reporter climbed onto the lower wing of the Jenny, then into the front cockpit. Here is how he described the takeoff:

"The first thrill is in getting a close view of the machine itself. To see the bright wings, the powerful motor, there in front of you — not up in the air but where you can see all the details — and to realize that this machine is to bear you up among the clouds, or close to them, at least, sets your heart beating a trifle faster.

"Then you climb in. The novelty of the situation is another thrill. You're not in an automobile, for the sides of the fuselage come up to your shoulders and you have to be buckled in, so that you can't fall out.

"The motor starts, the machine vibrates just a little. I'll be in the air in a minute! you think.

"In a moment, the plane begins its run for the takeoff. The wheels rumble over the rough ground, and the wind sings in your ears. The motor roars. You feel an invisible hand lifting you up, gently at first, then more rapidly. You're flying! Oh, thrills!"

The men who barnstormed in the slowpoke Jennies could do things with them that are impossible now. Can you imagine the captain of a gigantic 747 climbing from his seat onto the top of the plane in flight, crawling back to the tail, and piloting the plane from that rear position by manipulating the controls with his hands and feet? With nobody in the cockpit at all? Barnstorming stunt flyers did that in their Jennies. Without parachutes, at that!

These flyers truly were daredevils. They tried to top each other with midair stunts that grew constantly more risky and more frightening to the audiences down below. Although many of them died in crashes or falls when they pushed the law of gravity too far, the tragedies didn't stop others. The crazier the stunts were, the larger the crowds they attracted to the air circuses the traveling aviators staged in town after town, and the more the flyers earned.

As an example, the two young barnstormers in whose Jenny that awestruck reporter rode did stunts over the downtown shopping district of the city at an altitude of only one thousand feet. The copilot climbed from his cockpit onto the top of the fuselage, crept to the tail, stood upright without hanging onto anything and waved to the gawking spectators. Once he was back in the cockpit, the pilot set a course right along the city's main street. He flew upside down and did a series of low-level loop-the-loops, barrel rolls, wingovers, and other maneuvers. To climax the performance he climbed a bit higher, let the Jenny stall into a tailspin, and leveled it off safely a few hundred feet above the spectators' heads.

Even more startling was the feat by some trick flyers of doing a loop with a man standing on the top wing, even while the plane was flying upside down at the top of the circle. The wing man was held in place by guy wires invisible from the ground.

Some stunts were less dangerous than they appeared from the ground because of secret safety devices. The trick of a man hanging by his teeth from a leather strap suspended below the landing gear was an example. This thrilled and frightened the crowds looking up. They were

194

certain the daredevil would fall to his death if his jaw tired. They didn't know that he had a thin steel cable fastened from the landing gear crossbar to a strong harness under his flying coat.

One veteran of those barnstorming days recalled later how he had soloed at the age of twelve in a Jenny, without intending to do so. Flying was that casual then. While a boy in Corpus Christi, Texas, in 1921, J. O. Dockery was hired by a man selling surplus World War I planes to guard them. As a reward, he was taken on a ten-hour aerial tour of Texas. During the trip he followed closely everything the pilot did, putting his hands on the dual controls. Shortly thereafter, the pilot-salesman went away again, leaving the twelve-year-old guard on duty.

Nobody was around, and Dockery, an adventurous boy, was curious. What would it be like, sitting in the pilot's cockpit and pretending to fly? He climbed into the cockpit and got the engine started. With no one to stop him, he taxied the plane across the bumpy field. He was light and the gas tank was almost empty. The plane gathered speed. Suddenly the boy found himself flying level with the treetops. He had taken off without really trying to do so! Fortunately, he knew enough to get the Jenny back to earth safely. Fifty years later he was still talking about his surprise.

Changing from one plane to another while high in the air was a favorite crowd-pleaser in the air circuses. Spectators watched tensely as two biplanes drew alongside, wingtip to wingtip, and a man or woman stunt performer — yes, there were a few women barnstormers — jumped from one plane to the other. Even that wasn't risky enough for one stunt performer. He changed planes with one hand tied behind his back!

Today, refueling of long range military planes in midair by tanker plane has been developed into an intricate art. The first known midair refueling back in the 1920s was a haphazard stunt in a Jenny.

A pilot named Earl Daugherty announced that he intended to keep his Jenny aloft for twenty-four hours. It was obvious that the Jenny couldn't carry enough gasoline for that, but Daugherty took off, anyway, at the Long Beach Airport in California. Just when his fuel tank was nearing the empty mark, another biplane drew alongside. Standing on the top wing was a wingwalker, Wesley May. Strapped on May's back was a five-gallon can of gasoline. When the planes were almost touching, May stepped over onto Daugherty's wing, walked across it to the engine, and poured gasoline into the tank.

Since these traveling shows always needed fresh ways to thrill the crowds and sell tickets, the pilots kept busy thinking up new stunts. A parachute jump was a standard part of air shows. The audiences loved to see a man jump

196

from a plane, then a few seconds later see his parachute billow open and float him safely to earth right in front of them. This led one crew of barnstormers to announce plans for a man to leap from an airplane without a parachute. He did so, too, and survived.

While the biplane flew over the crowd, the jumper climbed from his cockpit down onto the undercarriage. There he swung by his knees on the crossbar that connected the two landing wheels. He had no parachute. The pilot flew low and as slowly as his plane would go without stalling. At the agreed moment, the man on the undercarriage let go and fell — right into a haystack!

Jimmy Doolittle was one of the pilots who tested his nerve and learned the tricks of flying during the barnstorming era. As Lieutenant Colonel Doolittle in World War II, he led squadrons of American bombers that took off from an aircraft carrier in the Pacific Ocean.

Jimmy Doolittle, barnstormer pilot

As a young aviator, Doolittle loved speed and pranks. He became the first pilot to fly across the United States in less than twenty-four hours. That was in 1922, only eleven years after Cal Rodgers required eighty-four days for the same flight, an indication of how swiftly aviation was developing. Doolittle later set many other speed records.

One of his jokes took place when he was flying an unusual high-winged monoplane in an air show. He attached an extra landing gear upside down on top of the wing and a dummy head projecting underneath the fuselage. Then he flew past the crowd upside down, leaving them baffled. A pilot's head and landing gear appeared both on the top and bottom of the plane. Which side was up? No one knew.

* * *

The list of lives lost among these pioneer airmen who did so much to make the world air-conscious during the 1920s was long and sad. They lived dangerously, usually in a happy-go-lucky way, flying at a time when few government restrictions existed to control their antics. During this period, passenger travel began to develop, and the first organized airlines started operation with only one or two planes. Speed and distance flying began to replace aerial acrobatics in the public's attention.

Those crazy barnstormers faded into the past as the age of commercial aviation dawned on the horizon.

— *Phil Ault*

198

What Do You Think?

1. What characteristic do you think was most important for a barnstormer? Explain your answer.
2. How did barnstorming lead to the development of aviation?
3. Imagine you were the man who jumped from the airplane without a parachute. Think of at least five words to tell how you would feel while you were in the air.

Taking a Closer Look

1. What was barnstorming?
2. What kind of airplanes were usually used for barnstorming?
3. How did the man who hung by his teeth from a leather strap really stay attached to the plane?
4. Summarize the things for which Jimmy Doolittle was famous.
5. How did the first world war lead to the barnstorming era?

Putting Ideas to Work

Look in your encyclopedia for an entry about Doolittle. Read and share what you learn with the class. Or prepare a time line showing the development of aviation from World War I to World War II. Save your time line until you finish this unit so you can add more information later.

High Flight

Oh! I have slipped the surly bonds of earth
   And danced the skies on laughter-silvered wings;
Sunward I've climbed, and joined the tumbling mirth
   Of sun-split clouds — and done a hundred things
You have not dreamed of — wheeled and soared and swung
   High in the sunlit silence. Hov'ring there,
I've chased the shouting wind along, and flung
   My eager craft through footless halls of air.

Up, up the long, delirious burning blue
   I've topped the wind-swept heights with easy grace
Where never lark, or even eagle flew —
And, while with silent lifting mind I've trod
   The high untrespassed sanctity of space,
Put out my hand and touched the face of God.

200
                                              —John Gillespie Magee, Jr.

White Wings
beneath the Waves

Whenever they could, Melvin and Georgianna Peters left their Kansas farm after crops were harvested to visit their son Clyde and his wife Eleanor and their grandchildren, Shelley, Allan, and Linda on the banks of Lake Yarina Coche in the Peruvian jungle. Clyde Peters piloted the first Seventh-day Adventist mission airplane, the *Fernando Stahl*. Georgianna Peters, a registered nurse, loved the adventure of flying with her son and his family into the jungles. She maintained medical supplies, prepared emergency kits, nursed sick mothers, and treated snakebites and all kinds of infections. But one such trip to the village of Amaqueria[1] gave this grandmother more adventure than she expected. This is part of a letter she wrote.

[1] Amaqueria (ah-mah-kay-REE-yah)

The beds were hard that night — just mats with blankets — but it was so relaxing to lie there and not hear any sounds of civilization. Once in a while a dog would bark or a bird would twitter. We could hear the rushing of the water in the river just a short distance away. It was in flood stage now and had risen more than a hundred feet, so that it was nearer the village than usual. As I drifted off to sleep, I never thought that this *could* be my last night on earth.

The villagers rise early, and we were up with them. It was bright and sunny. We ate and then trooped over to the house where the Sabbath school was to be. We would have our meeting early, then go on to the other station and hope to get back to Pucallpa[1] before the afternoon thundershower that always comes up during this season.

It was only a fifteen-minute flight from Amaqueria to Shahuaya.[2] The weather was good, but a light shower appeared to be approaching from behind. We headed for the plane. Clyde put Eleanor and Linda and me in the back and saw to it that we had our seat belts fastened. Then Melvin got in front and took Shelley on his lap. Allan squeezed in between Clyde and Melvin. Clyde said final good-bys, fastened his seat belt, checked the flight list, and started the engine.

As we taxied down the strip, we waved to the people gathered along the sidelines. At the end of the runway, we turned into a position for takeoff. There we paused for a short word of prayer, then began moving down the runway. Everything went well until we reached the riverbank. For some reason, we were not gaining enough

[1] Pucallpa (poo-KAHL-pah)   [2] Shahuaya (shah-HWIGH-yah)

speed and we could not seem to get airborne. But the strip ended at the riverbank, and there was a steep cliff. When we reached the river we would no doubt get some lift.

When our wheels left the ground and we were out over the water, the plane seemed to be struggling to gain altitude. No possibility of turning back. We simply had to keep hoping that we would get some lift from somewhere. Finally, however, we saw the water getting closer and closer. We realized that we were going to crash in the Ucayali[1] River. Clyde turned his head and said calmly, "Undo your seat belts."

I thought of what I had been teaching in my first aid classes back home: four to six minutes is the limit that one can remain under water. I wondered how many breaths until it would be over. No one talked.

There are only two doors to the *Fernando Stahl.* One is by the pilot and the other is in the back on the opposite side. Eleanor was by the door in the back. Now the plane was nosing down. Suddenly it just landed flat on the water, then tipped to the left, and Linda fell in front of me. I grabbed her and held her tightly in my arms.

[1] Ucayali (oo-kigh-YAH-lee)

Water began to rush in. This must have been when Clyde took Shelley and Allan out his door. I did not see them leave. The plane tipped to the other side. Eleanor was looking hard at the door handle. She must have opened the door, although she never remembered doing so, for we were soon out and into the water.

I seemed to be standing on something for a moment. I could see part of the plane above the water. Good, I thought. We can hang onto it.

I looked around. Clyde had Shelley and Allan and was helping them to keep afloat. Eleanor was looking around frantically. "Are we all here?" she asked, searching the water. "I had Linda, but I don't know where she is now." Just then Linda popped up right in front of me. She was swimming like a little duck with her head just above the water. Eleanor took Linda and let go of the plane, which was slowly sinking. Melvin was nearby.

"I can't swim," I called.

Just then the children's three trumpet cases and a plastic water jug popped up. "Get one of those and hang onto it," Melvin shouted.

I grabbed a trumpet case and put it under my right arm. Then I got the water jug, which was upside down, and put it under my left arm.

By this time the plane was gone. I could see Clyde with Shelley and Allan; Eleanor was with Linda. I could see Melvin. So far we are all safe, I thought. I breathed a prayer of thanks, although how long I could stay up was a grave uncertainty.

I noticed some men in their little dugout canoes coming to our rescue as fast as possible. It seemed I was

204

going downstream so fast in the swift current that they would never be able to get to me.

The canoe picked up Clyde, Shelley, and Allan. I saw them reach Eleanor and Linda, who were hanging onto the floating flannel board. Then they picked up Melvin.

It was hard to keep my nose and mouth above the surface. My trumpet case was filling with water; the jug was slippery, and I had a hard time hanging onto it. I remember thinking, If I could just turn it over and get hold of the handle . . . .

I will never make it, I thought. I struggled to get my nose and mouth above the water. Then I got another breath and tried to hold it. I shut my eyes and went under. I tried again to get a good grip on that water jug. Why couldn't I turn it over?

205

A man in a canoe paddled toward me with long, fast strokes, first on one side of the canoe, then on the other. But it seemed as though he would never reach me. Finally a man reached for me and tried to pull me into the canoe. My nylon nurse's uniform was wet and slippery, and I slid back into the water.

The next thing I knew I was hanging over the edge of the canoe looking at the bottom. And there on the bottom of the canoe lay the water jug. The cap was off the jug! If I had turned it over, it would have filled with water and never could have held me up. That water jug with the air inside it had been my life preserver!

A small launch with a thatched roof pulled alongside. I was loaded onto it. The others were there too. We hugged one another and cried a bit. All of us were safe now. We could go back and wait for a ride home.

But Clyde did not rejoice. He kept looking back at the place where the *Fernando Stahl* was slowly sinking to the bottom of the river. A part of him seemed to go with it.

We shivered — not that it was cold, but we were all in shock. The launch took us back upstream to Amaqueria. The people were so kind to us. We will never forget them. We were all without shoes except Clyde and Allan. We wanted to get out of our wet things, so we went back to the same little hut where we had spent the night so peacefully. As soon as we were alone we all knelt, and with our arms around each other thanked God for His deliverance from a watery grave.

— *Dorothy Aitken*

What Do You Think?

1. Have you ever been in a place where you noticed the silence? Mrs. Peters described the absence of civilization noises. What would it be like to be in a place where you heard only the sounds of nature?
2. Why did Mrs. Peters think of her first aid class during this emergency?
3. Why do you think the family "cried a bit" when they found that they were all safe?

Taking a Closer Look

1. How did Mrs. Peters help her son when she traveled with him in the jungles?
2. Why did Mrs. Peters want to turn the water jug over? What would have happened if she had?
3. On what continent does this story take place?
4. How was the writer able to stay afloat until she was rescued? Would you call this a miracle? Explain your answer.
5. As the plane lowered itself toward the water, what was Mrs. Peters thinking about?

Putting Ideas to Work

Use an open plastic bottle and a large bowl of water to show how the water jug served as a life preserver for Mrs. Peters. Place the bottle in the bowl with the open side down. Then turn the bottle over so that water can get in. What happens?

Around the turn of the century many people around the world were experimenting with flying machines that would carry a man. Here are two stories: one about a man who thought he failed and another about two brothers who succeeded.

The Turkey Buzzard and the Aerodrome

Samuel Langley, his cheeks red with the cold and his white beard glistening a little in the sun, walked down a country road on the outskirts of Washington, D.C. It was late autumn in the year 1888. As the professor made his way down the rutted road, he noticed that the puddles were frozen. In a nearby field corn stalks were piled up in irregular cones. Yellow pumpkins lay heaped up into a little golden hill.

"The sky is unusually clear. There's hardly a cloud in it," Professor Langley said to himself. And it's cold — unusually cold for this time of year, he thought.

Ordinarily Professor Langley did not mind the cold. He had camped just below the snow line on Pike's Peak to sketch an eclipse of the sun with fingers that were half frozen. He had sat on a stool in the snow on Mount Whitney in frigid weather trying to make a study of sunspots. "A scientist cannot be disturbed by discomfort," he had often told himself. Yet there was no denying it was cold that afternoon. He tied his knitted muffler tighter around his neck and walked on, pushing his hands deeper into his pockets.

After a time Professor Langley noticed a turkey buzzard. It was circling over the corn field on the left of the road. The big bird wheeled round and round, its eye doubtless on some hidden prey. He stopped to look at it. The bird's strong wings lay motionless on the air as it circled. Sometimes it seemed to tip slightly, but there was no other movement. Its motion was as easy as a leaf floating on a stream.

"How does it hold itself up?" Professor Langley wondered. He leaned against a fence to watch. The turkey buzzard circled and circled. Occasionally it tipped its wings a little. Then it circled lazily on as if it had abandoned itself to the rocking of some invisible wave.

"There is not the least quiver of its wings," the professor said. He remembered a scientific paper he had read which claimed that every bird is kept aloft by a tiny quivering of its wings. "I can see them quite plainly. I am sure there is no quivering at all."

A full hour passed; the turkey buzzard circled on; the professor continued to watch. A cold wind blew across the corn field, but the bird was undisturbed.

Even the most earnest scientific curiosity can be discouraged by the cold. Professor Langley's hands and feet were growing numb. He had to give up at last. He left the turkey buzzard still circling.

All that evening by his fire Samuel Langley thought about the turkey buzzard and its circling. Next morning he was up early, and on his way to his office. He was director of the Smithsonian Institution, in Washington.

When he reached his office, he asked the library for everything available on the subject of birds' flight. Within an hour messengers began bringing books and pamphlets to his desk. Putting aside other matters, Langley began to study.

"No one really understands birds' flight," he said to his assistant, peering at him over the top of a great heap of books. "Physicists make such efforts to understand the sun's rays and the ocean's tides. Why haven't they found out why a bird can soar?"

"A good many men have been trying to fly," the assistant answered. "There's Penaud, and Sir George Cayley, and Sir Hiram Maxim, and — "

"I know," Langley said, smiling at the younger man. "Everywhere people have been trying — but it does not seem to me that they have really understood the air . . . ."

No one has really understood the air, Langley kept thinking — the air that stretches upward, clear, invisible, with its winds, its moving currents. Is it some kind of strange ocean that sweeps around the earth? Why can the birds fly through that ocean when men cannot? What secrets do the birds know? How do their wings lift them up?

So Professor Langley made more than a hundred little models. Small artificial birds they were and he set them flying through the air of his workshop, with twisted rubber bands for power. The models were carefully and delicately made. The flat surfaces of their wings were set at exact angles. Weight in proportion to wingspan was carefully measured. As they went flying across his workroom, Langley's eyes danced. "See! See!" he cried, releasing one little plane and then another. "It will not be very long now before men can take to a new highway — the highway of the sky."

As he worked, a great discovery came to him. He himself could not tell why or how. It was a sudden understanding, like a flash of lightning on a dark night.

"I believe it's the movement of the air under the bird's wing that keeps it up," he said, "little moving ripples passing under the wing. The faster the bird goes, the more easily it is held up and the heavier it can be. I could make such a bird artificially. . . . These models are all too small," he said. "I want to make bigger ones and put engines in them. I think that engines have been developed well enough to use now."

So he began making bigger models with engines. He called them *aerodromes* from two Greek words that meant "runners in the air." Aerodrome No. 1 measured thirteen feet from one tip to another. Even with the engine it weighed only twenty-six pounds. When he brought it to the Potomac River to launch it, his friend Alexander Graham Bell came to watch. They shot Aerodrome No. 1 from a catapult on top of a houseboat in the river. It flew for half a mile before its fuel ran out and it dropped into the water.

Then Langley made still larger models, each one a slight improvement on the one before. And every one he shot from the catapult on top of the houseboat. That seemed to be the best way to get them into the air.

To his great excitement Aerodrome No. 6 flew for three-quarters of a mile. Bending toward the left in a great circle, it lighted on the water.

Samuel Langley with his helper Charles Manly rowed down the river to where Aerodrome No. 6 had dropped. They raised it from the water and set it carefully in the boat, its wings stretching beyond either side. Langley sat still, looking at it. There was no doubt: it had flown three-quarters of a mile.

I know it now, Langley kept thinking to himself. The movement of the air under the wings holds up the weight of the engine.

"So my work in aerodynamics is ended," he said aloud to Manly. "Now other men can work out the practical details. It should not be too hard for them to make the aerodrome big enough to hold a man."

Manly nodded. The boat moved slowly along the Potomac toward Washington. Aerodrome No. 6 lay glistening in the sun between them.

"There will be new highways — highways in the air," Langley said. He smiled. He and Manly were very happy as the boat made its way back to the shore.

The story ought to end there. Langley, so happy, rowing back to Washington with his friend and helper Manly. Aerodrome No. 6 had flown. He had made a flying machine. Aerodrome No. 6 could fly. But the story has a very different end.

In 1898, the *Maine* was sunk in Havana harbor, and the United States went to war with Spain. Theodore Roosevelt was Assistant Secretary of the Navy. McKinley was President. Roosevelt knew of the balloon observations that Thaddeus Lowe had made during the Civil War. But how much better it would be if the Navy had, not an anchored balloon, but an aerodrome. One could fly along with the Navy wherever it went. Theodore Roosevelt had heard of Langley's little models. He went and talked to President McKinley about them.

That is why a committee of brass-buttoned officials went to call on Langley in his office at the Smithsonian. "Will you make an aerodrome large enough to carry men?" they asked him.

"No," Langley said. "I am a scientist, not a manufacturer."

"But the country needs it — there is no one else to do it."

"It would cost a great deal of money," Langley said.

"Congress will provide the money."

So fifty thousand dollars was voted by Congress to meet the expenses of building a big aerodrome, and Langley set about designing and building it. He made it very much like his other aerodromes. Two propellers were driven by a motor which produced one horsepower. Langley had found that a steam engine was too heavy, so he decided to try a combustion engine. He had to go to Europe to find one that was suitable, and all this took a great deal of time.

But at last the aerodrome was ready to be launched from the roof of the houseboat on the Potomac. He felt sure that the best way to launch it was with a catapult, just as he had launched the smaller models.

There was a buzz of excitement along the shore when the day of the launching came. Congress had invested so much money in the building of the aerodrome that the newspapers thought it was a good story. A crowd of reporters came down to the shore to watch.

Langley stood up in a little boat that was tied beside the houseboat. "It's all right now," he said to the mechanics who were with him. He was very confident. He knew that the principles on which the aerodrome was built were scientifically right.

He signaled for the blocks to be pulled out from the aerodrome's wheels. It slid down the tracks on the roof of the houseboat, hung for a moment over the edge of the water, then dropped head first into the river. There was a sickening crash and a shower of spray.

Charles Manly had been seated in the aerodrome. He swam out from underneath, unhurt.

"I think one of the struts caught somehow. It never really left the top of the houseboat," he said.

Professor Langley examined the aerodrome. "The damage can be repaired," he said. "There is no reason why it should not fly."

Three months later they were ready to take off again. While the crowd on the shore watched, gasping, the nose of the machine rose into the air. It stood straight up on its tail a moment, and fell into the water on its back, broken. And again Charles Manly swam to shore.

Houseboat from which aerodromes were launched

Damaged aerodrome being recovered from Potomac River

"There isn't anything the matter with the principle of it," Langley kept insisting. "It was just the launching gear that didn't release it for some reason. We could build it again quite easily with the experience we've had now . . . ."

Quite easily — but where was the money to come from? The war was over now. Congress was not willing to spend any more money on human flight. Newspaper reporters who had watched from the shore of the Potomac were making fun of Langley's efforts now. "A professor who thinks he can fly," they wrote. "A professor who is wasting the people's money."

Professor Langley died only two years after that. He was hurt and broken by the sneering remarks of people who did not understand what he had done. Several years later Glenn Curtiss actually flew Langley's aerodrome. Afterwards they brought it back to Washington and put it in the Smithsonian, where Langley had worked. You can see it there today.

217

Bicycles and Flying Machines

All night he could not sleep. Wilbur Wright lay on his hard cot in the shack at Kitty Hawk and did not close his eyes. He heard the pounding of the surf on the beach and the showering of sand blown by the wind against the side of the shack. He saw the patch of moonlight on the floor. It changed its shape as the white moon moved across the sky. Beside him on the other cot his brother Orville slept, his breathing steady and deep.

But Wilbur lay awake. In his mechanic's brain calculations were coming and going — figures from the tables of air pressures they had worked out in their wind tunnel, angles of glides they had made, straight planes, and curving winds. Tomorrow — tomorrow would be the final test. They were almost sure that the rudder would hold. They thought the propeller shaft was strong enough. The hours passed, Wilbur lying there awake, Orville sleeping.

Tomorrow might mark the end of a long effort. It had started when they were still at school. One day they had been skating on the ice and someone had slipped, and Wilbur had been hit in the face with a stick. It had not hurt him badly at all, but he had to remain in bed for a long time. Orville had tried to keep him from being bored by bringing him books to read from the public library. They used to read them together. They were nearly all books about "flying machines." Everybody seemed to be interested in that subject at the turn of the century, though most people thought then that the very idea of flying was nonsense.

One day Orville came in empty-handed from the library. "There isn't a single book there that we haven't read," he said. "Let's write to the Smithsonian Institution in Washington, D.C., for the names of books that we might buy." So after they had left school and gone to work, they continued to read and dream about flying.

Later they learned of the Frenchman Octave Chanute[1] and his book *Progress in Flying Machines*. They read it, and decided to write to Chanute. Chanute was no great inventor himself. But he knew about the work of all the men who had ever dreamed of flying — Clement Ader, Langley, Alexander Graham Bell, Hiram Maxim — there were a host of them. They all had failed, and still people kept on trying. "There has been no one like Lilienthal[2] in Germany," he wrote them. "That man has wonderful gifts of patience and industry and scientific imagination."

But Lilienthal was killed when he tried to lift his

[1] Octave Chanute (ok-TAHV sh'-NOOT) [2] Lilienthal (LIL-ee-ən-thahl)

machine from the ground. "I don't believe he calculated the air pressure on his wing surfaces right," Orville said. And Wilbur said, "Could we go on where Lilienthal left off?"

The brothers had left school and opened a bicycle repair shop. Repairing and renting bicycles made them a living, but it didn't take all their time. It was not very long before they had made a glider for themselves. The material for it cost fifteen dollars; it weighed a little over fifty pounds.

"We're going to be careful," they told their father. "Anyway there isn't any danger in a glider. And we don't want to crash. We couldn't go on experimenting if we did."

But you couldn't use a glider very well in Dayton. There were too many houses and too many people around. "What we need," they said, "is a fairly level place where the wind is steady. If the place has soft sand to fall into, so much the better. And if the slopes are free from trees and shrubs, we'll run less risk."

They wrote the Weather Bureau in Washington, D.C. The Weather Bureau suggested Kitty Hawk, North Carolina.

Every year when they could take a little time from their bicycle business they went to Kitty Hawk, a tiny fishing village on an island off the coast. They built themselves a shack on the sand dunes, and fitted it up in what they called "royal luxury." They cooked their meals on a smoky oil stove and washed their dishes with sand. And they watched the buzzards and chicken hawks flying, to try to find out how they kept their balance in a wind. Day

who ran along beside it with a stop watch in his hand, estimated that it was in the air about twelve seconds.

With the help of the bystanders they brought it back to the shed and began a repair job. They had to work clumsily because their hands were so cold. Soon after eleven o'clock the repairs were finished. They were ready to try again.

This time it was Wilbur who lay down beside the engine, and Orville who held the stop watch. Again they slipped the rope, and again it started. Again the machine darted up and plunged down, but this time it went a little farther before it came to rest.

A third time they tried it, and a fourth. Now the controls worked better. That fourth time it stayed in the air fifty-nine seconds and traveled eight hundred fifty-two feet. Then it hit a mound of dirt and stopped. The rudder frame was badly broken.

Photograph taken by bystander during early flight trials

They took off the rudder, carried the flying machine back to the side of the shack, and set it down. But just then a gust of wind struck it. Everyone rushed to hold it, but it rolled over and over. The wind was too strong.

It didn't matter. They had flown. They had been first to drive a machine with a motor through the air. They had done what Langley had failed to do, what Lilienthal had lost his life in trying to do. All the work in aviation that followed was merely a matter of improving on what they had done.

They hurried to the Coast Guard Station to send a telegram to their father. It seems strange to think of them — thin, long-legged, running along the cold hard beach, with the waves and the wind and the sandpipers and the seagulls — two men knowing they could fly.

The telegram read:

Success four flights Thursday morning all against twenty-one mile wind started from level with engine power alone average speed through air thirty-one miles, longest 59 seconds inform press home Christmas
                                                    Orville Wright

After they had sent the telegram they packed up their things and started for home. Their father must have been happy when he received the telegram. He informed the press as Orville had requested. But he needn't have done it; the newspaper editors didn't want to bother with the story. Only two papers in the whole United States made any mention of the flight next day.

224

But Wilbur and Orville knew that they had done it. On the wall of their bicycle shop, they tacked the photograph of Orville lying on the wing beside the engine, and Wilbur running alongside with the stop watch in his hand.

Six years passed after that, and Wilbur and Orville Wright kept on with their flying. They gave public exhibitions in Dayton and in Cleveland. More and more people were convinced that it was possible for a man to fly in a machine that was powered by an engine. To be sure, no one had ever seen a plane fly very far. They simply crowded into some country field and stood gaping while the strange vehicle made of sticks and cloth cut awkward circles over their heads in the sky.

Was this all that could be done? Would it ever be possible to navigate on the currents of the sky?

— *Katherine B. Shippen*

What Do You Think?

1. Do you agree with Professor Langley that "A scientist cannot be disturbed by discomfort"? Why or why not? What does this mean?
2. Was Professor Langley a failure? Support your answer with details from the story.
3. Why do people often laugh at the failures of others? Explain your answer.
4. Why was owning and operating a bicycle repair shop helpful to the Wrights as they built their airplane?
5. Wilbur Wright said, "I don't believe anyone will fly in a thousand years." He also said, "I think we'll succeed." How do you explain this contradiction in his words?

Taking a Closer Look

1. What was the important discovery that came to Langley "like a flash of lightning on a dark night"?
2. What did Professor Langley mean when he said there would be "highways in the air"?
3. Why did the Wright brothers decide to use Kitty Hawk as their testing grounds for flight?
4. How had Wilbur Wright been injured when he was young? What effect did this have on his interest in flying machines?
5. Why couldn't the Wrights fly their glider near Dayton, Ohio, where they lived?

Putting Ideas to Work

Pretend you are a reporter at the scene of either Langley's or the Wrights' demonstration. Write a short news report of what you have seen. Be sure to tell who, what, where, when, why, and how.

Dreams

Hold fast to dreams
For if dreams die
Life is a broken-winged bird
That cannot fly.

Hold fast to dreams
For when dreams go
Life is a barren field
Frozen with snow.

— *Langston Hughes*

Imagine what it would be like to fly. Not in an airplane or a glider or a balloon — just to fly. When Ellen White was only seventeen years old, she traveled in vision. Her vision took her on a flight beyond the planets, all the way to heaven. In her own words as recorded in *Early Writings*, Ellen describes her first vision.

Beyond the Planets

Up to December, 1844, my joys, trials, and disappointments were like those of my dear Advent friends around me. At this time I visited one of our Advent sisters, and in the morning we bowed around the family altar. It was not an exciting occasion, and there were but five of us present, all women . . . .

While I was praying at the family altar, the Holy Ghost fell upon me, and I seemed to be rising higher and higher, far above the dark world. I turned to look for the Advent people in the world, but could not find them, when a voice said to me, "Look again, and look a little higher." At this I raised my eyes, and saw a straight and narrow path, cast up high above the world. On this path the Advent people were traveling to the city, which was at the farther end of the path . . . . Soon our eyes were drawn to the east, for a small black cloud had appeared, about half as large as a man's hand, which we all knew was the sign of the Son of man. We all in solemn silence gazed on the cloud as it drew nearer and became lighter, glorious, and still more glorious, till it was a great white cloud. The bottom appeared like fire; a rainbow was over the cloud, while around it were ten thousand angels, singing a most lovely song; and upon it sat the Son of man. His hair was white and curly and lay on His shoulders; and upon His head were many crowns. His feet had the appearance of fire; in His right hand was a sharp sickle; in His left, a silver trumpet . . . .

229

◄ Harry Anderson, Artist

Then Jesus' silver trumpet sounded . . . . He gazed on the graves of the sleeping saints, then raised His eyes and hands to heaven, and cried, "Awake! awake! awake! ye that sleep in the dust, and arise." Then there was a mighty earthquake. The graves opened, and the dead came up clothed with immortality . . . .

We all entered the cloud together, and were seven days ascending to the sea of glass, when Jesus brought the crowns, and with His own right hand placed them on our heads . . . .

Jesus raised His mighty, glorious arm, laid hold of the pearly gate, swung it back on its glittering hinges, and said to us, "You have washed your robes in My blood, stood stiffly for My truth, enter in." We all marched in and felt that we had a perfect right in the city.

Here we saw the tree of life and the throne of God. Out of the throne came a pure river of water, and on either side of the river was the tree of life. On one side of the river was a trunk of a tree, and a trunk on the other side of the river, both of pure, transparent gold. At first I thought I saw two trees. I looked again, and saw that they were united at the top in one tree. So it was the tree of life on either side of the river of life. Its branches bowed to the place where we stood, and the fruit was glorious; it looked like gold mixed with silver . . . .

With Jesus at our head we all descended from the city down to this earth, on a great mighty mountain, which could not bear Jesus up, and it parted asunder, and there was a mighty plain. Then we looked up and saw the great city, with twelve foundations, and twelve gates, three on each side, and an angel at each gate. We all cried out,

"The city, the great city, it's coming, it's coming down from God out of heaven," and it came and settled on the place where we stood. Then we began to look at the glorious things outside of the city . . . .

I saw a field of tall grass, most glorious to behold; it was living green and had a reflection of silver and gold, as it waved proudly to the glory of King Jesus. Then we entered a field full of all kinds of beasts — the lion, the lamb, the leopard, and the wolf, all together in perfect union. We passed through the midst of them, and they followed on peaceably after . . . .

Edward Hicks (1780-1849)
The Peaceable Kingdom
Circa 1840-1845
Oil on Canvas 45.8 x 61.2 cm.
The Brooklyn Museum, Dick S. Ramsey Fund

231

As we were traveling along, we met a company who also were gazing at the glories of the place. I noticed red as a border on their garments; their crowns were brilliant; their robes were pure white. As we greeted them, I asked Jesus who they were. He said they were martyrs that had been slain for Him. With them was an innumerable company of little ones; they also had a hem of red on their garments. Mount Zion was just before us, and on the mount was a glorious temple, and about it were seven other mountains, on which grew roses and lilies. And I saw the little ones climb, or, if they chose, use their little wings and fly, to the top of the mountains and pluck the never-fading flowers . . . .

And I saw a table of pure silver; it was many miles in length, yet our eyes could extend over it. I saw the fruit of the tree of life, the manna, almonds, figs, pomegranates, grapes, and many other kinds of fruit. I asked Jesus to let me eat of the fruit. He said, "Not now. Those who eat of the fruit of this land go back to earth no more. But in a little while, if faithful, you shall both eat of the fruit of the tree of life and drink of the water of the fountain." And He said, "You must go back to the earth again and relate to others what I have revealed to you." Then an angel bore me gently down to this dark world. Sometimes I think I can stay here no longer; all things of earth look so dreary. I feel very lonely here, for I have seen a better land. Oh, that I had wings like a dove, then I would fly away and be at rest!

— *Ellen G. White*

232

What Do You Think?

1. Why was the way that the Advent people traveled represented in this vision as a straight and narrow path?
2. What do Jesus' words mean "You have washed your robes in My blood, stood stiffly for My truth"?
3. What is meant by the expression, "clothed with immortality"?
4. Which of the scenes described in this vision do you find most appealing? What do you like best about that scene?

Taking a Closer Look

1. How old was Ellen White when she received this vision? Where was she? What was she doing?
2. Why did Jesus tell Ellen that she had to go back to earth?
3. In your own words describe the tree of life.
4. Who was the Son of man? Describe Him.
5. Name four ways in which heaven will be different from earth as it is now.

Putting Ideas to Work

Invite members of your class to help prepare a mural showing the scenes of the vision in the order in which they were described.

Scholars and dreamers have thought of flying for many years. About 1500 a scholar and artist named da Vinci knew that people could fly and that it would not be by miracles.

not By miracles

Leonardo da Vinci pushed open the heavily studded door of his workshop, and entered. In a corner a workman gluing fabric on a gigantic framework of bamboo put his brush down into the glue pot and came over to meet him.

"It's almost done, sir," the workman said, subdued excitement in his voice. "Another day, and you may push me from the second-story window. I shall fly across the rooftops and right across the piazza — and all the people coming down the steps from the church will see me. That is, unless you yourself — "

Leonardo laid his crimson cloak across a chair and put his hand on the shoulder of the excited workman.

"I'm sorry, Giovanni," he said. "Tomorrow I think we'll start to design the drains for the palace of the Duke of Tuscany."

Giovanni drew back, and consternation was on his face.

"But sir," he cried, "not finish it? Why, you have spent all you had on this flying machine. And I too, have worked more than a year, sizing the cloth and making the special glue, splitting the bamboo, and making strong joinings."

234

Giovanni paused. Evidently it was not necessary to tell Leonardo all this, since he himself had directed the work. Yet what made Leonardo behave so strangely? After all this time and work, was he going to abandon the flying machine?

Leonardo walked up to the great birdlike frame that stretched all the way from one side of the workshop to the other, and examined it.

"Your work has been good, Giovanni," he said. "No man could have done better. It is I who have failed. I have checked the mechanics of it again, and it is not right. These wings would not hold the great bird in the air. If we were to finish it and launch it, it would crash. A broken leg would do neither one of us any good."

"Ay, but sir," Giovanni answered, "I have prayed. It may be we will receive a miracle —"

Leonardo turned with an impatient shrug. "Flying will not be by miracles, or by any kind of wonders," he said. "It will be only by the laws of mechanics."

And then, more kindly, for he saw the disappointment in Giovanni's face, "Go home to rest after all your work."

When Giovanni had gone, Leonardo sat down at his littered table and pulled his notebook toward him. It was a strange room, this workshop in which he sat. On the walls he had tacked his sketches: the face of a peasant girl he had seen selling flowers, a man's figure, a hand with long delicate fingers. There were heaps of sketchbooks on the table, beautifully bound in tooled leather. But there was dust on the piles of sketchbooks, and the sketches on the wall were disordered, half untacked. A lute rested on a chair near the window, a bunch of

bright-colored ribbons tied to its handle. But the lute was dusty; it had not been touched for a long time.

Bottles and phials and bars of metal crowded each other on the tables. Pieces of pipe, samples of various kinds of minerals, shells, and specimens of various herbs — all lay in confusion and apparent neglect, dust-coated.

Over all these things, suspended from the ceiling, was the bamboo framework on which Giovanni had been working. It was nearly covered with linen cloth, and looked very much like the wings of a strange and gigantic bird.

Leonardo walked over to it and examined the place, still moist with glue, where Giovanni had been sticking the last patch. Then he turned and sat down at a low table near the window again.

"Maybe tonight I shall be able to find the principle..." He drew a shabby notebook from his pocket and began thumbing through the pages.

"A bird is an instrument working according to mathematical law," he had written. Underneath he had sketched a bird's body, with the center of gravity carefully marked. And down across the page in apparent confusion there were wings — wings bent and wings spread, wings with strong pinions, and wings with row upon row of delicate feathers. They were drawn in every possible position, at every possible angle, as if he had tried to catch and hold the motion of a sparrow's flutter or the wingbeat of an eagle.

On another page he had sketched a curious contrivance. It was a sort of a screw that he had hoped might lift a body up into the air, like a modern helicopter. And near this was a propeller — of birds' feathers. All those things were practical enough, he thought to himself. Some day his sketches would be transformed into models, he had no doubt. But how to find the mathematical law, the exact measurements by which an artificial bird could fly — this had eluded him.

His pencil checked over again the diagram of the great

frame on which Giovanni had been working.

"It won't do," he said. "It isn't right." He turned over to a fresh page, and fell to figuring and sketching, and figuring again.

It grew dark in the room, and he fetched a candle in a tall candlestick. When it was lighted, he went on with his work. A sleek black cat jumped up on the table. He stroked it absently, while it purred and curled up on top of a pile of his papers.

Leonardo must have worked very late in the quiet room. Paper after paper was covered with his equations. The cat slept on. The candle dripped down into a craggy mass of wax. The street outside his window was still. Then the pencil slipped from his hand, and his head sank down on his arms.

It was morning when he woke. The bells of Santa Maria del Fiore were ringing. And as his consciousness gradually came back to him the bells of San Lorenzo began to ring. Soon San Michele and Santa Felicita answered them, until the air was filled with the pealing joyous sound. He raised his head and listened, then pushed back his chair and walked toward the casement. Below him in the cobbled street, the city of Florence was already awake. On the doorsteps matrons stood gossiping, and although it was still early, a fair crowd of the pious were already on their way to church.

Leonardo looked down at them. "When a man can fly,"

◀Leonardo wrote his notes backward on his sketches. They could only be read with a mirror.

he said, "he will forget the cares of the earth. All the nervous worry, all the bartering and bickering, all the striving and contriving — they will disappear as the morning mist blows away from the surface of the Arno. If only I can find the mechanical principle. If only I can work it out."

He stood quietly by the window, looking down, yet hardly seeing the street below him.

He was aroused from his reverie by a very faint sound. It was so faint as to be hardly a sound at all — as light and soft as the touch of a fallen leaf. A swallow with glossy wings and bright little eyes was looking up at him. It spread its wings, and beat them once or twice; then with a sure, easy motion it glided on a current of air, wheeling up over the housetops until it was gone in the clear blue.

Leonardo stood watching the sky where it had gone. He had succeeded in so many things. People traveled from everywhere to see his painting of the Last Supper, at Milan. He had composed music and written sonnets and designed buildings of extraordinary beauty — yet here was this little bird that could fly. His glider would not fly; he knew it.

"Maybe I shall never learn your secret, little one," he said softly. "Maybe I shall never drift on the clear currents of the air. But if I do not, someone will. There will be a day when men can fly as well as you."

So he turned to his unfinished work.

— *Katherine B. Shippen*

There are many mysteries about the past. Scientists and historians have many questions and a few answers. Some people think they have the solution to this one. See what you think.

Mystery of the Ancient Balloons

The great holiday had arrived. Thousands of people left their irrigated farms. They headed toward the desert plains to celebrate.

Children played while grown-ups talked and ate. Nearby, workmen put the final touches on huge ceremonial figures cut into the earth.

Suddenly a giant shadow passed over the crowd. Everyone stopped talking and looked up. There, flying high above them, was a huge hot-air balloon carrying the king and priests.

From 1000 feet in the air the leaders inspected the people. They looked at the huge animal shapes and symbols on the desert surface. The workmen had removed the dark topsoil to uncover the light material underneath. This is how the huge figures were formed in the earth.

This scene sounds like something that might have happened in Europe in 1783. That was when the first recorded balloon flight took place.

But now some explorers claim the first balloon trip was not in Europe. This scene, they claim, took place in Peru, South America. And it happened 2000 years before the flight in Europe. It is believed that the fliers were Nazca[1] Indians.

[1] Nazca (NAHZ-kə)

The explorers believe the balloon flights are the answer to the mystery of the Nazca Plains drawings. These huge drawings have been a mystery since they were first discovered in the 1920s. The figures and designs are too large for people on the ground to see completely. Only someone high overhead could see the designs and direct the work going on below. But there are no nearby mountains.

The explorers started investigating. They had found a Nazca pot jar which appeared to show a hot-air balloon. This led them to think that the figures were drawn by people guided from a hot-air balloon hovering overhead.

Then the explorers made an important discovery. They found the papers of a missionary who had lived in Brazil many years before. He had been to Europe about 1707 with a model of a balloon he claimed the Indians used. The missionary had displayed his model seventy-four years before the first hot-air balloon flight recorded in Europe!

Some argued that the explorers were just guessing. So the explorers decided to prove their idea. Using the missionary's description, they built a copy of the Indian airship. They named the balloon *Condor I*.

Condor was made of fabrics similar to those found in Nazca graves. The balloon was eight stories high. Under it was a boat-shaped area for men to sit in.

The night before the flight the explorers started inflating the balloon. Heat from flaming dry wood was directed through a tunnel to the balloon opening.

By early morning the eight-story balloon was ready. Two explorers got in. They released the lines and

244

sandbags holding *Condor* to earth. It rushed up into the cool morning air — 600 feet in thirty seconds.

The explorers clung tightly to *Condor* and looked down at the Nazca drawings. They could see everything!

Then a sudden wind blew the balloon hard onto the desert floor. It hit with a thud, bouncing the two crewmen out. Free of their weight, *Condor* rose to 1200 feet and flew two and one-half miles in eighteen minutes before landing.

The flight didn't go quite the way it was planned, the explorers said. But to them it seemed to prove how people made the huge drawings. It also suggested that the history of flight might have begun 2000 years earlier than people had thought.

245

What Do You Think?

1. What did da Vinci mean when he said, "Flying will not be by miracles"?
2. Leonardo said, "When a man can fly, he will forget the cares of the earth." Do you think he was right? Why or why not?
3. If you could design any new invention you wanted to, what machine would you make?
4. Did the Nazca Indians fly in hot-air balloons? Use details from the story to explain your answer.
5. Why did the explorers say that the flight of Condor I didn't go quite the way it was planned? What happened?

Taking a Closer Look

1. For what two reasons did da Vinci abandon his efforts to build a flying machine?
2. List some of the things that Leonardo da Vinci had done successfully.
3. What did a missionary from Brazil take to France in 1707?
4. What made the explorers think the Nazca Indians had flown in balloons?

Putting Ideas to Work

Use reference books to find out more about da Vinci or flying machines, or to learn about the first recorded balloon flight. Write a paragraph that tells what you discover.

Taking Off

The airplane taxis down the field
And heads into the breeze,
It lifts its wheels above the ground,
It skims above the trees,
It rises high and higher
Away up toward the sun,
It's just a speck against the sky
— And now it's gone!

— Unknown

247

Joan Steinberger was winning the transcontinental air race. Then she entered mountainous thunderclouds and learned that another contestant was in trouble. She had an important decision to make. As you read, see if you think she made the right choice.

The Race with Two Winners

On the Fourth of July, 1969, the big airport at San Diego,[1] California, vibrated with excitement. Out on the field, ninety-two sleek light planes were warming up. Their wings glittered from polishing. Their finely-tuned engines buzzed with impatience.

A few minutes after nine o'clock in the morning, a single-engined Cessna with a big number 1 on its tail taxied up to a woman holding a flag at the end of the long runway. The flag dropped and number 1 zoomed down the runway and into the air.

[1] San Diego (SAN dee-AY-goh)

The twenty-third annual All-Women's Transcontinental Air Race had just begun. From here on, it would be full speed ahead all the way across the continent to Washington, D.C.

A few planes back was Joan Steinberger of California in the TAR 10 position (Transcontinental Air Race starting position number 10). The takeoff positions were won by lot, and Mrs. Steinberger was happy to get off to an early start in her single-engined Piper Cherokee. Much farther back, Doris Bailey of California was TAR 66 in a Cessna 172. Behind her, in the TAR 68 spot with a twin-engined Piper Comanche, was Mara Culp, also a Californian. Of these three women, one would become the surprise winner of the race. The other two would be part of a high drama more than halfway across the country.

249

The first leg of the race stretched to the northeast toward Las Vegas, Nevada. The pilots climbed above the green belt of the California coast and headed for the bleak mountains of the San Bernardino[1] Range. Every second counted. The winner of the race would be the pilot who hit the highest average ground speed from coast to coast in relation to her type of plane. In past races the difference between first and second place was often a matter of minutes.

The total distance was 2515 miles. This was no race for amateurs. Along the route the fliers would have to deal with every kind of land and every type of summer weather. The rules did not make it any easier. No instrument flying or night flying were permitted. Pilots were allowed only certain equipment so the contest would be fair.

Every woman in the race also had to have at least a private pilot's license plus an instrument or an instructor's rating. Though no airline hired a woman pilot until 1972, there were hundreds of qualified women with thousands of hours of flying experience. Joan Steinberger, for instance, flew emergency supplies to hospitals in California. Doris Bailey was a flight instructor. Mara Culp was a charter pilot.

Most of the fliers decided to spend a night at Saint Joseph, Missouri. Joan Steinberger was one of these. On the morning of Monday, July 7, she got out to the airport early and prepared her plane for a full day at top speed. But when she checked the weather, she wondered if she would get in a full day's flying after all. Already

[1] San Bernardino (SAN ber-nah-DEE-noh)

250

thunderstorms were building up on either side of the route to the next checkpoint at Mount Vernon, Illinois.

I might as well push on through and see how far I can get, she thought to herself as she filed her flight plan.

The pilots leaving Saint Joseph that morning began to meet the first thunderstorms after they crossed the Mississippi River. At first the storms were scattered. All that was needed to avoid them was a slight detour now and then. But as Joan Steinberger neared Mount Vernon, the sky was almost black. The dense clouds at the edge of the storm had a solid, rolling look. She knew this meant high winds and rough air far beyond the strength of her little plane.

As Joan Steinberger headed for the field from the northwest, she called the Mount Vernon tower. The news was bad.

"TAR ten, this is Mount Vernon tower. The field is below minimums. Visibility one and one-half miles in heavy rain. Hold south of the field and wait for further instructions."

Unless a plane is guided by instruments, by law a pilot must be able to see at least three miles and clouds must be no lower than a thousand feet before a plane can land. Since instrument flying was forbidden by the rules of the race, Mrs. Steinberger had no choice but to remain clear of the field until visibility was good enough for her to land.

At the field itself, air-traffic controller Charles Thomas was having a difficult day. His "tower" was a pickup truck with radio equipment in the back. The Mount Vernon airport was a small one and did not have the usual equipment. So Thomas had been sent over from a large airport at nearby Evansville, Indiana, to help the pilots on their way. As he stood by the truck, the wind-whipped rain lashed at him, and the lightning crackled on his radio. But that was not the worst thing. Thomas knew that every minute he made the new arrivals wait would reduce their chances of winning. There was nothing he could do, though. As long as the heavy rain continued to reduce the visibility, no plane could legally land.

Joan Steinberger followed the tower's instructions and turned south. Soon she passed over a highway which gave her a good landmark to circle while she waited.

Mrs. Steinberger was not the only one in the air around Mount Vernon, however. As she circled south of the field, she heard one of her competitors call in.

"Mount Vernon tower, this is TAR sixty-six. Can you give me a radio bearing to the field?"

"That's odd," Mrs. Steinberger thought. "She must be having some kind of trouble if she needs directions to the field."

"TAR sixty-six, this is Mount Vernon tower. Unable to give you a bearing. We don't have the right equipment."

"Mount Vernon tower, this is TAR sixty-six. Can you give me a steer? Over."

The tower repeated its message, but for some reason, TAR 66 was unable to hear the tower. This could be serious, Mrs. Steinberger thought as she listened in. She scanned the dark, storm-whipped clouds that boiled around the Mount Vernon airport. There was no sign of the other plane.

The storm had sprung a trap on Doris Bailey in TAR 66. Normally the course between Saint Joseph, Missouri, and Mount Vernon would have been a straight line. But severe storms lay directly across Mrs. Bailey's course. She had turned aside to try to get around the fast-moving storms, but they had closed in behind her. In an effort to remain clear of the clouds, she had wandered farther and farther from her course.

As Mrs. Bailey dodged the clouds, she searched the ground for landmarks. But in southern Illinois and nearby Indiana, everything on the ground looks very much the same, even on a clear day. This is beautiful, flat, farm country. For miles in any direction, a person in an airplane can see few things that stand out as landmarks. Nearly all the country roads run in straight lines from north to south and east to west. The towns are all about the same size and shape, and the little winding rivers all look alike. With the sky darkened by the storm, it was all but impossible to identify points on the land below.

With each passing minute, the needle of Mrs. Bailey's gas gauge moved slowly toward the empty mark. Airport or no airport, she would soon be down. Again she called for help.

This time Mrs. Steinberger answered. "TAR sixty-six, this is TAR ten. Can you read me?"

"Roger, TAR ten."

"The tower can hear you, but they can't give you a steer. No equipment. Try to tell me where you are, and I'll relay the message for you."

"I'm in the clear above a highway and a railroad. I can see a tower of some sort."

Mrs. Steinberger repeated the message to the traffic controller at Mount Vernon. On the ground Charles Thomas tried to visualize the countryside. He had flown over the area many times, but he did not quite recognize the landmarks that Mrs. Bailey had described.

"Tell her to keep circling and call in anything else she sees," he radioed to Mrs. Steinberger.

A few minutes later Mrs. Bailey described a river. She said she saw smoke from some sort of factory or power plant. When Joan Steinberger relayed this to Thomas, he could picture the scene.

"Tell her she's over the Wabash River now," Thomas called to Mrs. Steinberger. "She can probably contact Evansville tower." Thomas told her the radio channel for Evansville, and she relayed the information to Mrs. Bailey. Mrs. Steinberger tuned in Evansville herself. She listened to see if she could be of further help, even though every extra minute in the air would reduce her chances of winning the race. After a while she heard TAR 66 reach the Evansville tower by radio and get landing instructions. When Mrs. Steinberger was sure Mrs. Bailey was safely on the ground, she threaded her way through the thunderstorms back to Mount Vernon. The field was clear and she landed.

The incident took only twenty minutes. Joan Steinberger, Doris Bailey, and Charles Thomas made it sound almost routine. But routine it definitely was not. Mrs. Bailey's plane ran out of gas just as she touched down at Evansville. And by spending so much time in the air to help, Mrs. Steinberger had lost all chances of winning.

When the race was over and all the flying times had been recorded, Mara Culp was the winner. She made the 2515-mile trip in eleven hours and fifty-seven minutes — an average of 210 miles per hour. It was her very first time in this race, and a great personal triumph for her. A native of Latvia, she had moved to the United States and learned to fly. Now she had won the toughest and most professional women's air event in the world.

Joan Steinberger and Doris Bailey could not finish the race. More bad weather kept them from completing it by the deadline. But in the hearts of pilots everywhere, men and women alike, the flier who gave up the race to help another in trouble was a winner too.

— *Sherwood Harris*

What Do You Think?

1. Why were no women pilots hired by the airlines until 1972?
2. What could have happened if Joan Steinberger had decided winning the race was the most important thing in the world?
3. What did the author mean when he wrote, "The flier who gave up the race to help another in trouble was a winner too"? Do you agree? Why or why not?

Taking a Closer Look

1. Where did the race begin and to what point were the contestants headed?
2. How was the winner of the race to be determined?
3. Why was Mrs. Bailey lost?
4. List as many of the rules of this race as you can remember. Then compare your list to the facts in the story.
5. What kinds of professional flying had Joan Steinberger, Doris Bailey, and Mara Culp done before the race?

Putting Ideas to Work

What does a person have to do to become a pilot, receive an instrument rating, an instructor's rating, or a charter license? What is the work of an air traffic controller? To find out more about flying, interview a pilot or study reference materials such as the encyclopedia. Be ready to report your findings to the class.

The Web of Life

Unhappily the story of civilization includes the careless killing of wildlife, the polluting of streams, the draining of salt marshes, and the stripping of forest lands. But humans are slowly learning that their survival depends upon the way they treat their environment. The selections in this unit explain how humans and all things around them, living and nonliving, affect each other every minute of every day.

259

TO LOOK AT ANY THING

To look at any thing,
If you would know that thing,
You must look at it long:
To look at this green and say
"I have seen spring in these
Woods," will not do—you must
Be the thing you see:
You must be the dark snakes of
Stems and ferny plumes of leaves,
You must enter in
To the small silences between
The leaves,
You must take your time
And touch the very peace
They issue from.

—John Moffitt

260

AS SCIENTISTS STUDY LIFE in the forest, they must step softly, sit quietly, and look and listen in silence. If you could watch them, you would think they were alone, but how wrong you would be!

TOWN IN THE FOREST

Every town has its secrets. And a passing stranger may wonder: Who lives here? How do the residents make their living? Why did they choose this place?

The town may be one of the human-built towns, strung out like knots that tie together a fishnet of country roads.

Or the town may be deep in the forest. Its exact location may be a bog, or a cave, or a small hill, or a hollow log.

A dead log may, in fact, be rich with life. Here a thousand varied creatures live, making up a community. In some brisk autumn dawn, these log-dwellers stir. Black crickets and green-gold beetles search busily for food. The last wildflowers of the year strain toward the dwindling sun. A crab spider scurries out of the range of a passing lizard, back to its web.

Within a hive in the log, an aging queen of bees is already in winter sleep, full of the eggs she will lay in the spring. A caterpillar wraps itself carefully into a cocoon. And the log rot gives slow growth to living molds and mosses.

In the burrow formed when the falling oak tore itself from the earth, a chipmunk family breakfasts on a wind-fall of seeds and berries.

This is the Logtown community. Here a toad shares citizenship with a toadstool. The redbud is neighbor to a green snake curled against the warmth of the decaying log. Countless other creatures live here that are visible only through a magnifying lens.

From the eye level of an insect, this community bustles with life. Like the human community, it has its share of quarrels, its small tragedies, its daily rhythm of food-gathering, resting, mating, homemaking.

The inhabitants of the log are not as separate as they may seem. They are each and all members of a real community, bound to one another in countless ways. Their town has a clear-cut form and pattern.

The forest is filled with such towns, all parts of the wider woodland community. And just as there are

263

towns in the forest, so there are cities in the sea and villages on the prairie. Of all the communities on this planet, only the smallest number is peopled by human beings.

A wide range of animals may share lightless lives in the never-ending darkness of a deep cave—all of them whitish and blind. Strange bedfellows may be found living in a sea sponge. An interesting group of creatures may make their home together on some rocky crag. The communities in the rain forest harbor a rich variety of living things. And still another type of community is the tiny sea island where assorted beings live in the shadow of a smoldering volcano.

Wherever such wildlife communities appear, they stir the same haunting questions: Who and how and why? These towns in nature are webbed with a thousand mysteries.

But the questions are not idle ones for human beings to ask. Our own lives are woven deeply into the answers.

Nature withheld few secrets from the American poet-naturalist Henry David Thoreau.[1] He was a Harvard graduate, class of 1837. Some of his classmates went into law, others into the ministry. Thoreau took to the woods.

"Many a forenoon have I stolen away," he recounted, "preferring to spend thus the most valued part of the day; for I was rich, if not in money, in sunny hours and summer days, and spent them lavishly."

[1] Thoreau (thə-ROH)

He described himself as a self-appointed inspector of rainstorms, surveyor of forest paths, and keeper of the wildstock. He roamed silently through the woods. His pockets bulged with the gear of the naturalist—a spyglass, a jackknife, twine, and a small microscope. He carried an old music book for pressing plants, and a notebook in which he captured the sights and sounds of the wildlife in soaring poetry or in singing prose.

Thoreau built a tiny cabin on Walden Pond near Concord, Massachusetts. There he enjoyed the company of woodsmen and woodchucks. And there he observed nature in a special way.

"You only need sit still long enough in some attractive spot in the woods that all its inhabitants may exhibit themselves to you by turns," he wrote.

It was in this fashion that Thoreau became a part of the natural community.

He was not an expert in any species, nor was he a great collector or experimenter. He had no laboratory other than the "sweet wild world" of the woodland itself.

He was an eyewitness of the order and life in the natural community. He could look at a neighbor's field, and then remark as he did once, "I had no idea that there was so much going on in Haywood's meadow."

Many of nature's secrets are discovered only in this kind of broad view. Some of the most puzzling events of the woodland are explained only as plants and animals are observed living together against the natural setting of the soil and the season. Certain

facts about species can be learned only by watching the free-flowing life of the natural community.

On a spring night in the year 1842, Thoreau found himself on a strange woodland adventure. As he poled his boat gently across a silent New England pond, his pine torch lit up the scene below. To his delight, the crystal depths appeared like a living city, its roofs raised to reveal the private community of the fishes.

"There they lie in every variety of posture," he later wrote, "some on their backs with their white bellies uppermost, some suspended in mid-water, some sculling gently along with a dreamy motion of the fins, and others quite active and wide awake — a scene not unlike what the human city could present. . . ."

Thoreau's genius was in seeing life whole. One can learn much about a clock by taking it apart — but not find its tick. Thoreau observed nature in its wholeness instead of piecemeal, learned its rhyme and its rhythm.

There is an old rhyme that begins with the loss of a horseshoe nail. This small cause eventually leads to the loss of a battle, and finally to the loss of a kingdom.

In the same fashion, every small happening in nature touches off other happenings. Spring thaw and rock slide, the birth of a fawn, the fall of an oak — such events set up a series of results within the living community. From a single cause flows a running stream of effects.

A poet once said that one could not pluck a flower

without troubling a star. This is another way of saying that the living and the nonliving are all linked together. Lives are altered by changing temperature, climate, and moisture, by the very shape of the land and the chemicals that are in it.

The courses of streams are shifted by dam-building beavers. Rock is turned into soil by the action of frost and plants, of water and small animals. The population of mosquitoes is reduced by the first cold snap. An entire forest may be set ablaze by a flash of lightning.

The naturalist Charles Darwin had a story that showed the endless chain of causes and effects. In Great Britain, he pointed out, roaming cats eat field mice at the edge of town. It seems that the number of wild bumblebees is controlled by the mice, which destroy their nests. If the mouse population is kept down by the cats, then there are more bees to pollinate the red clover plants. As a result of all this, the British fields are deep in clover.

In dealing with nature, people are often puzzled by strange turns of events. Unseen causes may lead to hunger and illness, to crop failure and human tragedy.

The people of Ireland once depended upon the potato as their main source of food. The summer of 1845 proved to be a poor one for potato-growing. It was a good year for a tiny fungus that destroys potatoes.

In the tragic days that followed, famine struck the island nation. When it was all over, a million people had died. Two million more had to leave their homeland.

A chain of events may be touched off by our own doings. It may begin with the crack of a rifle or the bite of an ax.

An upland forest is cleared of trees. The area is turned into a pasture which soon becomes overgrazed and bare. Now the rain water is no longer held in the ground by the deep roots of trees and shrubs. Instead, the water runs swiftly off the surface, forming gullies. On the hillside farms the good wells run dry. In the valleys below, the raging streams rush wildly together, flooding the countryside.

The explanation of such events that have long puzzled people seems tangled in a thousand threads. Today scientific study is beginning to clear up some of the old problems and many new ones as well. The science of cause and effect in the natural community is called ecology.

One of the newer branches of biology, ecology is concerned with the associations of living and nonliving things. It begins its study of life—as Thoreau did— in the wildlife communities, seeking answers to very important problems in the patterns of nature.

The work of the ecologist has sometimes been called "the science of everything." The ecologist studies the "why" of nature. Usually, the answer is contained in a thousand bits and fragments of fact. Clues may be as varied as the flyways of geese or the surge of an underground stream, the busy work of bacteria or the damming of a river.

The behavior of living things is often strange and complicated. But certain patterns of life do repeat themselves. An orderly design can be discovered. Developments can be predicted. Events can be understood.

The methods of the ecologist, like those of other scientists, begin with the careful study of the facts. Precise information is gathered, checked and rechecked endlessly. Out of a large body of facts emerges a small but growing set of scientific principles.

The name "ecology" was formed about a hundred years ago out of the Greek word *oikos*, which means "home." Ecology is the study of the home life of living things, how they relate to one another and to their nonliving environment.

Ecologists work in the laboratory. But they can probably be found most often in the field. They may be taking a census of earthworms. Or they may study how the population of the arctic fox varies with that of lemmings or how the number of red oaks in a forest depends on the number of acorn-burying squirrels.

In its quiet beginnings, the new science of ecology is becoming an important problem-solver. It is more than that. It is the growing edge of our understanding about the living fabric of nature.

270

The life of the seas and the uplands, of the prairies and the forests, is a web of species. In some places the fabric is time-tested and strong. In other places the weave is loose and can be unraveled by the tearing of a single thread. At times, the texture within a particular region is richly patterned. Or else it may be riddled and threadbare.

Humans, the most powerful of the species, are woven throughout the fabric of life. To the ecologist, humans are increasingly important in the whole design of living things. Ecology deals with the web of life as it has been changed by human beings.

Ecologists may investigate the number of acres of prairie that will properly support a herd of sheep. Their main interest may be the health of an olive grove or an oyster bed. Their searches may take them to the gloomy sea depths, where natural communities tend to be old and stable. Or they may be at work on the problems of an entirely new kind of community — the life-support system aboard a spaceship.

A group of ecologists at a midwestern university have set up a tiny living community. This tightly sealed "hothouse" is a mock-up for some future spacecraft. This is the kind of community that may be used to support life on an expedition to the moon or a visit to a neighboring planet.

Small mammals and insects, assorted grasses and shrubs live inside, amid apparatus and instruments. The animal life is being carefully studied to determine its needs. The plants are chosen to keep the air clean, to reclaim waste materials, and to offer high yields of suitable foods in a limited growing area.

This is a "closed system," where plants and animals are all in balance. Each form of life supports the other, and each makes use of what the other produces.

The essentials for long-time support of life are the same everywhere—whether in an outpost flung into space or in some wild place in the forest. These communities are small worlds where plants and animals share life together.

—*S. Carl Hirsch*

What Do You Think?

1. In your own words tell what the poet meant by "one could not pluck a flower without troubling a star."
2. Describe what ecologists do and the methods they use in their work. If you were an ecologist what methods would you use?
3. Give examples to show how people are affecting the ecology of your area.
4. Reread the paragraphs about Henry David Thoreau. Do you think you would have liked him? Why?

Taking a Closer Look

1. Name the inhabitants of the "Logtown community." Why did the author call this dead log a town?
2. The author said that Thoreau "observed nature in a special way." Describe this special way. What tools did he use?
3. According to the naturalist Charles Darwin, how did cats affect the amount of clover in British fields?
4. What are some of the effects of clearing a forest of trees?
5. Find two examples in the article to support this statement: "Every life depends upon other living and nonliving things."

Putting Ideas to Work

Looking at the photographs in this story, which animal pictured have you seen? Write a paragraph about the animal and the natural community it lives in.

The last frontier on earth is the ocean, which we have not yet fully explored. Dive with Eugenie Clark, a daring and inquisitive scientist, and her brave companions. Meet the mysteries of the Pacific.

Adventure on the Last Frontier

For ages we have used the ocean to discover new lands. Now we are spending a great deal of time and money discovering the ocean. We already know a great deal about this last frontier, as it has been called. But we still need to learn much more about it. We know that the ocean is rich in minerals that the world needs. We know, too, that it contains enough food to provide protein for all the world's people. We know that if the salt could be taken from it, the ocean could turn the deserts into farm lands. We have begun removing salt from the ocean water, but the process is still too costly to be practical except in special situations.

Today's scientists explore the sea in ships outfitted for this purpose. One of these, the *Kane*, even has a large computer aboard to process the information which the scientists receive each day. Some scientists have descended into the sea's depths in specially built objects called bathyspheres. Sitting in their bathy-

274

spheres, the scientists are able to turn on very strong lights, which shine through the ocean's darkness and show them the strange sea life inhabiting the depths of the sea.

There are also scientists who work by themselves, depending on the native inhabitants of certain ocean areas to help them. Such a one is Eugenie Clark. She founded the Cape Haze Marine Laboratory in Florida and directed it for sixteen years. In the following story, she tells of some exciting days in Pacific waters when a native diver called Siakong[1] was her helper.

Siakong was just over fifty when I knew him. He was the best spearfisherman in the Palaus.[2] I'm not saying this because he taught me spearfishing and

[1] Siakong (SEE-ə-kong)   [2] Palaus (pə-LOWS)

one hundred other things about the underwater world. His great skill was an accepted fact among all the Palauans.

Siakong knew a native, Niraibui,[1] who owned an inboard motorboat that could hold up to six people. Sometimes, besides the three of us, we took with us some of the other scientists who had come to these islands in search of specimens.

Siakong knew the best places to get the kind of fish I was after and these seemed to be where there were the most beautiful coral reefs. These reefs were a long way out from the town of Koror, the most important community in this group of islands. We usually went there by way of a harbor where we could look deep down into the clear water and see sunken battleships from the war days.

[1] Niraibui (ni-RAH-bee)

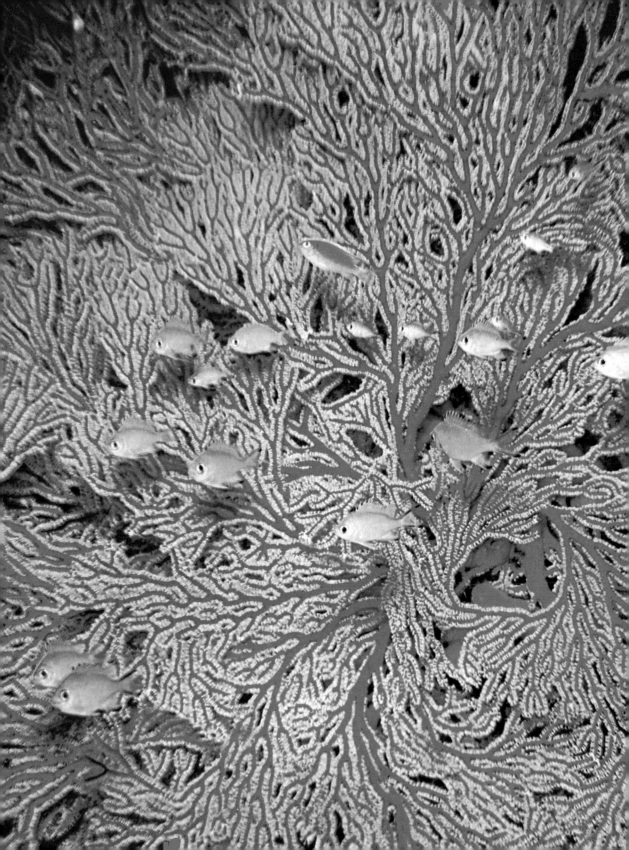

It was great fun to watch Siakong spear fish from above the water. He would stand on the bow of Nirai-bui's boat as we putt-putted to the outer reefs, a long spear in each hand. I would sometimes stand up searching the water too, but I could never spot a fish before Siakong did. A spear was flying through the air as I opened my mouth to call out, "There's a fish!" If the first spear missed, the second one was on its way in a flash and Siakong seemed to predict the direction in which the fish would dodge the first spear.

Underwater it was different. He never made a sound, but I could see him grinning broadly and his eyes sparkled through his water goggles. Here, there was no doubt about whether or not Siakong would get the fish he was after. It was only a question of how long it would take him and by what trick he would get it.

Siakong was powerfully built. He wore only a small red loincloth and homemade goggles when he went underwater. The rest of the time he wore an old pair of khaki shorts over his loincloth.

Once I pointed out a fish to him, it was as good as mine. He was a keen observer. His years of underwater experience made him an expert in the ways of hundreds of varieties of reef fishes. He didn't always go directly after a fish but would watch it a few seconds, determine its next move, and then head it off into a place where it could easily be caught.

One of Siakong's methods of spearing fish underwater was breathtaking, as well as remarkably simple. He would find a reef well inhabited by fish and then dive calmly to about ten or twenty feet, sometimes weighting himself with a rock so he could sink without swimming. He'd get a firm grip on the reef with his legs or his free arm, hold his spear in readiness, and then *wait* for the fish to come to him!

The first time I watched him do this it alarmed me. He dived and lay motionless on the reef, like an animal about to spring on its prey. His brown body and red loincloth blended in with the varied colors of the surrounding reef. The fish began to regard him as part of the corals and came very close.

I was watching from above. Not used to Siakong's extraordinary lung capacity, I began to worry after a long time passed and he didn't move. So I swam down to him and tapped him on the head to make sure he was all right. He turned and looked up at me with his usual underwater grin as I reached for a piece of coral to hold myself down. I tried to make a gesture with my face to ask him what he was doing, but he was looking at my hand and the grin had dropped from his face. He reached for my arm as I felt the "coral" under my hand suddenly move.

I was holding onto the side of a giant "man-eating" clam. The clam had just snapped shut and my fingers were only a fraction of an inch from the opening between the two halves of the shell. These close with a grip so tight that it can hold a diver's arm or leg until he drowns.

As we swam up to the surface, Siakong pointed to the wall of coral along which I had carelessly descended. Partly hidden in the corals were dozens of these clams, all with their shells gaping open. The shells looked like gray dead corals. Inside, the soft flesh had the beautiful colors of surrounding living corals and the plants and animals that encrust them. Some were bright green, others blue, purple, and shades of brown mingled with irregular darker patches. They were well camouflaged, but from then on I learned to distinguish them from anything else.

Siakong taught me, however, that even the largest of these clams can be handled safely and that they are among the most sensitive of sea creatures. He would dive down to an open clam and wave his hand over it. Often this was enough to stimulate the light-sensitive flesh inside and the clam would close. If not, he tapped the side of the shell. Then he pried the clam loose and brought it up with him.

Ordinarily rain didn't stop us from spearfishing. The reef water was so clear that it took more than average rain clouds to make vision bad. The first time we started spearfishing in the rain, however, I thought it would prove a waste of time. When I got into the water and looked around, it was full of wavy lines and everything was blurred as if I weren't wearing my face mask. But Siakong and Niraibui were diving without concern. Then I took a dive too and when my face reached about four feet below the surface, the water became its usual clear self. Then I realized that the blurring near the surface was the result of the fresh rain water mixing with salt water. I've never come across an English word for it, but German chemistry books call the phenomenon *Schlieren*.[1] So for spearfishing in the rain, one merely has to dive below the *Schlieren* layer and reach the sea water to see clearly.

It was on such a rainy day that we came across the largest giant clam I ever saw alive. Siakong and I were

[1] *Schlieren* (SHLEER-en)

swimming across some open water toward the reef where the boat was anchored. Niraibui was sitting in it keeping his head dry under Siakong's straw hat. We swam along, diving now and then below the *Schlieren* layer for a look around.

Whenever I swim in deep open water, I keep glancing around through my face mask with a mingled feeling of fear and hope. I don't want to miss seeing it if a large shark should be cruising nearby. But on each of these dives I saw only empty water in all directions. Not the smallest fish was in sight. From above I could see Niraibui was still over one hundred yards away, and I looked forward to reaching him and seeing the comforting walls of reef and the mass of familiar fish that would be swimming there. It is a strange feeling to swim underwater away from any signs of rock, coral, the bottom, or sea life. It's like swimming in the middle of the ocean. It was nice to be able to find Siakong in the water nearby.

I was getting a little ahead of Siakong, as he was stopping for deeper dives, when I heard him call me back.

"Nechan,[1] come see here."

I swam over to him, dove under the *Schlieren,* and looked where he was pointing down below. I couldn't make out much until I was down a few more feet. Then I could see a sandy bottom and sitting in the sand was a clam. It looked like an average-size, giant clam. However, there was nothing around to compare it with and I couldn't estimate the depth.

[1] Nechan (NEE-chən)

283

We swam to the surface and treaded water easily and forced a long series of deep breaths. We had been swimming for quite a while, and I wasn't prepared for a deep dive. When I felt a little rested and filled with fresh air, I nodded to Siakong. He started to dive toward the clam and I followed, swallowing to adjust my ears to the increasing pressure.

I've never measured how deep I can dive; but I know that at more than twenty feet under, my face mask cuts into my head and my ears and nose feel uncomfortable. Usually I don't go much deeper for I have always found enough activity in the top twenty-five feet to keep me occupied and satisfied. But this time I followed Siakong until I felt I was well below my usual limit and I knew my breath wouldn't last descending any deeper. Perhaps if I had dived with a weight and not spent so much energy swimming downward, I might have been able to stand another ten feet—but I still wouldn't have been anywhere near bottom. From the depth I did manage to reach, I could see Siakong far below me getting smaller and smaller until he reached the clam.

Then I saw it was truly a giant.

Siakong looked like a midget beside the clam which seemed nearly four feet across. I saw him give it a kick to close the huge jaws which could have held all of Siakong with ease. And then I had to shoot for the surface. I was still panting heavily when Siakong finally came up with no sign of strain.

We got Niraibui to come over with the boat. The anchor wouldn't reach bottom. It hung loose, far above the clam. We couldn't find anything long enough to

reach bottom and help us haul up the clam. The three of us dived toward the clam again, but I stopped at a comfortable depth and clung to the dangling anchor while Niraibui continued on with Siakong. I doubted that even the two of them together could lift it an inch.

The clam's jaws were open again. Siakong reached it and kicked it shut. Niraibui hovered about Siakong's head for a second and then headed back for the surface, where we met, both well out of breath.

"O kina ne!"[1] (It's a big one, isn't it?) Niraibui exclaimed to me.

Siakong still had not come up. Niraibui and I dived under again. As we descended I made out a sight that sickened me with horror. *Siakong was caught in the clam.*

The jaws of the gigantic clam were shut tight and

[1] *O kina ne* (oh KEE-nə nay)

Siakong's arm was in it up to the elbow. Siakong wasn't moving. I expected Niraibui to dive all the way and at least attempt a rescue, but the fellow swam back to the surface. In the excitement my breath was shorter than ever. I came up gasping and started hollering at Niraibui in panic. My poor Japanese came out all mixed up and he looked at me surprised and then blankly. I felt helpless and desperate. Siakong was trapped and would be dead in a few seconds if we couldn't find some way to help him. How could Niraibui tread water there so calmly.

Short of breath and good for nothing, I nevertheless adjusted my mask to dive again. But just then Siakong popped up beside us—panting but grinning! He lifted his arm out of the water, the one I had seen in the jaws of the clam, and held up the biggest adductor muscle I had ever laid eyes on.

I was doing a mixture of laughing and crying as the three of us climbed back into the boat. Niraibui of course had understood all along that the clam—which must have weighed at least a quarter of a ton—was impossible to lift off the bottom and that Siakong had broken the lip of the huge shell enough to reach into the clam and cut loose the adductor muscle with his knife. The two men got a big kick out of my fright.

"She was ready to kill me because I didn't try to save you!" Niraibui told Siakong, who howled with delight. I started to feel a little silly, but when they continued to kid me I got angry. Finally they stopped and the rain which was still falling cooled me back to normal. Soon we all sat contentedly in the boat, munching on our lunch. Niraibui and Siakong stuffed their mouths to keep from laughing any more.

I never saw Siakong spear a shark underwater, although several times he showed up with six- and seven-foot specimens neatly speared through the gills. He explained that the gills were the best place to spear a shark because the skin was too tough and if you missed getting the spear in, the shark might not give you the opportunity for a second try.

All of Siakong's spears were of the primitive hand type. He had none of the fancy arbalests or CO_2 cartridged spearguns that shoot sixty feet through the water—the equipment of the hundreds of modern skin divers these days. When Siakong speared a fish, his powerful arms were the only propelling force behind the spear. And the fish, though it be a shark, was then caught on one end of the spear while Siakong held on to the other.

One day Siakong and Niraibui put on an underwater turtle rodeo. They were in a clowning mood. Siakong caught hold of Niraibui's foot and tickled the bottom of it until Niraibui had to laugh out all his breath and almost drowned before Siakong let him go to the surface for air. They were having great fun. Then Niraibui

spotted a large sea turtle resting quietly on the bottom and he sat on its back. Siakong latched onto Niraibui's back and they began taking turns knocking each other off the turtle and riding the bewildered animal around underwater. They could steer it any way they liked by holding the shell just behind the poor turtle's neck, pulling back to make it swim upward, pressing down to make it dive, and leaning sideways to make it bank and turn. All the while the turtle flapped its finlike legs desperately and strained its long neck forward trying helplessly to get rid of the playful tormentors.

Finally they brought the turtle on the boat. Niraibui was pleased when I took his picture with it and I promised to give him a print.

As my weeks in the Palaus came to an end, Siakong asked when I would be back again. "Perhaps many years later," I said because I hated to tell him, "Probably never." "That's O.K., Nechan, I'll still be a good spearfisherman when I'm eighty." And he might have been too. But a few years later I learned that Siakong, when on a fishing trip, took a deep dive after a turtle and never came up again. The area was combed by other divers, but they couldn't find a sign of him nor a clue to his disappearance.

— *Eugenie Clark*

What Do You Think?

1. What qualities do you think a scientist must have to be successful on an expedition like the one described in this selection? Think about whether you possess some of these qualities.
2. If you were an ecologist, which field of interest would you choose to work in? Why?

Taking a Closer Look

1. In this selection the author tells about several of her adventures. Find in the story where each begins and ends. Think of a good title for each adventure.
2. Skim the opening paragraphs of this selection. Find three ways in which the ocean can benefit people and three ways scientists can study sea life.
3. Describe the ways Siakong helped Eugenie Clark in her study of sea life.
4. Compare Siakong's method of spearing a fish from a boat and from underwater. Which did you find more interesting? Why?
5. What dangers might a scientist face while studying sea life? How could these dangers be avoided?
6. Explain in your own words the term *Schlieren*.
7. What are some facts you learned about clams?

IN MY MOUNTAINS

In my mountains,
Where the wind blows cold and fresh,
The scent of wild flowers float on the breeze,
Animals are roaming everywhere,
Fish are swimming in the streams,
Streams that are pure and clear,
Streams that are cold.

The sound of night
With stars shining bright,
Of the stream gurgling on its way,
The animals creeping in the distance,
And the smell of the dying campfire,
Yes, I love my mountains.

—*Jill Yokomizo*

THE RARE AND THE WILD

MANY SPECIES OF ANIMALS have been endangered by human carelessness, greed, and ignorance. This selection describes how humans have endangered some of these animals. As you read notice the ways people can help preserve "the rare and the wild."

The Earth is only a small planet, but it is an unusually beautiful one. It is rich with plant and animal life. In their short stay on Earth, humans have only begun to understand the other life in the biosphere around them.

Over the centuries, some plants and animals have become extinct. This process still goes on. Just as the last of the dinosaurs died out years ago, other kinds of animals are becoming extinct today.

More than five hundred kinds of animals are listed as rare or endangered. The blue whale is simply being hunted to death. Other kinds of animals die out because their special living areas, or habitats, are destroyed. The Everglades kite, for example, is a bird that depends on a single kind of snail for most of its food. The marshes and lakes of Florida where the snails live are being destroyed by humans. The kite cannot adapt to a new kind of food, so its numbers drop as its habitat shrinks in size.

You may ask, "Does it really matter if people cause the extinction of this bird? It probably would have died out in a few hundred more years anyway."

Some answers to this question come from biologists, the scientists who study living things. They point out that each creature on Earth is unique. Just as humans are unique in some ways, so too are other animals. As citizens of the Earth, humans have no right to wipe out other creatures. Once gone, a species cannot be brought back. For all their power, humans cannot make a whooping crane or a grizzly bear.

Biologists are especially concerned that humans may simplify life on Earth too much. They have noticed the problems that sometimes occur in the Arctic, where the communities of plants and animals are very simple. Not many plants and animals can survive in the Arctic. Those that live there depend on a few other living things for life. If one part of the system is damaged, many other parts may be affected. Arctic plant-animal communities are easily damaged by humans or by some natural disturbance. Once upset, it may take centuries for the system to recover.

The opposite is true in the lush tropics. There the plant-animal communities are much more complex. There are many kinds of living things and they are not dependent on just a few other plants and animals, as in the Arctic. The numbers of animals don't change greatly from year to year, as they often do in the Arctic. When tropic communities are damaged by humans, they usually recover quickly.

You can see why biologists want to keep the Earth as full of a variety of life as possible. Already, in farming, the dangers of simplifying life can be seen. A farmer may plant hundreds of acres to a single crop, keeping out weeds and getting rid of fencerows where a variety of life might live in the brush and weeds. The huge planting of a single crop is an invitation to an outbreak of a disease or an insect pest. The pests can thrive but there is no habitat for the birds or other enemies that might normally control the harmful insects.

The farmer may be able to protect a crop with poisons, but the danger of a crop disaster is always present. The plants could also be protected by a network of brushy fencerows that support a variety of life, including birds and insects that prey on insect pests.

Biologists point out another reason for treasuring each bit of life on Earth. Some of our great gains in science and medicine have come from research upon some plant or animal that seemed of little value at the time. New knowledge about human blood came from the study of rhesus monkeys. Research on wolves and baboons is giving scientists a better understanding of the behavior of all mammals. For our own welfare, then, we ought to make sure that a great variety of life survives on the Earth.

To maintain that variety, humans must make sure that many kinds of plant-animal communities exist. In the United States and Canada, some of these communities are saved in wilderness areas, wildlife refuges, and in national, provincial, and state parks. With so much of North America already changed by people, these areas have special value as "outdoor laboratories" for study of the natural world.

But many other wild areas are disappearing. As we build more highways, factories, houses, and shopping centers, we wipe out entire habitats—draining a

297

swamp, cutting down a forest, flooding a valley. In each case, humans have lost a place where they can learn about the natural world of which they are but a part.

In some parts of the world the human population is so great that it has already caused the destruction of most wild land and the extinction of many kinds of animals. In parts of Africa, the wild hoofed animals are being wiped out so that cattle can be raised. The cattle do not do well, however, because of diseases and low rainfall. They strip most of the plant life from the land, wiping out their own food supply and leaving the soil exposed, to be washed away by rain or blown away by the wind. Biologists believe that the land would produce more food for humans if the native wild game was allowed to live there. But the slaughter of wildlife goes on.

The situation is even worse in India, a country that was once rich with wildlife. Food is scarce for India's 500 million people. Wild animals are thought of only as food, or as a threat to crops.

The habitat of many Indian animals has been destroyed, and wildlife must compete for food with vast herds of cattle and buffalo. The numbers of wild animals drop even lower due to shooting by poachers, who kill for meat even within the borders of India's few parks and game refuges. As a result, some animals found nowhere else on Earth have vanished, even before they could be studied in the wild. Many other kinds of animals, such as the Asiatic lion and the one-horned rhinoceros, are close to extinction.

Even in the United States, where concern for wild animals is great, the survival of some species is threatened because of greed or ignorance. The numbers of American alligators dropped low because their skins are so valuable when used in handbags and shoes. Recent laws forbid the sale of products made from alligator skins, and these laws may stop the illegal killing of these reptiles.

In the northern United States and in Canada, people are still shooting, trapping, and poisoning wolves. Many people think of wolves as dangerous, "bad" animals. But biologists have discovered that wolves have many good effects in the wild areas where they live.

Wolves eat large plant-eating animals such as moose. The wolves usually kill those moose that are easiest to catch—the injured, the sick, the old. In this way they help to keep the moose population healthy. By keeping the population under control, the wolves also help prevent the moose from becoming so plentiful that they destroy their own food supply.

In areas where wolves have been wiped out, populations of animals such as moose, deer, and elk often get out of control. The population increases until the animals run out of food and starve, or until a disease sweeps through the herd. This was the problem at Yellowstone National Park, where thousands of elk had to be removed or killed each year in order to keep the herd in balance with its food supply. Some biologists suggested that wolves be brought to Yellowstone, where they once served as natural controls on the elk population. Now the wolves *are* at Yellowstone once more.

Bringing wolves back to Yellowstone will help the wolf species to survive. It also helps bring a national park a bit closer to its original wildness and makes it a better outdoor laboratory where scientists can study nature. If humans are to understand nature, they must find ways like this to save the rare and the wild.

—*Laurence Pringle*

What Do You Think?

1. Why do you think people have allowed so many animals to become rare and endangered?
2. What is being done in your area to preserve wildlife? Do you think enough is being done? If not, what more do you think should be done? What can you do personally?
3. Is it possible that there may be no such thing as "bad" animals? Explain your answer.

Taking a Closer Look

1. According to the author what are some causes that contribute to the extinction of animals? What might be some other causes?
2. What does the author mean by the statement, "Biologists are especially concerned that humans may simplify life on Earth too much"?
3. Explain how some farming methods have endangered wildlife.
4. What are some of the reasons the author gives for "treasuring each bit of life on Earth"?
5. What are plant-animal communities? How can they be useful?
6. Wolves have been thought of as dangerous, "bad" animals. How does the author show that wolves have good effects on the balance of nature?

Putting Ideas to Work

Think of an animal or form of plant life that you do not want to become extinct. Write a paragraph explaining why you think it should be saved.

On Eagles' Wings

But they that wait upon the Lord shall renew their strength;
they shall mount up with wings as eagles;
they shall run, and not be weary;
and they shall walk, and not faint.

— Isaiah 40:31 KJV

THIS STORY TELLS OF PERHAPS ONE HOUR in the life of a family of golden eagles. It shows what humans can do to endanger the eagle, and how the eagle responds to the challenge of survival.

THE GOLDEN EAGLE

From the rocky bank of the small, swift stream at the bottom of the canyon, the cliff rose up, straight as a wall for nearly seven hundred feet into the sky. About sixty feet below the rimrock at the top, there was a shelf that thrust out over the empty air for ten feet and ran along the face for twenty. Near one end of it there was a cave four feet wide and six deep. A person kneeling could just about move around in it. From this cave and the shelf there was a wide view of the canyon, across it over the lower ridge on the other side, and beyond to the Colorado plain, fading off into the haze to the east.

In the middle of the shelf there was a golden eagle's nest. It was made of crisscrossed sticks and brush and was covered on the outside with gray-green moss that blended into the gray rock of the cliff face.

There were two young eagles in the nest, one much

larger than the other. This was the female. She would always be a third larger than her brother, after the manner of birds of prey. They were both about ready to fly. The crown and hackle feathers on the male's head were dark and would grow paler as he matured. The female's were already dark gold and gleamed in the sun.

They had been quiet for a time, lying together in the nest. But presently the female, whom we shall call Kira, began to grow restless. She stood, bowed her bright head, and stretched the great seven-foot wings up over her back. After she folded them again, she looked at her brother and decided to bedevil him. She often did this, and he knew he would be roughly handled. He scrambled out of the nest and ran along the ledge to the mouth of the cave. Kira started for him, but after several steps she noticed the hindquarters

of a jackrabbit in her path. Her foot, longer than a person's hand and armed with great, curving, needle-sharp talons, shot out and clamped upon it. She dropped it; caught and dropped it again. She picked it up with her hooked beak, tossed it a foot away, and ran after it. This play foreshadowed battles of the future that would not be playful. Her foot came out again and took the hindquarters in its grip. She looked at

the prey in her foot, dropped it, flapped her wings, and screamed in triumph.

It was not a very impressive scream for a bird of her size. But golden eagles are rather silent creatures. Many hawks scream more frequently and with greater volume. It is not their screaming that makes eagles noble. It is their great power and courage and their regal dignity. Their race circles the world.

Kira had got her mind off her brother. She moved to the ledge's lip, and her dark, hooded eyes searched the canyon. Her sight was excellent, fashioned to find prey at immense distances. She saw, among the scrub oak and cottonwood along the stream, wand lily, creeping holly grape, stonecrop, and bracted alum root blooming. Several tiny chipmunks ran in and out among the rocks. The old coyote who lived in the canyon had moved out of cover and lay drowsing in a sunny opening, muzzle on forepaws.

She raised her head, searched the sky, and fixed her gaze to the east. Far off, a tiny dot in the blue, the old female eagle was coming in high above the other ridge. She set her wings for the long glide to the ledge, and as she came nearer, Kira saw that there was prey in her foot and began to move about with anticipation. The young male had seen his mother too, and ran back from the end of the ledge. Over the canyon the old bird dropped a little, swooped up to slow her speed and as she landed on the ledge, opened her foot and dropped a half-grown jack-rabbit. As it slid toward them, both young eagles started for it. Kira's foot flashed out and she caught it. She looked at her brother and he moved back a little, remembering just in time that he was over-matched and had better wait his turn.

He watched hungrily until Kira had eaten as much as she wanted and had climbed back into the nest, then he moved in to finish what was left. His mother, calm and unruffled, beautiful in repose in the clear light of the Front Range, watched him with her head tilted, her golden hackles bright in the sun.

The three men, carrying ropes, came out of the pines which ended a few yards back from the edge of the cliff. It was the male eagle (called the *tiercel* because he is a third smaller than his mate) who saw them first. He had swung back over the ridge when he came in from the prairie; he approached from behind the men, several hundred feet over the pines, with a five-foot rattler, which he had decapitated, in his foot. When he saw the men directly over the nest, he began his alarm cry: Kiah! Kiah! Kiah! The sound echoed among the great rocks and stony spires on each side of the cliff face. A lonely trout fisherman in the stream far below heard it and looked up but could see nothing for his roof of leaves.

The tiercel swung past the edge of the cliff and circled higher, still screaming his ap-prehension. The old eagle on the ledge heard him, cocked her head, and saw him mount-ing into the sky. She knew at once that there was trouble, and jumped off the ledge. Her great wings opened and took hold on the air; she slanted off across the canyon to a place where there was usually an updraft which would help her gain altitude. She found the warm and rising current of air and began to circle higher in it. The canyon dropped beneath her, and she saw the men.

She screamed at them too, but continued to rise. Her temper was shorter than the tiercel's and the young were more her concern. Had the creatures upon the top of the cliff been anything but people, she would have swooped at them in fury, roaring down on folded wings to drive them away. There were few animals in her world that she wouldn't meet in battle, but her ancestors had survived the schemes of Indian plume hunters for so many generations that it had become an instinct to avoid humans.

They watched her as she mounted higher and drifted off to circle with the tiercel in the distance. Then they dropped a rope's end over the cliff and payed out the rope until it reached the shelf. Having thus measured the length they wanted, they took the other end into the pines, ran the rope around the nearest pine—which was to be used as a snubbing post—and made the rope fast to another tree further back. They came back to the cliff's edge again, pulled up the rope, and arranged it around the lightest man so that while he sat in a loop of it, he was also supported under the arms.

He walked around to assure himself that it was fast at all points, and comfortable. "I think it's all right," he said. "Suppose there are two of them?"

"Take one. We don't need them both."

The men put a big musette bag over his shoulder, and one of them walked back to the snubbing post. The other took hold of the rope. The one who was going over the cliff turned his back on it, and holding the rope backed over the cliff's edge. It was rounded there;

there was no sharp edge to fray the rope, and the man sitting in the loop, holding himself off with his feet, began his descent as the rope was slowly payed out. He looked very small against the cliff.

The young eagles on the ledge had been puzzled by the tiercel's screaming, for they had never heard the alarm call before. They watched their mother take off, and when her voice was added to the tiercel's, they began to grow uneasy. Their familiar routine had been disturbed, something was happening to which they had no key, and some of the old bird's apprehension came through to them. They both ran to the familiar nest, climbed into it, and crouched down. Then Kira's eye caught movement above as the man started down the cliff. She looked up, staring at him. The young tiercel followed her glance. Swaying a little on the end of his rope, the man seemed all sprawling arms and legs. He was a deadly enemy, and momentarily growing nearer.

As the man descended, the young eagles moved back in the nest until they were on the inside edge of it, pressed against the rock. Confusion held them there until the man was almost level with them. As he came closer he grew more menacing, with his pale face looking down and the scuff of his shoes on the rock. Suddenly Kira was freed of the paralysis of fear that had held her. She jumped from the nest and ran along the shelf to the cave, and her brother followed her. They scrambled into the cave; its roof and walls closed protectively around them and shut out the sight of the man.

The man kicked out from the cliff, and by pulling himself up a little as he swung back, landed on the shelf. He had a little slack now and signaled for more by giving two jerks on the rope. The men gave it to him. He could move about a little now, but he didn't like his position. He thought of being pulled up again to be dropped before the cave but decided against this. He crawled along the shelf, pressing against the rock, to the cave. When he appeared in the mouth of it, breathing quite audibly, his outlandish crawling shape outlined against the sky, the young eagles jammed their backs against the rock. Their hackles rose and they stared with menace and fear.

The man grinned at them and crawled closer, spreading his arms to keep them together. It was his plan to move in a little more, crowding them still with his arms wide, and then make a quick, sweeping grab for the legs of one of them to immobilize its feet. He could ignore the strong, hooked beak. Eagles do not use their beaks for offense. But he had great respect for the damage the talons could do to him. Once they were locked in him somewhere, it would be impossible for him to get them loosened by himself. The power of an eagle's grip is unbelievable.

He crawled an inch closer, and suddenly Kira could stand it no longer. She had always been an aggressive bird, and now this trait sent her forward. Her advance was certainly more for escape than for attack, but some of both were in it. She ran toward the man, who was badly startled and fell back a little, jumped toward him, touched one of his extended arms, and pushed against it to launch herself through the mouth of the cave.

She had often exercised her wings on the shelf, rising and holding herself up two or three feet above it, but solid footing had always been under her and she had never dared the empty air. Now she was in it. Her feet dropped and for an instant she tried to walk upon the air, but it had no substance; she was falling through it. She had a moment of terror, but then

313

the memory of the supporting air under her wings as she exercised them, and her nerve reflexes took over. Her wings took hold on the air and her tail spread and buoyed her up. She was flying. It was a shaky and uncertain performance; she almost lost her flying speed and stalled several times. When rising from flat ground, eagles start slowly and heavily because of their weight. They have to exert themselves to get airborne. But Kira had the impetus of her drop and plenty of empty space under her and wasn't confronted with this condition. All she had to do was glide at such an angle that her flying speed was maintained. This preoccupied her so much that at first she didn't realize how fast the other side of the canyon was sliding toward her. When she did realize it, she fell into confusion, tried to turn, and came very close to stalling again. Her mother had seen her jump from the nest and although her instinct told her to stay far from the men, she broke her circle, came roaring down, braked, and rose beneath Kira. Her presence and her solid back supported the young eagle and gave her confidence again. By skillful maneuvering beautiful to see, alternately rising beneath her and dropping away, she managed to help Kira land on a wide shelf on the other side of the canyon.

It wasn't a graceful landing, but at least Kira was on the ground again. She was somewhat ruffled, but now that she had dared the air and had got safely out of it for the first time, she shook her feathers into place, looked around, and bowed and talked excitedly to herself in congratulations. Her mother rose away and took up her distant, watchful circling. Kira watched her go and began to run about on the shelf, opening her wings and making several short, clumsy

flights from one rock to another. The feeling of being
airborne remained with her
for a time, so thrilling that it
dulled the memory of her
fright. She remembered the
feel of the air, the exhilarating freedom of it, and the
speed of her flight, when she
was borne up, weightless,
high above the earth.

While she was preoccupied
with these things, the man,
with her brother hooded and
crammed into the musette bag
over his shoulder, emerged
from the cave and was pulled
up the cliff face, walking up
the rock on the end of the
rope. He reached the top and
went over it. His companions
untied the rope, coiled it up,
and all of them vanished into
the pines.

After they had gone, Kira's
mother slid down the air from
her high post, screaming in
relief from the tension that
had held her. This unusual
sound in the canyon brought
an old horned owl, who lived

315

in a pothole far below and had slept through the tiercel's alarms, blundering out to see what the screams were about. The eagle saw him. He was something to vent her rage and frustration upon, and although they had managed to live in peace together since early in the spring, she stooped and struck the owl a terrible blow. One of her rear talons opened him up like a cleaver. There was an explosion of feathers and the owl fell dead toward the stream. Before he vanished through the trees, the old eagle had swung up and landed beside Kira on the shelf.

The tiercel, knowing himself safe now, came out of the sky on a long, sloping stoop with his wings half backed. He still had the rattler in his foot, and when he landed Kira ran to him, snatched it, and began to break into it. She was hungry again from all the excitement. Her first experience with humans was over and she had got well out of it. But there would be more experiences, more encounters brought about by ill will, before she lived out her life.

—*Robert Murphy*

What Do You Think?

1. As a symbol, what does the eagle stand for?
2. Think of three titles you could give this story.
3. The author does not say, but why do you think the men in the story wanted to capture the eagle?
4. Imagine that you are an eagle. Describe what it would be like to live at great heights.

Taking a Closer Look

1. Reread the first paragraph. Try to form a mental picture of the cliff, the ledge, and the surrounding area. For what reasons was the ledge a good home for the eagles?
2. What were the steps the men followed to capture the tiercel? Begin from the moment they came out of the pines until they disappeared again into them. Why was it necessary to have three men to capture just one eagle?
3. The dictionary defines the eagle as a large strong bird with keen eyes and powerful wings. Find several facts in the story that prove this statement.
4. The last sentence hinted that Kira would experience more trouble with humans. What are some of the troubles she might face?
5. In this story what effect did humans have on ecology?

Putting Ideas to Work

Pretend that you are an animal on the endangered species list. Write about what it would be like to be the last one of your species.

When God created the world, He designed each delicate portion of the web of life. In this psalm the psalmist praises God for His care for each portion of the web and His control that keeps the web intact.

The Heaven and the Earth

Praise the Lord, my soul!
  O Lord, my God, how great you are!
You are clothed with majesty and glory;
  you cover yourself with light.
You spread out the heavens like a tent
  and built your home on the waters above.
You use the clouds as your chariot
  and ride on the wings of the wind.
You use the winds as your messengers
  and flashes of lightning as your servants.

You have set the earth firmly on its foundations,
    and it will never be moved.
You placed the ocean over it like a robe,
    and the water covered the mountains.
When you rebuked the waters, they fled;
    they rushed away when they heard
        your shout of command.
They flowed over the mountains and into the valleys,
    to the place you had made for them.
You set a boundary they can never pass,
    to keep them from covering the earth again.

You make springs flow in the valleys,
    and rivers run between the hills.
They provide water for the wild animals;
    there the wild donkeys quench their thirst.
In the trees near by,
    the birds make their nests and sing.

From the sky you send rain on the hills,
   and the earth is filled with your blessings.
You make grass grow for the cattle
    and plants for man to use,
so that he can grow his crops
   and produce wine to make him happy,
   olive oil to make him cheerful,
   and bread to give him strength.
The cedars of Lebanon get plenty of rain —
   the Lord's own trees, which he planted.
There the birds build their nests;
   the storks nest in the fir trees.
The wild goats live in the high mountains,
   and the badgers hide in the cliffs.

You created the moon to mark the months;
    the sun knows the time to set.
You made the night, and in the darkness
    all the wild animals come out.
The young lions roar while they hunt,
    looking for the food that God provides.
When the sun rises, they go back
    and lie down in their dens.
Then people go out to do their work
    and keep working until evening.

Lord, you have made so many things!
    How wisely you made them all!
    The earth is filled with your creatures.
There is the ocean, large and wide,
    where countless creatures live,
    large and small alike.
The ships sail on it, and in it plays Leviathan,
    that sea monster which you made.

All of them depend on you
   to give them food when they need it.
You give it to them, and they eat it;
   you provide food, and they are satisfied.
When you turn away, they are afraid;
   when you take away their breath, they die
   and go back to the dust from which they came.
But when you give them breath, they are created;
   you give new life to the earth.

May the glory of the Lord last forever!
   May the Lord be happy with what he has made!
He looks at the earth, and it trembles;
   he touches the mountains, and they pour out smoke.

I will sing to the Lord all my life;
   as long as I live I will sing praises to my God.
May he be pleased with my song,
   for my gladness comes from him.
May sinners be destroyed from the earth;
   may the wicked be no more.

Praise the Lord, my soul!
Praise the Lord!

—Psalm 104 TEV

What Do You Think?

1. In a single sentence, try to state the central theme of the psalm. What was the psalmist trying to say?
2. What part of this psalm did you like most? Why?
3. Think of another appropriate title for this psalm. Explain your choice.
4. The psalmist suggests that the ability of the birds to build their nests is related to the rain. Explain his reasoning. Do you agree?

Taking a Closer Look

1. List the birds, mammals, and fish that are named in this psalm.
2. To what are the following things compared:
    a. the heavens
    b. the clouds
    c. the ocean
   Are these appropriate comparisons? Why or why not?
3. Explain how water is a benefit to the donkeys.
4. How does the rain fill the earth with blessings?
5. What is the source of gladness?

Putting Ideas to Work

This psalm is a song of praise to God. Think of some of the things for which you are thankful and write your own song of thanks and praise.

Wings for My Flight

The stories in this unit are about young people who, at a moment in time, had decisions to make and more than ordinary problems to solve. They each met the problems and challenges in a different way, but it was always courage and unselfishness that gave them "wings for their flights."

THE FIRST WINTER

CONSTANCE HOPKINS, her father, and her step-mother Elizabeth were among those who landed at Plymouth Rock in November of 1620. In this journal account the author, a descendant of Constance Hopkins, describes the incredible hardship the colonists endured during their first winter in the New World.

January 1621

They have actually started building a Common House! We can hear the cold ring of the axes—carried clearly in the winter air—and the thick solid sound of a tree as it hits the earth. Even though the women still have little to do save their usual tasks, there is a feeling of progress that infects us all. The men come back on board at night, so weary they nigh stagger. Yet once they have bolted their food they sit for hours talking of their plans.

Father is constantly working. He lifts great logs the others cannot move, heaving them into place across the sawpit where they are cut into thick planks for building. Elizabeth says all the men will catch most fearful chills if they do not take better care of themselves. First heavy work that puts them a-sweating, and then a rest period when they stand in the bitter cold, or gather round a fire—burning their faces and freezing their backs. In truth, Christopher Martin confessed tonight that he felt quite unwell, but there are those who think he may be malingering. Since he was deposed from governorship at the start of the journey by William Brewster's followers he has been at times vexatious, finding great fault with what the others decide to do. Malingering or not, he has a fearful cough!

January 1621 Continued

The sailors call it scurvy, and say that they have seen men step from their hammocks announcing that they are in good health, walk a few feet, and fall dead from the disease. Dr. Fuller gives it no name, but does what he can with bloodletting and such remedies as the juice of thyme, which he claims to be excellent for irritations of the chest. And yet we are dying! My stomach churns with fear.

Those who are taken ill, and there are more each day, are carried from the ship to the Common House, which has at last been built. A few other houses are almost finished, but there is hardly a soul strong enough to work on them. Ours is at least a roof over our heads, although the cruel cold seeps in between the many cracks. I huddle in it most of the day, staying as far as I can from the horrible Sickness. Elizabeth insists on nursing those poor wretches who lie dying in the Common House.

"Someone must do it, Constance," she says.

"Not me! I will not go near them!"

"Then mind Damaris and Oceanus for me, and feed your father and Giles. I will come back whenever I can."

"And bring the Sickness with you that we may all die of it? I will go back on the ship and stay there!"

"There are those with the Sickness on the ship now too, Constance."

"But I thought . . . I thought they were being brought ashore!"

"There is no more room in the Common House. The floor is already filled with pallets, without a spare inch to lay another, save when someone dies. Rose Standish died this morning."

334

"*Rose?* But . . . but I *saw* her just a day or two ago! She was talking to Mistress Mullins!"

"Mistress Mullins is dead too. And her husband lies ill—" Elizabeth bit her lip hard. "I cannot stand here idle, Constance. Look out for the babes for me." And with that she left the house and walked down the hard-packed dirt path, disappearing into the Common House. I saw the door close behind her.

After Father helped Captain Standish bury Rose that night, he returned to the house, standing his spade against the wall, where the crumbs of earth from Rose Standish's grave fell softly to the dirt floor. I set my mouth tight and went to the hearth where I filled his trencher with hot boiled fish, silently handing it to him.

335

"No, Con. I want nothing to eat," he said, and lay down on the bed without even taking off his boots.

I stood watching him in amazement. For Father to refuse his food was unbelievable!

"Are you well, Father? Is there aught wrong?" But already he lay drowned in sleep and did not answer.

Sometime deep in the night I heard the thick, choking sound of his breathing, and forced myself to get up from the pallet and go to him. In the firelight I could see his face flushed and red, and his head turning restlessly on the pillow. Ted Dotey heard it too, and came creeping down the ladder from the loft where he and Ted Leister sleep. He stood beside me among the half-shadows, and I was grateful for his nearness.

"He's got it, Constance," Ted whispered. "The Sickness. This is the way it starts."

"Rouse Giles, while I wake t'other Ted. We'll carry him to the Common House."

"But there is no room there! Elizabeth said so."

"There must be a place. With so many dying—"

"No! Don't take him there! If you do, he'll die too! I know he will! Leave him be. I'll care for him."

"It's a filthy task, Con. 'Twill turn your stomach! Let us take him."

I whirled on him and knew that my eyes were blazing. Sounding to myself just like Father, I shouted, "You will do as I say! Leave him be! Now help me get his boots and clothes off. He must be made more comfortable. And get more wood for the fire! I will not have him chilled!"

"Aye, miss," Ted mumbled, and did as he was bid.

My voice had wakened Giles, although Father had not

opened his eyes at all, and he came shuffling sleepily to the bedside.

"What is it?" he asked, yawning. "Is something wrong with Father?"

"He has the Sickness," I said crisply.

"What are you going to do, Con?" My brother's eyes were wide with fear.

"Make him well! Fetch me some cool water and a cloth and then go back to sleep!"

"Water? What shall I bring it in?" Giles asked, gaping at me.

"Bring it in your open mouth," I snapped, tugging at Father's boot, "or in your shoe, for all I care! But bring it!"

A moment later the water was there beside me in one of Elizabeth's wooden tankards, but Giles did not go back to sleep. Instead we sat the night there, one on each side of the great bed. I knew little of what to do for Father, save to bathe him with cool water when his fever rose, and cover him with an extra rug when the shivering took him. Once he opened his eyes, fixing them hard on me, as though trying to see through thick mists.

337

"Leave me be, Con, leave me be," he said. His voice was so weak I could hardly believe it to be Father's. "Let someone help me to the Common House—away from you and the babies."

"You will stay here," I told him.

"Thunder, Con, you will do as I say!"

"No, Father. You will do as I say! Hush now. You are only wasting strength."

The faintest sort of smile touched the corners of his mouth.

"'Tis a sad thing when a man cannot command his own daughter," he murmured. Then, closing his eyes, he lapsed back into the Sickness.

Giles wanted to take him to the Common House. "Dr. Fuller is there, Con. He may have medicines—he knows better what to do."

"Giles, if he goes there, he will die. I know it! I will not have him moved!"

"What will Mother say?"

"Elizabeth has enough to take care of without Father," I told him, and then noticed Father's body start its straining again. "Giles, get the basin and hold it and stop yammering, or else get out!"

My brother looked at me as he shoved the basin under Father's chin, giving me one of his long straight glances with mischief dancing way deep in his eyes.

"I pity the man ye marry, Con," he said, "You're as stubborn as Father, and ye fight just as hard. But I'm not leaving."

And that was how the night passed.

In the morning I fed 'Maris and Oceanus, spooning gruel into the baby whilst Damaris fed herself and Giles fed Father. Sometime late in the morning Elizabeth came back from the Common House, her eyes dull and shadowed with weariness.

338

When she saw Father she gave a little moan, and knelt beside the bed.

"You should have called for me, Constance," she said, her hands smoothing his forehead, feeling how hot it might be.

"I knew you were busy. We have done all right. Giles has helped me."

"Have you slept, Constance?"

"I am not tired." I filled a bowl of gruel and handed it to her with a wooden spoon. "Here. 'Twill do you good."

Elizabeth ate, her eyes on Father. "He does not seem as ill as some of them," she said.

"He is better this morning. The little food we gave him has stayed in his belly."

She took a few more spoonfuls and then gave the bowl back to me. "I can eat no more, child." She bowed her head into her hands, and when she spoke again her voice was muffled and thick with tears.

"In spite of all we can do for them, they die. Christopher Martin was the first, and since him—Rose Standish, and both Priscilla's parents; her little brother, Joseph, lies there now, with no more strength in him than a kitten. Elizabeth Winslow is dead too, and Will White—"

"Baby Peregrine's father?"

"Yes. And both Anne and Edward Tilley sicken more each hour; they lie side by side, their hands clasped . . ."

I wanted to comfort Elizabeth, to touch her, to soothe her somehow, but I could not. Elizabeth and I—well, I know she is most fond of me, and she is always kind and patient and good to me. But somehow I seem to hold her off. I do not want her to be my mother! I seem not to be able to let her love me, or to let myself love her. I do not understand this, I

339

only know that I scorn myself for acting so, and yet I cannot change. I knew at that moment I could have eased her grief with a touch, or a word of sympathy—and I could not give them. I could only pull my pallet out from under the big bed, and lay a rug beside it.

"Rest now," I told her. "You must rest. Father sleeps, and I will watch him."

Poor Elizabeth. She was so tired she could not protest, but fell onto the pallet like a child, and slept.

February 1621

Father recovered, I know not how, but he is one of the few who have. A week after he was taken ill he was able to leave his bed and walk about the room a bit, and then I left him to care for himself and went to the Common House to work with Elizabeth and the others.

Prissy Mullins' brother has died, and the poor girl is stricken with grief and loneliness. She has put herself to caring for the small children whose mothers are either dead, or dying. 'Tis strange how few of the children are stricken—I know not why this is. Bess Tilley and Mary Chilton help Prissy, and so, without 'Maris and Oceanus to look after, I have been free to help with the nursing.

Were there time to think about it perhaps I might wonder why, after my horror of the awful Sickness, I was willing to assist. It may be that after tending Father and finding myself still uncontaminated, my fears were eased. Or it may be simply that every hand is needed and I could not, in all pride, be the one to shirk. Or—perhaps—this is all a part of growing up. In any case, I went.

When I first walked into the Common House I could not
believe what I saw. The floor was covered with mats and
pallets, with barely room to step between them, and on each
lay some miserable creature, blazing with fever. There was
a strange hush in the room, with a constant low sound
of weeping, soft moaning, or whispered voices. The great
fire, which the men keep blazing, threw a fearsome flickering
light over everything, making a weak hand, raised in suffering,
become a skeleton shadow on the wall. For a moment I
stood in the doorway, doubting whether I could force myself
to enter. The nauseous stench, the sounds of agony, the
nightmare look of the place, made me want to turn and run.
Then I saw Captain Standish, kneeling beside some poor
wretch, bathing a face drawn with pain. Looking up, he saw
me too, and smiled.

"Another pair of hands, Constance?" he said. "God bless you! Here, empty this basin, girl, and rinse it well. The water is there in the cask beside the door."

And that was it. As I carried the cleansed basin back to Myles, I saw John Cooke and his father lifting Edward Fuller from the floor in the corner of the room. As they carried him past me I saw that he was dead. Dr. Fuller held the door open for them, and as he watched his brother being taken from the house his face was wiped clean of all expression. I had just handed the basin back to the Captain when I felt a touch on my ankle and looked down. It was Ann Fuller.

"That was my husband?" she whispered. In the wavering light from the pine knots and the fire her face seemed all bones, with great black holes for eyes. "That was Edward?"

I knelt beside her. I could not answer—I just nodded.

"Sam—my little Sam—is he—"

"Samuel is well," I told her. "He is with the other children. Priscilla is tending them."

She grasped my hand; her own was scorching hot, the while she shivered. "Watch over him, Constance. Little Sam— see he is taken care of. Please!"

"I will. I promise. Try to sleep now, ma'am."

She turned her head away from me, and there were slow tears seeping from her closed eyes. The next night she was buried beside her husband.

Somehow, I know not how, I was going from one to another, emptying their basins, sponging their faces, spooning gruel into the mouths of those with enough strength left to swallow. There was no time to bathe the dead, nor prepare them properly for burial; we must needs tend the living. Day and night were much the same, save that we removed the dead by

342

night. Sometimes Elizabeth would be working with me, Desire
Minter, and Mistress Brewster, the only one who took time
to breathe a prayer over each corpse as it was carried out.
Several times I saw John Cooke, his face tight with disgust at
the chores to be done, helping with a gentle tenderness
that did not seem strange to me.

It went on for weeks, and days and time meant nothing.
There was little talking—no one had the strength to spare for
unnecessary words. There was a certain order to our work;
there were those who cooked and those who tended the
children, whom we kept away from the sick ones as much as
we could. There were those who dug the graves and buried
the dead. There were those who bore most of the nursing.
And there were those who—in spite of everything—continued
to build houses! And still they died.

And then one night I saw Father come into the Common
House, carrying little 'Maris. He handed the child to Elizabeth,
and together they stood gazing down at her tiny little face.
I tried to go to them, and something stopped me—they were
so alone with her. Elizabeth sat the night holding the babe,
rocking her gently and crooning songs without words. All
the next day Damaris seemed to sleep, though she turned
restlessly from one side to the other, fretting in small unknowing
sounds. Elizabeth went back to nursing the others, stopping
by 'Maris' small pallet each time she passed. Kneeling for
a moment, her hand caressed the child's hair and her flushed
face. I sat with her for a while, bathing her with cool water,
trying to ease the fever. Once she opened her great dark
eyes and looked at me and smiled a little, and then started
to cry weakly, so that Elizabeth came back to her.

Sometime in the night I stretched myself on a bench to

sleep briefly, and woke a short time later to see Elizabeth and Father together before the fire. Father was taking Damaris from Elizabeth's arms. As he walked slowly out of the Common House, carrying his tiny daughter, I saw the tears that streamed from his eyes and heard the dreadful sound of a man sobbing. Elizabeth stood watching them go, one hand against her throat. She made no noise, not even when I went to her and held her in both my arms.

And the days and nights go on, and the sick are brought in, and the dead are carried out. Mary Allerton died, too weak after bearing a stillborn son to withstand the Sickness. And the whole Tinker family died, and Degory Priest died, and Mary Chilton's parents died, and John Goodman and Thomas Rogers and Richard Gardiner died, and Francis Eaton's wife Sarah died, and John Crackston and John Rigdale and Thomas Williams died, and Anne and Edward Tilley died, and John and Bridget Tilley died, and Jasper Moore and his sister Ellen died, and John Hooke and Robert Carter died . . .

Dr. Fuller said today he thinks the Sickness is ebbing, that fewer people are falling ill. A few or many—what does it matter? Soon there will be none of us left.

And who will bury the gravediggers?

March 1621

And then one morning, just last week, I opened the door of the Common House to look at the day, and it was spring. The air was warm and soft, but with the salty smell that is always here, and I could hear a thousand birds all talking at once in the trees! Priscilla Mullins sat on a rock below me, near the shore, and she was talking to John Alden. He stood like a tall ghost—pasty white and weakened from the Sickness,

344

but standing! He's going to get well, I thought suddenly.
He's not going to die!

I looked around as someone touched my shoulder gently,
and Will Bradford stood there, one hand against the doorframe
to steady himself. "You're up!" I said, like a ninny. "Ought
you to be? Are you strong enough?"

He smiled his very slow smile. "I am all right, Constance.
Weak, shaky, and badly in need of a shave—but all right."

I looked at him and knew it was true. They were beginning
to recover. Those who were left were sitting up, or trying their
weak legs in a few shaking steps—but they were getting well!
Elizabeth came and stood beside me, breathing in the
freshness of the morning.

"They're getting well," I said. "I don't think any more are
going to die!"

"I have felt the same thing. Pray God we are right!"

345

Father came toward the Common House, his feet stepping with their old strength on the dirt path. He stopped in front of us, and stood looking at his wife. Elizabeth's sleeves were rolled up, her hair was an uncombed sight, her dress was reeking with filth. Her face was smudged and drawn and shadowed. Yet her eyes held a peace, a look of ease I had not seen in weeks. Father stared at her, seeing all I saw, and then he grinned.

And with his arm around her, they walked down the short lane from the Common House and up the hill. I watched them go, and Will Bradford, still standing beside me, watched them too. From somewhere we heard the sound of hammers and the pull of a saw through wood.

"Plymouth is a-building, Constance," Will said. "Its people are getting well, and houses are rearing their walls, and the spring is come. God is still with us."

But of the one hundred and two people who sailed from England, fifty-one are dead.

—Patricia Clapp

What Do You Think?

1. In what ways was life more difficult in 1621 than it is today? Are there any ways in which you think life was less difficult than it is today? How?

2. Would you like to have lived during some period in history other than the present day? If so, during what period? Why would you like to have lived during this period?

3. Have you read about or been in an emergency situation involving great numbers of people—such as a flood, a forest fire, an earthquake, or an epidemic? Tell about the experience. What did people do in the emergency?

Taking a Closer Look

1. Why didn't Constance want to help the sick at the beginning of the story? Why was Elizabeth more willing to help them?

2. What did Constance do when her father became ill? Did you expect her to respond in this way? Why?

3. At what point in the story did Constance begin helping the sick in the Common House? How did Constance explain the fact that she was now willing to help?

4. Constance wanted to comfort Elizabeth who was exhausted and saddened from working with the sick and dying. Why do you think she wasn't able to?

5. Which character did you admire most—Constance, her father, or Elizabeth? Why?

6. What words would you use to describe the people who first settled Plymouth?

7. What facts did you learn about life in Plymouth during the first winter?

During a winter in the 1850s when the weather was cold and rainy, Caddie slipped away on a dangerous mission. She knew she had to act quickly. Read to find out about her mission and the way she brought peace to the settlement.

Caddie
and
Indian John

Clip-clop-clip sounded Betsy's hoofs across the field. There was a treacherous slime of mud on the surface, but underneath it the clods were still frozen as hard as iron.

Then the bare branches of the woods were all around them, and Caddie had to duck and dodge to save her eyes and her hair. Here the February thaw had not succeeded in clearing the snow. It stretched gray and dreary underfoot, treacherously rotted about the roots of the big trees.

Caddie slowed the mare's pace and guided her carefully now. She did not want to lose precious time in floundering about in melting snow. Straight for the river she went. If the ice still held, she could get across there, and the going would be easier on the other side. Not a squirrel or a bird stirred in the woods. So silent. So silent. Only the clip-clop-clip of Betsy's hoofs.

Then the river stretched out before her, a long expanse of blue-gray ice under the gray sky.

"Carefully now, Betsy. Take it slowly, old girl." Caddie held a tight rein with one hand and stroked the horse's neck with the other. "That's a good girl. Take it slowly."

Down the bank they went, delicately onto the ice. Betsy flung up her head, her nostrils distended. Her hind legs slipped on the ice and for a quivering instant she struggled for her balance.

Then she found her pace. Slowly, cautiously, she went daintily forward, picking her way, but with a snort of disapproval for the wisdom of her young mistress. The ice creaked, but it was still sound enough to bear their weight. They reached the other side and scrambled up the bank. Well, so much done! Now for more woods.

There was no proper sunset that day, only a sudden lemon-colored rift in the clouds in the west. Then the clouds closed together again, and darkness began to fall. The ride was long, but at last it was over.

Blue with cold, Caddie rode into the clearing where the Indians had built their winter huts. Dogs ran at her, barking, and there was a warm smell of smoke in the air. A fire was blazing in the center of the clearing. Dark figures moved about it. Were they in war paint and feathers? Caddie's heart pounded as she drew Betsy to a stop.

But, no, surely they were only old women bending over cooking pots. The running figures were children, coming now to swarm about her. There was no war paint! No feathers! Surely she and Father had been right! Tears began to trickle down Caddie's cold cheeks. Now the men were coming out of the bark huts. More and more Indians kept coming toward her. But they were not angry, only full of wonder.

"John," said Caddie in a strange little voice, which she hardly recognized as hers. "Where is John? I must see John."

"John," repeated the Indians, recognizing the name the white men had given to one of their braves. They spoke with strange sounds among themselves, then one of them went running.

Caddie sat her horse, half-dazed, cold to the bone, but happy inside. The Indians were not on the warpath. They were not preparing an attack. Whatever the tribes farther west might be plotting, these Indians, whom Father and she trusted, were going about their business peacefully.

If they could only get away now in time, before the white men came to kill them! Or perhaps she could get home again in time to stop the white men from making the attack.

Would those men whom she had heard talking by the cellar door believe a little girl when she told them that Indian John's tribe was at peace? She did not know.

Indian John's tall figure came toward her from one of the huts. His step was unhurried and his eyes were unsurprised.

"You lost, Missee Red Hair?" he inquired.

"No, no," said Caddie. "I am not lost, John. But I must tell you. Some white men are coming to kill you. You and your people must go away. You must not fight. You must go away. I have told you."

"You cold," said John. He lifted Caddie off her horse and led her to the fire.

"No understan'," said John, shaking his head in perplexity. "Speak too quick, Missee Red Hair."

Caddie tried again, speaking more slowly. "I came to tell you. Some bad men wish to kill you and your people. You must go away, John. My father is your friend. I came to warn you."

"Red Beard, he send?" asked John.

"No, my father did not send me," said Caddie. "No one knows that I have come. You must take your people and go away."

"You hungry?" John asked her and mutely Caddie nodded her head. Tears were running again and her teeth were chattering.

John spoke to the squaws, standing motionless about the fire. Instantly they moved to do his bidding. One spread a buffalo skin for her to sit on. Another ladled something hot and tasty into a cup without a handle, a cup which had doubtless come from some settler's cabin.

Caddie grasped the hot cup between her cold hands and drank. A little trickle of warmth seemed to go all over her body. She stretched her hands to the fire. Her tears stopped running and her teeth stopped chattering. She let the Indian children, who had come up behind her, touch her hair without flicking it away from them. John's dog came and lay down near her, wagging his tail.

"You tell John 'gain," said John squatting beside her in the firelight.

Caddie began again, slowly. She told how the whites had heard that the Indians were coming to kill. She told how her father and she had not believed. She told how some of the people had become restless and planned to attack the Indians first. She begged John to go away from the Wisconsin country with his tribe while there was still time.

When Caddie had finished, John grunted and continued to sit on, looking into the fire. She did not know whether he had understood her or not. All about the fire were row on row of dark faces, looking at her steadily with wonder but no understanding. John knew more English than any of them, and yet, it seemed, he did not understand. Patiently she began again to explain.

But now John shook his head. He rose and stood tall in the firelight above the little white girl. "You come," he said.

Caddie rose uncertainly. She saw that it was quite dark now outside the ring of firelight, and a fine, sharp sleet was hissing down into the fire.

John spoke in his own tongue to the Indians. What he was telling them she could not say, but their faces did not change. One ran to lead Betsy to the fire and another brought a spotted Indian pony that had been tethered at the edge of the clearing.

"Now we go," said the Indian.

"I will go back alone," said Caddie, speaking distinctly. "You and your people must make ready to travel westward."

"Red Hair has spoken," said John. "John's people go tomorrow." He lifted her onto her horse's back, and himself sprang onto the pony. Caddie was frightened again, frightened of the dark and cold, and uncertain of what John meant to do.

"I can go alone, John," she said.

"John go too," said the Indian.

He turned his pony into the faint woods trail by which she had come. Betsy, her head drooping under a slack rein, followed the spotted pony among the dark trees. Farther and farther behind, they left the warm, bright glow of the fire. Looking back, Caddie saw it twinkling like a bright star. It was something warm and friendly in a world of darkness and sleet and sudden, ice branches.

From the bright star of the Indian fire, Caddie's mind leaped forward to the bright warmth of home. They would have missed her by now. Would Katie tell where she had gone? Would they be able to understand why she had done as she had?

She bent forward against Betsy's neck, hiding her face from the sharp needles of sleet. It seemed a very long way back. But at last the branches no longer caught her skirts. Caddie raised her head and saw that they had come out on the open river bank. She urged Betsy forward beside the Indian pony.

"John, you must go back now. I can find my way home. They would kill you if they saw you."

John only grunted. He set his moccasined heels into the pony's flanks, and led the way onto the ice. Betsy shook herself with a kind of shiver all through her body, as if she were saying, "No, no, no!" But Caddie's stiff fingers pulled the rein tight and made her go.

The wind came down the bare sweep of the river with a tremendous force, cutting and lashing them with the sleet. Betsy slipped and went to her knees, but she was up again at once and on her way across the ice.

Caddie had lost the feeling of her own discomfort in fear for John. If a white man saw him riding toward the farm tonight, he would probably shoot without a moment's warning. Did John understand that? Was it courage or ignorance that kept John's figure so straight, riding erect in the blowing weather?

"John!" she cried. But the wind carried her voice away. "John!" But he did not turn his head.

Up the bank, through the woods, to the edge of the clearing they rode, Indian file. Then the Indian pony stopped.

Caddie drew Betsy in beside him. "Thank you!" she panted. "Thank you, John, for bringing me home. Go, now. Go quickly." Her frightened eyes swept the farmstead. It was not dark and silent as it had been the night before. Lanterns were flashing here and there, people were moving about, voices were calling.

They're starting out after the Indians! thought Caddie. Father hasn't been able to stop them. They're going to massacre.

356

She laid her cold hand on the spotted pony's neck. "John!" she cried. "John, you must go quickly now!"

"John go," said the Indian, turning his horse.

But, before the Indian could turn back into the woods, a man had sprung out of the darkness and caught his bridle rein with a strong grip.

"Stop! Who are you? Where are you going?" The words snapped out like the cracking of a whip, but Caddie knew the voice.

"Father!" she cried. "Father! It's me. It's Caddie."

"You, Caddie? Thank God!" His voice was full of warm relief. "Hey, Robert, bring the lantern. We've found her. Caddie! My little girl!"

Suddenly, Father was holding her close in his arms, his beard prickling her cheek, and over his shoulder she could see Robert Ireton with a bobbing lantern that threw odd shafts of moving light among the trees. John, too, had dismounted from his pony, and stood straight and still, his arms folded across his chest.

"Oh, Father," cried Caddie, remembering again her mission and the last uncomfortable hours, "Father, don't

let them kill John! Don't let them do anything bad to the Indians. The Indians are our friends, Father, truly they are. I've been to the camp and seen them. They mean us no harm."

"You went to the Indian camp, Caroline?"

"Yes, Father."

"That was a dangerous thing to do, my child."

"Yes, Father, but Kent and some of the men meant to go and kill them. I heard them say so. They said they wouldn't tell you they were going, and you weren't there. Oh, Father, what else could I do?"

He was silent for a moment, and Caddie stood beside him, shivering, and oppressed by the weight of his disapproval. In the swaying lantern light she searched the faces of the three men — Robert's honest mouth open in astonishment, Father's brows knit in thought, John's dark face impassive and remote with no one knew what thoughts passing behind it.

Caddie could bear the silence no longer. "Father, the Indians are our friends," she repeated.

"Is this true, John?" asked Father.

"Yes, true, Red Beard," answered John gravely.

"My people fear yours, John. Many times I have told them that you are our friends. They do not always believe."

"My people foolish sometimes too," said John. "Not now. They kill no white. Red Beard my friend."

"He brought me home, Father," said Caddie. "You must not let them kill him."

"No, no, Caddie. There shall be no killing tonight, nor any more, I hope, forever."

Over her head the white man and the red man clasped hands.

"I keep the peace, John," said Father. "The white men shall be your brothers."

"Red Beard has spoken. John's people keep the peace."

For a moment they stood silent, their hands clasped in the clasp of friendship, their heads held high like two proud chieftains. Then John turned to his pony. He gathered the slack reins, sprang on the pony's back and rode away into the darkness.

"Oh, my little girl," said Father. "You have given us a bad four hours. But it was worth it. Yes, it was worth it, for now we have John's word that there will be peace."

"But, Father, what about our own men? They meant to kill the Indians. I heard them."

"Those men are cowards at heart, Caddie. Their plans reached my ears when I got home, and I made short work of such notions. Well, well, you are shivering, my dear. We must get you home to a fire. I don't know what your mother will have to say to you, Caddie."

But, when they reached the farmhouse, the excitement of Caddie's return was overshadowed by another occurrence. Katie, who had sat pale and silent in a corner all during the search, rushed out of the house at the sound of Caddie's return.

"Caddie!" she cried, "Caddie!" Then suddenly she crumpled like a wilted flower, and had to be carried away to bed.

In the excitement of fetching smelling salts and water, Mrs. Woodlawn had only time to cry, "Caddie, my dear. You ought to be spanked. But I haven't time to do it now. There's a bowl of hot soup for you on the back of the stove."

In the kitchen all the children crowded around Caddie as she ate, gazing at her in silent admiration, as at a stranger from a far country.

"Caddie, didn't they try to scalp you?"

"Did they have on their war paint?"

"Did they wave their tomahawks at you?"

Caddie shook her head and smiled. She was so warm, so happy to be at home, so sleepy . . . .

360

The day after Caddie's ride to the Indian camp, life settled into the old routine. The neighbors went home again. No charred black ruins awaited them. The sturdy wilderness houses were just as they had left them, only dearer than ever before, and in the log barns hungry cows bawled lustily for food.

Everyone recognized now that the "massacree scare," which had started in the tavern, had been a false alarm. But the terror which it had inspired was not easily forgotten. Many people left the country for good, making their slow way eastward, their few possessions piled high in wagon or cart, their weary cows walking behind. Tales of bravery and cowardice during the "scare" were told and retold around the winter fires; and, at last, people were able to laugh at them instead of trembling.

But, although it all came to nothing and folks could laugh at the "massacree scare" at last, still it left with many people a deeper fear and hatred of the Indians than they had ever felt before. The Indians themselves understood this. Now that the excitement was over, they were safe from even the most cowardly of the white men. But, nevertheless, they prepared to leave their bark huts and move westward for a time.

They felt the stirring of the sap in the trees. A smell of spring in the winter air lured them. The old women made bundles of their furs and blankets and cooking pots and put them on pole-and-buckskin litters. The ponies pranced; the dogs barked. The Indian men refitted bowstrings, polished knives and guns, and prepared the canoes for a long portage over the ice.

One day, soon after the "scare," when Caddie came

home from school, she saw an Indian pony tied to the rail fence near the kitchen door. Clara ran out of the front door to meet her.

"Oh, Caddie," she said, "do hurry. Indian John's in the kitchen and he wants to see you. He won't say a thing to the rest of us. Father's away and Mother and Mrs. Conroy are nearly frightened out of their wits. He's got his horrible old dog with him and his scalp belt too."

Caddie ran around the house and opened the kitchen door. Between the cook stove and the table sat John, bolt upright, with a large piece of dried apple pie in each hand. Solemnly he bit into first one piece and then the other, Mother and Mrs. Conroy peeping timidly at him from the dining room door. His scalp belt lay on the kitchen table beside the empty pie tin and the clean fork and plate which city-bred Mother had laid for him so daintily. At his feet lay his dog, licking its front paw with a slow red tongue.

"Why, John, I'm glad to see you," said Caddie. She stooped and patted his dog. The dog stopped licking his paw for a moment and looked at Caddie with affectionate eyes.

"Him hurt," said John. "Him caught foot in trap."

Caddie bent closer over the foot. "Why, so he did. Poor thing!"

"You like him dog?" asked John. Absently he opened a square of calico which he had tied to his belt, disclosing an odd assortment of bones, bits of fat, and odds and ends of food. To this collection he added the last scrap of the dismembered pie, folded up the cloth, tied it again to his belt, and then knelt down to examine the dog.

362

"Of course, I like him. He's a good dog."

"Missee Red Hair got no dog?"

"No," said Caddie slowly, her eyes filling with tears. "Nero, our dog — he's lost."

"Look. John he go 'way. John's people go 'way. John's dog no can walk. John go far, far. Him dog no can go far. You keep?"

"Yes, John," said Caddie. "I'll keep him for you. May I, Mother?" Mrs. Woodlawn nodded at her from the dining room door. "Oh, I'll be so glad to keep him, John. I'd love to have a dog."

"Good," said John. He straightened himself and folded his arms.

"Look, Missee Red Hair. You keep scalp belt too?"

"The scalp belt?" echoed Caddie uncertainly. She felt the old prickling sensation up where her scalp lock grew as she looked at the belt with its gruesome decorations of human hair.

"Him very old," said John, picking up the belt with calm familiarity. "John's father, great chief, him take many scalps. Now John no do. John have many friend. John no want scalp. You keep?" John held it out.

Gingerly, with the tips of her thumb and first finger, Caddie took it. "What shall I do with it?" she asked dubiously.

"You keep," said the Indian. "John come back in moon of yellow leaves. John go now far, far. Him might lose. You keep?"

"Yes," said Caddie, "I keep. When you come back in the moon of yellow leaves, I will have it safe for you, and your dog too."

"Missee Red Hair good girl," said John.

He drew his blanket around him and stalked out. From the doorway Caddie watched him go. His dog limped to the door, too, and Caddie had to put her arms around his neck to keep him from following.

"Good-by, John," she called. "Have a good journey!" John was already on his pony. He raised an arm in salute and rode quickly out of the barnyard.

"Well, of all things!" cried Mrs. Woodlawn, bustling into the kitchen with a great sigh of relief. "You do have a way, Caroline Augusta Woodlawn! I declare, this kitchen smells of smoky buckskin. Let's open all the windows and doors for a minute and let it out. And, Caddie, put that awful scalp belt somewhere in the barn. I couldn't sleep nights if I knew it was hanging in my house."

Caddie took the scalp belt and the dog out to the barn. She hid the scalp belt in a safe dry place, where she could easily get it to show to the boys. They had gone part way to

364

Eau Galle[1] to meet Father. Wouldn't they be green with envy when they knew what they had missed?

There was an empty box stall in the barn. In it Caddie made a nice bed of hay for John's dog. She washed his hurt foot in warm water and brought him a bowl of warm milk. Then she covered him with an old horse blanket, and sat beside him, stroking the rough head. He was an ugly dog, without Nero's silky coat and beautiful eyes, but he licked her hand gratefully, and already Caddie loved him.

"I've got a dog," she whispered to herself. "I've got a dog of my very own to keep until John comes back." And she was unaccountably happy.

[1] Eau Galle (OH GAL-ee)

— *Carol Ryrie Brink*

What Do You Think?

1. Why did Caddie begin to cry when she saw that the Indians were not in war paint and feathers?
2. Who was the most uncomfortable, Caddie when she visited John's village, or John when he visited Caddie? Why?
3. Imagine you were one of the children who saw Caddie when she returned from the Indian camp. How would you have felt? What would you have said and done?

Taking a Closer Look

1. In what part of North America does this story take place?
2. Why did Caddie feel she must warn the Indians?
3. Why didn't Caddie's father warn the Indians?
4. Where had the massacre scare started?
5. What things were different about Caddie's ride to the Indian village and her ride back home? What things were the same?
6. In your own words describe John's visit to Caddie's home.

Putting Ideas to Work

If you enjoyed this true story and want to read more, look in your nearest library for the book *Caddie Woodlawn* by Carol Ryrie Brink.

DAWN

Quick cold hands
One by one remove
The bandages from the darkness
I open my eyes
     I am alive

MADRUGADA

Rápidas manos frías
Retiran una a una
Las vendas de la sombra
Abro los ojos
     Todavía

     —Octavio Paz
     Translated by Eliot Weinberger

Have you ever had to babysit a little brother or sister? For Jerry such an everyday thing as that turned into an exciting experience.

The West Wind Blew Danger

The footprints in the hard-packed sand glistened quickly under the pressure of the boy's bare feet. Then just as quickly the shininess disappeared, and only where tiny waves chased each other to the shore was the beach anything but dull, tan sand, dotted here and there by small stones and shells.

The boy walked straight and erect, his eyes now on the smoothness before him, now on the small summer cottage his family shared each year in July. It sat snugly in the green reeds and twisted pines.

Reaching the cottage, he paused to admire his proudest possession, a gleaming aluminum rowboat lying upside down in the deeper sand.

It had been one of those typical Maine days when the wind came steadily from the west, flattening the surf and blowing the warmer surface water of the Atlantic out to sea — a day for basking in the sun and cooling off only by fast in-and-out dips in water far too cold for swimming.

368

A voice from the porch snapped the boy out of his dreams. "Jerry," it called. "Come in a minute, will you?"

He turned and grinned at the figure of his mother, looking pretty and small beside the huge form of his father, then trotted through the soft sand.

"What's up?"

"We're going out," his mother said. "I told you this morning."

"Oh, I remember," Jerry said. "Say, you two are sure dressed up."

His father smiled down at the muscular, tanned figure and rubbed the close-cropped hair. "We'll be at the planetarium."

"Oh, no!" Jerry mumbled. "I forgot."

"Forgot what?" his mother asked.

"I have to sit with that sister of mine."

"Kathy's already in bed," his mother told him. "She's got a little cold but she should sleep. If anything goes wrong, call us."

Jerry shuffled his sandy feet on the steps. "I'm old enough to take care of her, but too young to use the outboard," he muttered, trying once more to start his favorite discussion.

His father groaned. "Not that again, Son. Next summer, yes. This summer, no. We've been through all that and we haven't time for a rehash now. Take care of things."

Jerry's mother bent and kissed him. "Take good care of Kathy," she said following her husband down the path.

He heard the car start, and slowly he wandered across the porch, pulled open the screen door, and went inside. In his own room he started to strip off his bathing trunks, found they were dry, and pulled an old pair of khaki pants on over them. A striped T-shirt completed his outfit, and he crept silently along the hall past Kathy's room.

"Jerry?"

The voice was sorrowful, wondering, and he pushed inside. "What's the matter?" he demanded, knowing that a short answer usually ended in a short discussion.

"I'm hot," Kathy said. "I want to go swimming."

Jerry moved to the side of the bed and looked down at the three-year-old pink and gold figure.

"You're a little goose," he said, tucking the blanket tighter between the springs and mattress. "The water's like ice. Go to sleep." Then he leaned down and kissed her roughly, quickly, on the forehead. "Good night," he said. "And be quiet."

At the door, he turned. "Holler if you want me, but don't play around."

Kathy grinned at him and closed her eyes.

Sitting down at the kitchen table, he ate his supper leisurely, then carved off a huge slice of red watermelon.

When that was gone, he heaved himself out of the chair, and tiptoed down the hall to listen at Kathy's door.

Silently, he turned the knob and pushed it open a crack.

The bed was empty, the light cotton nightgown in a crumpled heap on the floor.

Jerry dashed to the bathroom. It was empty. He turned and raced through every room in the house calling her name. In the living room, he looked wildly around, then yanked open the front door and stared frantically up and down the beach.

The narrow strip of sand between sea and breakwater stretched barren and lonely for half a mile on either side, quite empty but for the tiny figures of an elderly couple strolling far out of earshot down toward the point at his right.

As he spun back to the door, a tiny bright object on the rolling surface of the sea caught his eye and froze him to stillness. Gripping the porch rail, he squinted his eyes against the glare, fear already a choking lump in his throat. He stared only a moment before dashing into the house and yanking the fieldglasses from the mantel-piece. Then the object on the sea came sharply closer and Jerry's stomach knotted in panic. It was Kathy.

She wore her bright red bathing suit and paddled serenely in her yellow rubber ring, totally unaware of her danger or that the strong west wind was carrying her farther from shore with every passing minute.

Once again came the numbing spasm of a clutching terror. Dazedly he put the fieldglasses down on the rail, stood for a moment undecided, then raced into the house for the phone.

He forced himself to dial the right number slowly and carefully, then waited for the sound of the ring. An eternity of seconds passed and then came only the monotonous buzzing of the busy signal.

His first reaction was a half-choked sob — then sudden anger as he slammed down the receiver and ran blindly from the room.

He worked then in a fear-driven fury, almost falling down the steps in his rush to the boat. He dragged and hauled it over the breakwater, over the loose rocks that edged the beach, and down to the water's edge.

Racing back to the porch, he stripped the canvas cover from the forbidden outboard and with heaving, gasping sobs carried it down to the boat. He struggled it into position and tightened the wing nuts against the stern.

He was crying by the time he finally secured the motor and began dragging the boat into the water — crying from the knowledge that Kathy wouldn't last a minute if she slipped from the ring.

The icy cold numbed his ankles as he tugged and wrestled the boat into the shallows, and at knee depth he flung himself over the side and scrambled to the stern seat. In a matter of moments, the wind had pushed the light craft several yards from shore.

He made himself slow down. The starting rope had to be wound around the flywheel — just so — the choke adjusted carefully to the same degree he'd seen his father do so often.

"Please, God," he prayed and yanked.

The motor sputtered, coughed, and caught, and Jerry swung the bow out to sea with a quick push on the steering handle.

Half rising from his seat, he scanned the endless expanse of water, blue-green now under the low-slanting rays of the sun, and so very big, so much too big for Kathy all alone. From his lower angle the tiny bobbing form was nowhere in sight. Then a distant swell revealed an instant's glimpse of the yellow-and-red dot.

He sat again and jammed the throttle over to its fullest. The motor responded with a roar and the boat tipped into its fastest angle — stern down, bottom slapping the waves into a foamy wake.

Twice more, half standing, he spotted the bright blob of color that was Kathy. Lights began to blink on in the houses on the rocky point several hundred yards to his right. The sun was only balanced on the rim of the shore behind him, its rays barely holding back the gathering darkness.

Kathy waved when she saw him — a wave half greeting, half reaching out for help.

374

Jerry cut the motor and the boat glided silently across the few remaining yards until he could grip Kathy by the arms and haul her, rubber ring and all, over the side.

She was trembling violently and her lips were purple as she stared silently up into her brother's eyes. Fear had finally reached her, and she clung to him and cried for her mother.

"Don't cry," Jerry coaxed and stroked her hair as he held her tightly. "You're a little goose," he said, gently.

Kathy shivered even more violently, and Jerry put her down on the middle seat. Quickly he stripped off his T-shirt and khakis. He slid Kathy's chubby legs into the pants and pulled the shirt over her head, wrapping the loose folds around her. Then he picked her off the seat and placed her on the bottom of the boat, noting thankfully that the wind was dying down. The tide was coming in too. The trip home would be faster.

As he stepped back to the stern, he noticed his heavy rubber "frogman" swim fins. He yanked them free and turned back to his sister. Gently, he lifted her head and tucked them under to serve as a cushion against the metal.

The sun was now only half a red ball settling with almost visible speed.

Hurriedly, he wound the starting rope on the deep-rimmed wheel and pulled. The motor spurted into life, coughed harshly, and sputtered to silence. He rewound the rope, yanked again, but there was no reaction at all. Only then did he remember his disregard of the oars racked side by side on the porch, and his insides knotted in dread.

He unscrewed the large cap on the gas tank, shoved two fingers inside, and rocked the motor back and forth on its swivel. There was no sound of sloshing gasoline — no wetness on his fingers.

A wail from Kathy, and Jerry felt the sudden panic rise again to choke him.

And then the red sun jumped from sight and only the bright-colored clouds in the western sky bounced daylight out to sea.

More lights flickered in the houses on the shore — warm and inviting but a mile away. Jerry bowed his head and whispered a prayer for help.

Crouching forward, he wrapped Kathy more tightly in the too large clothes. "Go to sleep," he said gently. "You're OK. We'll be home soon." Then his eyes fell on Kathy's pillow, the rubber fins, and he brightened. "We'll be home in no time," he added.

376

It took him a moment to replace the fins with the yellow ring, yank them onto his feet, and whirl back to the dead motor. Bracing himself on one knee, he loosened the wing nuts and pulled the heavy motor high enough to free its brackets.

Then his left hand lost its grip and, suddenly off balance, he was yanked forward. His chest banged painfully against the stern, and the motor slipped just beneath the surface. For a moment he held on, but the weight was too much for him.

"Here," he choked, as though the sea was his own personal enemy. "Take it." And the shiny machine slid silently into the blackness.

He turned slowly and rubbed knuckles against his eyes to keep Kathy from seeing the tears. "Are you OK?"

Kathy nodded, her round eyes with the long, tangled lashes wide with wondering.

Quickly he bent over her and tucked the loose clothing tighter around the shivering body. "Now listen," he said. "I'll be right here all the time. Don't move, do you hear?" He moved back to the stern seat and turned again. "You want something, holler." Then he grinned at her, keeping his fear to himself, grasped the stern with one hand, and vaulted into the water.

Two powerful kicks of his finned feet swung the bow toward shore, and only then did the shock of the cold strike him — a biting cold that ached in his ankles and quickly became an overall numbing of his legs and lower body. He clung to the stern with both hands and began a rhythmic, powerful kicking.

Slowly at first, too slowly to judge whether he was moving at all, he pushed the light craft toward the distant shore. The wind had died, leaving the ocean glassy smooth. Jerry kept his bearings by occasional glances toward the rocky point.

And he kicked. He kicked till his legs were nothing but two hurting things that wanted to rest, that screamed for relief, that brought gasps of pain with every breath. His shoulders cramped in the awkward angle, and his stomach muscles were merciless agony.

Desperately, he wanted to stop — to haul himself into the dry comfort of the boat even for only a little while. Then Kathy called again — one word in a sleepy, scared voice. "Mummy!"

Jerry shifted his grip and peered along the side toward home. He was closer, far closer than he dared hope. "Soon, Kathy," he panted. "Soon. You're OK."

Darkness and cold, wet misery were all around him now, but the lights of shore were bigger and welcoming. He forced his legs back into the smooth, even, kicking pattern, and the boat glided silently.

Minutes passed and then he heard a slapping sound that wasn't the sound of his feet, but the irregular beat of little waves on sand.

Suddenly he shuddered, not with cold but with delayed reaction to what might have been.

"Little goose," he muttered and kicked harder.

And then he heard his father, voice hoarse and breathless, calling to him, and felt the rough, tweed-coated arms lifting him gently from the sea.

His mother was there too, reaching for Kathy, cradling her in her arms.

His job was done. He closed his eyes, pressed his face against the harsh, scratchy cloth on his father's shoulder, and turned free the tears he'd held so long.

Three minutes later he was in his own bed, piled high with extra blankets to still the shaking. The tears stopped and he looked up into the smiling, grateful eyes of his father.

"I lost your motor," he said.

"So what?" his father said softly.

"Kathy snuck out on me," Jerry began, "and I — "

"Hush," his father said. "You know old Mr. Newman? Lives out on the point? He saw the whole thing. He spotted Kathy a moment before you got there and did the only thing possible. He called the Coast Guard, but you were already on the beach when they arrived. He guessed your mother and I'd be at the planetarium so he called us. We came as fast as we could."

"The motor . . ." Jerry began again.

"Tomorrow, we can go into town and get you another," his father interrupted.

Jerry's eyes widened. "Get *me* another?"

His father rose to his feet and smiled down. "I somehow get the idea you're old enough to have one of your own," he said. "Try to get some rest now. I'll send your mother in." He bent hurriedly and kissed his son on the forehead. "And Jerry?"

"What?"

"Thanks." With that, he turned and walked from the room as his wife entered.

She went directly to the bed and knelt beside it, pulling Jerry close in a strong, silent embrace. He struggled free after a moment and lay back on his pillow.

"How's Kathy?" he asked.

"Cold as an icicle, but the doctor says she'll be all right."

Jerry closed his eyes.

"Little goose," he mumbled, drifting off to sleep.

— *David Savage*

What Do You Think?

1. How did Jerry feel about taking care of his sister while his parents were out?
2. Was Jerry to be blamed because Kathy went into the water? Why or why not?
3. Do you think Jerry did the right thing when he used the forbidden motor? Explain your answer.
4. How did Jerry feel about Kathy? Did his feelings change during the story? Support your answer with details from the story.

Taking a Closer Look

1. What did Jerry mean when he said, "I'm old enough to take care of her, but too young to use the outboard"?
2. How old was Kathy?
3. What did Jerry forget to put in the boat?
4. What two uses did Jerry find for his rubber fins?
5. Who saw what happened and what did he do?
6. Why wasn't Jerry's father unhappy with Jerry or Kathy?

The word is *challenge*. . . .
A challenge is there. Meet it. . . .
It is the very act
of meeting it that makes us
more than animals. . . .

—James Ramsey Ullman

This story is about a period of time many years ago, in the early 1920s. The main characters are based on real people — the author and her sister. Read the story to see how "The Last Day" tested their courage and unselfishness.

The Last Day

Julie and Elizabeth had finished breakfast and now were in their upstairs bedroom getting ready for the last day of school. Next to Christmas, the Last Day was the best day of the year, since it marked the beginning of summer vacation. Three months without school! The Last Day was joyously here and now. And today, of course, the girls would wear their best dresses and their brand-new patent-leather Mary Jane slippers.

Elizabeth stuck one foot out and wiggled it as she admired the sheen of the black leather. Suddenly she put her foot down.

"Will Ethel Tucker have on shoes today?" she asked Julie.

Elizabeth, who was a year younger than Julie, thought her sister the wisest person in the world next to Father and Mother. And, of course, Clara, who was Father's cousin and had come to help when Elizabeth was born eight years ago. Happily for all the Allens, Clara had stayed on, helping.

Julie was over at the window looking into the top branches of the ash maple growing beside the back steps. Yesterday she *thought* she had seen an oriole's nest there, and now she was leaning out of the window, her face almost touching the wide, flat leaves. She appeared not to have heard her sister.

Elizabeth crossed the room and touched Julie's shoulder. "Will Ethel Tucker have on shoes today?" she asked again.

Though most of the boys had been going barefoot for the past couple of months, none of the girls, except Ethel Tucker, ever did.

Julie drew her head in and considered Elizabeth's question.

From down the hall came Father's voice, singing with fierce energy as he shaved. Though perfectly tuneless, his songs were always well·worth listening to, for, while the first line and the rhythm were always the same, the words varied to fit the occasion. Now as the two girls wondered about Ethel Tucker, they heard:

"And then he told those children
And those children they did say,
That no more they'd leave their father,
For today was the Last Day."

386

The phrases of the song came jerkily between strokes of the razor.

When it had ended, Julie said, "Maybe she'll just stay home."

Her words were hardly a direct answer to her sister's question, but Elizabeth understood what she meant. Ethel would stay home because she didn't have shoes for the Last Day.

Ethel had started coming to school only two weeks ago. While there was little to distinguish her from several other girls in Miss White's room, she was distinctly in a class by herself. True, she was a skinny little thing with large blue eyes looking out of a thatch of stringy blond hair. But there were other girls in that room almost as skinny. Several of them rarely had their hair combed. And though she was the only girl who came to school barefooted, this, in itself, would not have been enough to set her apart. Ethel's claim to distinction at Orchard School lay in the fact that she was poor. She was poor among a group of children none of whom was rich. It was suspected that she didn't always have enough to eat. To cap it all, Ethel Tucker had no mother. She was poor indeed.

The Tucker family had established itself in the little shack next to the blacksmith shop a block up the street from the school. This was handy for Mr. Tucker, who worked at the blacksmith shop with Mr. Rodgers, the owner. But the house was hardly more than one room and a lean-to, so the six Tuckers must have been badly crowded inside it.

Here Ethel kept house for the four younger children and her father. She did, that is, until a truant officer called at the blacksmith shop one day and insisted that she be allowed to go to school. After that visit, Ethel went to school. Stretching a point, Miss Harvey, principal of Orchard School, allowed little Chester, aged three, to tag along with the other Tuckers. Every morning and afternoon he took a nap in the first-grade cloakroom on two straight chairs shoved together. There his older brother, who was in first grade, could watch over his slumbers and lift him back whenever he rolled off the chairs, as he sometimes did.

Though at first the Tuckers had caused a stir of interest at Orchard School, it wasn't long before everyone was taking them in stride. Ethel's poverty and bare feet came to be accepted, just as Herman Dilling's unquenchable badness had come to be accepted. Every school had at least one bad boy in it; so inevitably, every school had to have some poor children in it. Ethel Tucker, the poor girl, became at last simply poor Ethel Tucker.

"How will she get her report card if she doesn't come on the Last Day?" persisted Elizabeth.

"Someone could take it up to the blacksmith shop," answered Julie. "Miss White would."

Elizabeth nodded, feeling assured. You could count on Miss White.

They came out of the bedroom and went down the long shadowy hall toward the head of the stairs. At the bathroom door they paused to say, "Good-by, Father."

Instantly, the door was snatched open and a man stood on the threshold, peering at them over a mask of white

388

lather. "Make your poor old father proud this afternoon. He isn't long for this world." His voice, issuing through a hole in the mask, was dolefully solemn.

The girls giggled. A sturdier, healthier man than Father could hardly be imagined. He had been talking like this for as long as they could remember.

"You're sure you know your pieces?" he demanded, his dark eyes darting anxiously from one grinning face to the other. The girls nodded. "Good!" he cried, turning back into the bathroom and slamming the door. As Julie and Elizabeth continued down the hall, another tuneless song followed loudly after them:

> "And then he told those children
> That their pieces they did know,
> And the reason that he told them
> Is because they told him so."

Down in the kitchen they stopped for their mother's inspection.

"Let me look at you," she said, as she did every morning.

This morning the inspection was rather prolonged, because, of course, this was the Last Day.

"You look very nice," she said at last. "I shall be proud of you this afternoon."

Like Father, Mother was referring to the parts they were to take in the program.

She gave Elizabeth's hair ribbon a parting twitch, and said to Julie, "Remember, dear, it's not 'thus on its sounding anvil-shape,' but 'thus on its sounding anvil — shape each burning deed and thought.' Pause after 'anvil.' "

Julie, who loved horses, had chosen "The Village Blacksmith" for the Last Day. Now she nodded, moving the high lights on her smooth dark bangs.

"I'll remember," she promised.

Elizabeth had chosen "Abou Ben Adhem." She knew the poem perfectly and understood most of it.

They kissed their mother good-by and moved on through the kitchen to the screened back porch. Clara was there putting a dish of something into the big wooden icebox.

"Got your lunches?" she asked without turning around.

Sometimes they wondered if Clara had eyes in the back of her head. Of course, in all the excitement of the Last Day, they had forgotten to pick up their lunch pails. As they went meekly back into the kitchen they heard Clara's sniff behind them. It could mean almost anything, that sniff. This morning it plainly signified disgust, but the girls felt no concern. Clara always acted terribly afraid that Julie and Elizabeth would guess how much she loved them.

The girls went carefully out the back screen door, swinging it wide and stretching their feet to the second step. Fanny, Father's Irish setter, was sprawled along the top step. The screen door swung safely out over her. Fanny had not the slightest fear that anyone would step on her, because no one ever had. Now, as the children maneuvered past her and down the steps, she thumped her fringed tail lazily a couple of times, sighed mightily, and let them go.

They walked through the fenced kitchen garden to the driveway and down to the county road. Swinging their lunch pails, they started trudging steadily the mile and a half that lay between them and their destination. At the elderberry bush which marked the north boundary of their home place, they turned to wave. Once past the elderberry bush, they would be out of sight of the tall white house and completely on their own. They thought of the bush as a marker between the known and whatever lay beyond. Now, though at some distance, they were still under the eye of the double kitchen windows. They could see their mother's figure at one window and they knew she was waving, though they were too far away to tell. Then another figure appeared at the second of the pair of windows and they knew that Clara was waving too. They waved back, then turned and walked on past the elderberry bush and out of sight of home.

Julie and Elizabeth, though a year apart, shared the same classroom. Julie, a fifth-grader, sat next to the windows. Elizabeth was with the fourth-graders on the other side of the room. Ethel Tucker, though the oldest child in the whole room, sat across the aisle from

Elizabeth. Evidently Ethel had missed a good deal of school during the twelve years of her life.

The moment Elizabeth entered the classroom, she saw with dismay that Ethel had not stayed home after all. There she sat behind her desk, her face unusually animated as she watched the children coming in. Had Ethel, too, caught the excitement of the Last Day? For once her hair was combed. It was neatly parted in the middle and hung in two tight braids, each fastened with a rubber band. It wasn't until Elizabeth had taken her seat that she was able to check on Ethel's feet. Today, as on all other days, they were bare. Carefully Elizabeth looked at the other children. As near as she could tell, they all had on shoes. Even Herman Dilling was wearing shoes today. She tried to catch Julie's eye across the room to signal the dreadful news that Ethel Tucker was the only child without shoes on the Last Day. But Julie was already deep in a book and wouldn't look up.

A second row of windows ran along the back of the room, and in the corner where the two rows of windows met, Miss White had her desk.

Miss White had red hair and usually wore a green dress. Sometimes she wore a skirt with a white blouse under a green jacket. But you could count on Miss White's wearing green. You could count on her for other things too.

Every day, right after lunch, Miss White read to the whole room. Everybody was almost good all morning so that Miss White would read to them after lunch. Following the reading, things livened up. Notes found their way up and down the aisles, and here and there a child dared to whisper. Herman Dilling nearly always ended the day standing in the corner. But even Herman was fairly good during the morning.

"Good morning, boys and girls," Miss White greeted them, the tuning fork in one hand and a book open in the other.

"Good morning, Miss White," chorused all the children.

Miss White twanged a note out of the tuning fork, gave it to the children, and all the voices rose in the song with which they began each new school day.

> "Father, we thank Thee for the night.
> And for the pleasant morning bright;
> For rest and food and loving care,
> And all that makes the world so fair."

Then they settled down to work.

"I think we will take time this morning to go over the recitations once more," said Miss White. "Alberta Swall, we start with you."

394

Alberta rose and minced to the front of the room. She was a rather stout little girl with a wide, blank face, wide vacant gray eyes, and a small demure mouth which she kept folded up like a buttonhole. Now she made a curtsy to the class, at which they all giggled, and, unabashed, began her recitation.

It concerned a heroine named Grace Darling who had rowed across a storm-tossed sea to some shipwrecked people and rescued them. Alberta had learned the piece perfectly, as she learned everything, and she recited it with enthusiasm. In spite of themselves, for no one could really like Alberta, the whole room listened with respect. When she had finished, she curtsied again and sat down to applause that was only partly derisive.

"Are you sure you want to curtsy this afternoon?" Miss White asked her.

"My mother thought it would be more gracious," returned Alberta primly.

"Very well," said Miss White with the faintest trace of a sigh. "Lester Andrews, you're next."

Lester had chosen a short poem about circles. It was just about the shortest poem he could find anywhere. But Miss White liked it so much she said he might learn it if he looked up all the words. The only words Lester hadn't known were *heretic* and *flout*. He had explained them to the class. So now he spoke easily and with conviction.

> "He drew a circle that shut me out —
> Heretic, rebel, a thing to flout.
> But Love and I had the wit to win:
> We drew a circle that took him in."

Lester's bony wrists protruded beyond the sleeves of his jacket. Just once he started to put his hands into the pockets of his corduroy knickers, remembered, and drew them back. He looked almost strange to his classmates in his ribbed black stockings and the new shoes with the little tabs sticking out the back of them. And his straw-colored hair had not yet had time to become comfortably rumpled. Intrigued by his unfamiliar appearance, few of the children bothered to listen to what he was saying.

But this morning, for the first time, the poem spoke to Elizabeth. She listened with excitement as the words began to have real meaning for her. A very special meaning. "We drew a circle that took him in."

She glanced across the aisle to where Ethel Tucker sat, one bare foot resting upon the instep of the other.

Quickly Elizabeth reached down a hand and unbuttoned the strap of one Mary Jane slipper. Next, she unbuttoned the other. Now for the stockings. While Miss White commented on Lester's recital, Elizabeth dug frantically to free them. She had one off before Miss White said, "Now we'll hear from the fourth-graders. Elizabeth Allen, will you favor us, please?"

Elizabeth, her face rosy from her struggles, slid off the second stocking and rose. She cast a beseeching eye toward Julie and padded to the front of the room in a perfect stillness. Her eyes were lowered to her white, naked feet, so she missed Julie's shocked eyes, the boys' delighted grins, and Alberta Swall's buttonhole mouth, now a round O of surprise.

In the continuing silence, she began, "Abou Ben

Adhem, may his tribe increase . . . ,'' and went on to the end with a throat so dry she wondered that any sound could come out of it. Incredibly, the words tumbled from her in a frantic rush. It seemed as if she merely held her mouth open and they came spilling forth of their own momentum. At last it was over and she was back in her seat, her face scarlet and her heart pounding. What would Miss White say?

"I think, Elizabeth," came the teacher's calm voice from behind the desk in the corner, "I think it would be better if you spoke more slowly this afternoon. You will have a larger audience, remember, and each word must be heard and understood to the very back of the assembly room."

You could count on Miss White!

Two other children were called on and then it was Julie's turn. Elizabeth hadn't dared raise her head since she had finished her recitation. But now she lifted it to look at her sister. And her heart nearly leaped out of her chest. *Julie was barefooted too!*

Again Miss White refused to take note of anything unusual. She even praised Julie for remembering to pause after *anvil*.

With Julie's performance, the recitations came to an end. All the other children in the room were to be bunched with the soloists in a singing of "Onward, Christian Soldiers!" Miss White's room would perform last and thus the program would conclude on a suitable note.

So now all the children rose and arranged themselves at the front of the room in the places they would have on the stage. Miss White had put the soloists in the back row, thus equalizing honors for the audience of parents. This placed Ethel Tucker smack in the middle of the front row.

The whole school was seething with excitement when the pupils trooped back to their rooms following the noon recess. The performance would begin at two. But much before that time, the parents would start arriving. And as each automobile or horse-drawn vehicle pulled up in front of the schoolhouse, every head in the classrooms on that side of the building would twist to see who it was.

The Allens would come in the big red Peerless with the shining brass radiator, because Father would be here today. Only Father could drive the Peerless. Only he had the power in his shoulders to crank it, though even he panted like everything by the time the motor caught and turned on its own power. Sometimes it took a lot of cranking and considerable fiddling with the magneto to accomplish this. Today, unless the magneto failed, the Peerless would be out under the trees.

398

This certainly gave Elizabeth pause as she sat turning over in her mind the plan which she and Julie had cooked up during their lunch hour. It was nothing less than to leave off their shoes and stockings when their turn came to recite. It was a daring plan and one which they well knew might upset their parents. Never in all their lives had they gone barefooted, and to appear so in public might stretch their mother's love and understanding to the breaking point. They felt somewhat less worried about Father. He could nearly always be counted on to see their side of things. But this was different. They had never risked public disgrace before.

Miss White had not appeared after the noon recess. And no one felt any concern, for this was the Last Day. Even Miss White's daily routine might be affected by it. In her absence, an eighth-grade girl was "keeping order," and Herman Dilling was having the time of his life.

With genuine relief, Elizabeth noted that Ethel Tucker, too, had not returned from lunch. Evidently she had wisely decided to stay home. Now the drastic plan which she and Julie had determined upon would not be necessary.

Steadily the clock on the wall above Miss White's desk ticked off the seconds. By this time there was a long mixed row of automobiles and horse-drawn vehicles under the trees. But the big red Peerless was not among them. The magneto again! With Ethel out of the picture, Elizabeth wanted with all her heart to have her family present for the Last Day exercises.

Two o'clock came and still Miss White had not returned.

Occasionally there was the sound of applause from the assembly room upstairs where the upper classes had begun performing. Tension began to mount. Where was Miss White? At last, at half past two, the door opened and there she stood. She looked flushed and a bit harried as she beckoned the children to her. Their time had come! Quietly they slipped out of their seats and toward the door. On tiptoe, she led them across the big hall and up the wide stairs and down another hall past the assembly room to the door which led to the back stage area. And there in the gloom, the first person Elizabeth spied was Ethel Tucker! She hadn't stayed home, after all. She was standing in an almost dark corner and there were several children between her and Elizabeth. But it was Ethel, all right.

The sisters exchanged glances and in the feeble light each read the despair in the other's eyes. They must go through with their plan, and, as one, they bent to take off their shoes.

They watched with hopeless eyes Alberta's and Lester's shadowy outlines as each in turn mounted the short flight of steps to the stage, parted the curtains, and stepped before the audience. In terribly short time they were back with hearty applause ringing behind them. Then it was Elizabeth's turn.

Blindly she pattered toward the steps, unaware of Miss White's desperate attempt to reach her. She stumbled painfully once, but kept resolutely on. Nothing was going to stop her now. Ethel Tucker was not going to be the only child without shoes on the Last Day. Fumbling, she parted the curtains and faced a blur of faces in the bright light from the windows ranging along one side of the assembly room. If she heard the faint gasp which greeted her appearance, she paid it no heed, and stood resolute, her naked feet pressed close together.

Faintly she began, "Abou Ben Adhem, may his tribe increase." With those familiar words, the audience swam into focus and Elizabeth recognized three faces gradually emerging from among those on the back row. Father and Mother and Clara had indeed arrived! Mother's face looked shocked, Father's bewildered, and Clara was just delivering herself of a huge sniff. But Elizabeth kept staunchly on until the merciful moment when the poem ended and she could disappear between the stage curtains. The applause behind her was polite, almost questioning.

Coming through the curtains, she bumped into Julie, who stood barefooted and ready to pounce on the stage the moment Elizabeth left it.

"It's not your turn," Elizabeth whispered. But Julie gave her a shove and stepped into the light.

Elizabeth, wondering, pattered down the stairs to join the others in the gloom of backstage. There, "Under the spreading chestnut tree," came to them in ringing tones.

The waiting children remained utterly still while Julie's voice went confidently on. She even remembered the "anvil — shape" business and spoke the line correctly. You would almost have thought she was wearing shoes!

When at last she had finished and returned to Elizabeth's side, she was tensely quiet. Without a whisper between them, the sisters waited while the last

two performers spoke their pieces. Just once Elizabeth asked softly why Julie had gone ahead of turn, but Julie only shook her head and placed a finger on her lips.

Now it was time for the grand finale. All the children started up the stairs to the stage, the ones in the first row going ahead of all the others. Among these was Ethel Tucker. Elizabeth fastened her eyes on the little figure for whom she and Julie had dared so much, and her heart almost turned over. *Ethel Tucker was wearing shoes!*

She turned to Julie, her eyes shocked and questioning.

"Miss White got them for her this noon," whispered Julie. "She told me while you were reciting. That's why I went right after you."

"But you were barefooted too," said Elizabeth.

Julie nodded as they took their stations in the back row and waited for the curtain to be drawn open. "Miss White tried to stop you, and I was afraid she would try to stop me, so I stayed up by the curtain. I knew she wouldn't make a fuss there. I didn't want you to be the only one."

"Will the whispering in the back row please stop?" said Miss White.

Now the curtain was drawn wide. Sudden, crashing chords shook the scarred old upright piano below the stage as Miss Harvey, working from the shoulders down, sounded the first notes of "Onward, Christian Soldiers!"

With one upsurging movement, the audience came to its feet. "Onward, Christian soldiers . . ." rang out gloriously from the stage, across the assembled parents, through the windows, and beyond the school grounds. Now the whole audience was singing, and Elizabeth thought the song had never sounded so grand.

They were all in the Peerless, whizzing down the road at a good thirty miles an hour. Julie and Elizabeth sat on the wide back seat with Clara between them. Inside them both was a wonderful warm feeling.

Miss White had explained everything and Mother had promised to call a meeting of the Grange ladies at once to take up with them the matter of the Tucker family.

"Sometimes it takes something mighty special to make you able to stand in another person's shoes. Or out of 'em." Father spoke with a wink at Julie and Elizabeth. "But whatever put the idea in your heads?" he asked. For a moment silence followed his question, and then Elizabeth spoke.

"It was a poem," she confessed shyly. "Lester's poem about circles. I wanted to make a circle that took her in."

Nobody said anything more until they were past the elderberry bush and the tall white house had come into sight. Then Father burst into tuneless song:

"And then he told those children
That those children can't be beat,
And he's proud to be their father
Though there's nothing on their feet."

— *Doris Gates*

What Do You Think?

1. This story happened many years ago. How is the last day of school different for you than it was in the school in this story?
2. At the end of the story Elizabeth said, "I wanted to make a circle that took her in." How did these words explain why Julie and Elizabeth stood barefooted before the audience?
3. What was Father really saying each time he burst into song?

Taking a Closer Look

1. The poem Lester recited had a very special meaning for Elizabeth. In what other situations in or out of school do you think it would apply?
2. How do you know that Ethel Tucker had certain standards of her own?
3. What kind of person was Miss White? Support your answer with details from the story.
4. Why did Julie recite her poem out of turn?
5. Why didn't Elizabeth know that Ethel wore shoes to the Last Day program?
6. Explain in your own words what the poem about the circle means.

Putting Ideas to Work

Read more poetry by Edwin Markham, the poet who wrote about the "circle that took him in."

In this true story that happened in the 1930s, a storm in the bush country of Ontario creates a special problem. Only Pierre and his sister, Marie, can help. And if they don't, there will be a deadly disaster.

Saving the 559

Pierre tore up another piece of paper, tossed the scraps away, and sent his pencil whirling across the table.

His sister Marie looked up from her history book. "The School on Wheels will be here Monday, Pierre, and you won't have your homework done."

Pierre scowled. "I hate writing compositions," he said. "I never have anything to write about."

He reached over and turned off the big oil lamp on the table. Marie and he had worked right through a bad storm. Now the sun was shining again, and they no longer needed the lamplight.

"Maybe you can write about the storm," she said. "Let's go out and see if it did any damage." They left their schoolwork and ran to put on their boots.

Pierre and Marie went to a school that was not like any other school. Their schoolhouse was a railroad coach. In the bush country of northern Ontario where they lived there are no towns or villages. So a school coach travels on the railroad.

The coach stays on a siding at each place for just a few days. The schoolmaster lives in the coach with his family. The children come there, and the schoolmaster looks over the homework they have done and shows them how to go on with new work. Then the coach is coupled to a train and rolls on to another place. It returns several weeks later and the children go to school again.

Pierre and Marie were startled when they saw the damage the storm had done. Branches broken from trees were scattered everywhere. Great puddles of water lay all around, making the house look as if it were an island.

"There must have been a cloudburst," Pierre said, "right here in our valley."

"Do you think Father and Mother will be all right?" asked Marie.

"Of course," Pierre replied. "I don't think the storm hit anywhere except in this valley. Anyway, Father and Mother left so early they would be in town when it hit."

Then Marie cried, "Look, Pierre, over there! I see flashes. Is the storm coming back?"

Pierre looked in the direction that she pointed, and laughed excitedly. "That isn't a storm, Marie. That's Robert. He's sending us a message with his signal mirror."

"Oh, Pierre! What does he say?"

Slowly Pierre began to spell out Robert's message. "He says 'O-K-question mark.' He's asking if we are all right."

"Why, Pierre," Marie cried. "It's like having a telephone."

The signal mirrors were prizes which Pierre and Robert had won a few weeks earlier in the school races. The

408

schoolmaster's wife had shown them how to use the Morse code. This was the first time Robert had used his mirror to send a message across the valley.

Pierre took his signal mirror from his pocket and flashed slowly, "A-L-L O-K H-E-R-E T-H-A-N-K-S."

Robert flashed, "G-O-O-D."

Pierre signaled, "A-N-D Y-O-U-question mark."

The reply came back quickly. All was well at Robert's house. Then the sun went behind a cloud, and they had to stop.

Pierre put his mirror into his pocket. He said, "Maybe we had better go see what happened to the cow. Father always does that after a storm."

They sloshed across the wet, muddy ground. When they reached the field, they found the cow calmly chewing her cud. She had been wise enough to stay on high ground. It was a good thing, too, for a big pine had fallen flat in the lower part of the field.

"We're lucky that it missed the cow," Pierre said. Then suddenly he remembered the railroad cut across the lower end of their land. "Maybe we had better look at the tracks, Marie," he said.

They hurried down to the railroad cut. There they found a small lake several feet long.

"Stay here, Marie," Pierre warned. He slid down the bank to the water.

The ground was soft. Mud and water sloshed underfoot. Pierre jumped quickly to where the ties should be. Bending down, he felt around in the water. Suddenly he knew something was wrong. The rails were fastened to the ties. They could be seen like two long pencil lines ruled straight through the water, but the bed of gravel and cinders under the ties was *gone — washed out!*

"Marie!" he shouted, "What day is it?" He had to be sure.

"Why it's Friday!" she called back. "You know, school starts on Monday."

Friday! The day the 559 came through! His mind worked fast.

Engine No. 559 came pounding through every Friday at noon. Along with her sixty-two cars of freight, she would be pulling two tank cars filled with oil for the Ontario mines. The engineer would know nothing of the storm. The train would come rolling downgrade and would hit the washout! There would be a wreck — a terrible wreck if the oil went up in flames!

"Marie!" Pierre shouted. "It's a washout! I'm going up the track to Hilltop station to stop the 559. You take the road to Fifty-Mile Siding and telephone the telegraph operator at Hilltop from there. It will take you longer, but I may not get through, and if the freight is late, he could stop it."

He started through the water, jumping from tie to tie.

"Oh, Pierre! Do be careful," Marie called, as she hurried off in the direction of Fifty-Mile Siding.

"Hurry, Marie!" he shouted back over his shoulder.

It was a long stride from tie to tie. The ties were wet and slippery. Some were covered with loose gravel. He almost fell. It was hard to hurry, but he had to. He had to reach Hilltop in time to stop the 559.

Once over the cut the going was better, and he started to run. The road twisted and turned as it climbed, and he couldn't see far ahead. Twice he fell, but picked himself up again. Would he be in time?

He thought of Marie, and he wondered if the road was safe. Maybe he shouldn't have sent her.

Then the track straightened. He could see the Hilltop station now. The 559 had not arrived yet. He was in time. In his excitement he tripped, pitched forward, and rolled into the ditch.

Before he could scramble back to the track, he caught the sound. Sin-n-ng! Zin-n-ng! The steel rails were beginning to sing!

He leaped to his feet and saw the smoke of the 559 as the train was running into Hilltop. Now it was blowing for the station. Pierre looked at the semaphore. The arm of the semaphore was up, the signal that the road was clear. The train wasn't going to stop at Hilltop. He couldn't possibly make it in time now. He was too late.

He thought of waving, but he knew it wouldn't work. He had done that too often in greeting the engineer.

Sing — ng — ng — Zing — ng — ng! The 559 was picking up speed.

He must do something!

Words his father had said came to him, "When things get bad, your head is often better than your heels."

If only he had a telephone, he could warn the telegraph operator. A telephone! Suddenly Marie's words came to him, "It's just like a telephone."

Hurriedly he reached into his pocket and pulled out the signal mirror. Somehow he had to stop shaking, had to steady his nerves.

Sing-ng-ng! Zing-ng-ng! The 559 was leaving the station. It was picking up speed. The song of the rails grew louder every minute. If only the sun stayed out. He kept his eyes on the mirror.

S-O-S! S-O-S! S-O-S! He began to send the call for help. The engineer wouldn't understand, but the telegraph operator might — *if he were looking down the track!*

S-O-S! S-O-S! S-O-S! He kept the flash going.

The singing on the rails grew louder and louder! The 559 roared up to him. Gravel and cinders sprayed over him. He was lost in the shadow. He looked up. He tried to shout. The engineer waved from the cab. The 559 roared on! He knew he had failed as the sunlight touched him again, but something made him keep flashing his message.

S-O-S! S-O-S! S-O-S! He had no hope left, but still he kept on, sending his signal after the train. It was the only thing he could do!

Suddenly there was a startling scream of brakes, and a terrible shudder ran through the whole train.

It was a moment before he understood. Then he knew. The 559 had stopped! It was saved. He felt himself shaking from head to foot.

A figure was swinging off the end car. He saw to his surprise that the car was not a caboose, but a passenger coach.

"Pierre!" a voice called. "Pierre, what's happened?" Pierre looked up into the schoolmaster's face. The School on Wheels had been coupled onto the freight!

"I was riding on the platform. I caught your signal and pulled the emergency cord. Pierre, what's wrong?"

Pierre told his story to his schoolmaster, the engineer, and the trainmen.

"It's lucky we hooked on the school car," someone said.

Pierre heard only the schoolmaster's voice. He was saying, "Fine work, lad! Fine work! Learning the Morse code paid."

Pierre himself was thinking of something else. He knew what he was going to write for his school composition on Monday. He had plenty to write about now.

— *Zillah K. Macdonald*

What Do You Think?

1. Would you like having a railroad coach for a schoolhouse? Why or why not? In what ways would it be different from the school you attend now?
2. Why did Pierre think that he never had anything to write about? Were there things in his life that would be interesting to read about? What things would you like him to write about?
3. What has happened in your life that would be interesting to others? Explain your answer.

Taking a Closer Look

1. Why did Pierre dislike writing compositions?
2. Explain why the train was in danger.
3. How did Pierre and Robert use their signal mirrors?
4. What made Pierre think of using his mirror to signal the train?
5. Where were Pierre's parents during the storm?
6. Why didn't the engineer stop the train when he first saw Pierre?
7. What part did the schoolmaster have in saving the train?

Putting Ideas to Work

Look up Morse Code in an encyclopedia or dictionary. Copy the code symbols that spell your name and try flashing them with a mirror or other shiny object that will reflect light. Practice with a friend.

Measure Me, Sky

Measure me, sky!
  Tell me I reach by a song
Nearer the stars;
  I have been little so long.

Weigh me, high wind!
  What will your wild scales record?
Profit of pain,
  Joy by the weight of a word.

Horizon, reach out!
   Catch at my hands, stretch me taut,
Rim of the world:
   Widen my eyes by a thought.

Sky, be my depth,
   Wind, be my width and my height,
World, my heart's span;
   Loveliness, wings for my flight.

—Leonora Speyer

Snow Treasure

by Marie McSwigan

CHAPTER ONE

"Beat you to the turn!" Peter Lundstrom shot his sled down the long steep slope.

"No fair. You started first," his friend, Michael Berg, protested. Nevertheless, he flew along in Peter's tracks.

School was over for that day at least, and Peter and Michael were enjoying one of the sled rides the children of Norway never seem to tire of.

"Hey — wait a minute!" A dark-eyed girl drove her sled into the place the boys had just left. Her black curls bobbed like sausages under the cherry red of her hood. She was Helga Thomsen and somewhat of a tomboy. Behind her on the same sled was a smaller girl, fair as Helga was dark. The smaller girl was Lovisa, Peter's ten-year-old sister.

"We'll catch them at the lookout. Hold on!" Helga dug her heels into the snow and began another swift descent.

Catch them at the lookout they did, for the sled track made a sharp twist; below that, nearly a thousand feet, lay the sea. Peter and Michael had to slow down to avoid crashing a wall that protected the road.

Helga, daring as any boy, drove straight at them so there was a clamor of yells and a tangle of windbreakers, caps, sweaters, and mittens.

The mountains seemed asleep that April. Along the sea the world was lifeless. Except for the fiords, the harbors here in the north were ice-locked, their channels great fields of white. The fiords alone seemed alive with their black rushing waters and bobbing ice cakes. These forceful streams flow too fast for freezing and so are always a highway to the open sea.

The four friends at the lookout continued their lively play. Peter and Michael tried to wash Helga's face but the snow was too hard and dry and the face washing could hardly have been called successful. Helga managed to get a handful of snow down Peter's back.

Tired of the tussle, the four squatted on their sleds. When Michael idly tossed a lump of snow in Helga's lap she got up to shake her dress. In doing so she turned toward the sea.

"Why, Peter, there's your Uncle Victor!" She was surprised. "And Rolls, his mate! Look!"

"You're crazy!" Peter didn't bother to get up.

"But it *is* your Uncle Victor. Honest!"

"Now what in the world would he be doing here? You don't suppose he's fishing this time of the year, do you?"

"But it is, Peter. Come, see."

She was so sure about it that he got up, if only to be able to tell her she was wrong.

Below, miles away by road but only a little distance for a stone, Uncle Victor was making footprints in the hard snow. Behind him was the stocky figure of Rolls, second in command of the Lundstrom fishing fleet.

"Yoo hoo, Uncle Victor!" Lovisa was on her feet and looking over the wall of the lookout. But she could not make him hear.

"Yoo hoo," the four of them yelled in chorus, cupping their hands to make the sound carry farther.

Then Victor Lundstrom heard them and looked up. But there was no great roar of greeting the children had expected. He only waved his arm and went on walking. Rolls saw them too, and gave an equally casual salute.

420

Peter scowled. The greeting was unlike Uncle Victor. Why he should have been overjoyed to see them, especially after a long trip! He was Peter's favorite relative and, in all truth, his hero. He led a life of adventure in contrast with Peter's father, a banker. He was one of the most successful fishermen in that land of able fishers. He had a whole fleet of boats and sailed about everywhere, his nephew supposed. When he came back from a voyage he had stories to tell that no one could match. Uncle Victor was as fond of his brother's children as they were of him. So it wasn't like him not to seem glad to see them.

"What's he doing here?" Michael wanted to know.

They watched him walk along the beach toward the cliff beyond Riswyk Fiord.

"He's on his way to the Snake," they decided.

The Snake was a tiny arm of the big fiord so twisted and narrow that it deserved its name. Unless you knew about the Snake you never would have guessed it was there. Almost entirely hidden by cliffs, even from the air it would be hard to trace.

"To the *Cleng Peerson*," Lovisa's eyes danced, for the *Cleng Peerson* was Uncle Victor's own fishing boat, the one that he alone might sail.

"But why is he here?" Peter pondered. "He never comes north until the ice is gone." But he had no time for further reflection when a snowball broke in his face.

"So you thought I was crazy!" Helga taunted.

"Crazy as a hare!" Michael's snowball landed on Helga's hood. It spattered and her eyes and face were white. She lowered her head and shook it from side to side like a fierce young animal and then she charged at the tormentor.

And so, the battle went on. The boys, for all their strength and size, did not seem able to subdue the quickwitted girls, and none of them seemed to tire of the brisk exchange of snow.

"It's getting dark!" Peter was first to realize that the afternoon was over. Absorbed in the fight, the four of them failed to note the passing time. "We're all going to be late for supper and we'll get what's coming to us." What that was, he didn't have to explain for they all understood it was no pleasant prospect. "Come on. Let's get out of here."

As Peter predicted, he and Lovisa were late for their evening meal. But "what's coming to us" never came.

When they told of seeing Uncle Victor, a strange thing happened.

Their father pushed back his chair and jumped up from the table. Peter and Lovisa were surprised because they had never before seen him leave a meal unfinished.

"My hat and coat, Per Garson," he called to the old family servant. "Victor's back from Oslo. I've got to go out!"

CHAPTER TWO

When Peter told his father about seeing Uncle Victor that afternoon he saw a look of alarm come over his face.

Now that was strange because, although the two brothers were different in every way, there was a strong bond between them.

422

Was Uncle Victor in some sort of trouble? Peter wondered. But when he asked his mother she shook her head.

"Well, why did Father go out?" he asked. "You know he never does at night. He says he's tired after a day at the bank and likes to stay home."

"Yes, I know," his mother replied, "and he's busier than ever right now and so must be very tired. A treasury official has been here from Oslo and your father has had to work very hard. He's worried."

"Is there something wrong with the bank?" Lovisa asked.

"Not that I know of, Lovisa," her mother answered. "The bank has more gold than ever."

"Well, then why is Father worried? Is it about the war?" he asked as an afterthought. "About the Nazis taking Poland?" For even in the Arctic Circle the disturbance of that year could not be overlooked.

"Yes, Peter. It has something to do with that. But don't worry. Your father's a capable man. Everything he gets his hands on turns out all right."

Peter was awakened out of a sound sleep that night. Bang, bang, bang, bang, boots kicked the outside wall to shake off snow. He wondered what could be the matter. He got up to see.

His father was speaking when Peter got to the door of the living room.

"They'll never get our gold!" His father turned to face the men he had brought home with him. His voice was low and hoarse. "Not an ounce of it will they touch! Of that I am determined."

423

"How much does it amount to, now that the last shipment is here?" John Olsen, the clock maker, asked.

"It's bullion, of course," Mr. Lundstrom replied, "and it's more than thirteen tons." And Peter was banker's son enough to know that bullion is the gold before it is made into money.

"Thirteen tons!" Michael Berg's father exclaimed. "Why that would be thirty million kroner!"

"More," his father replied. "It's nearer forty million."

"Whew!" came a whistle and Peter saw his Uncle Victor. "That's around nine million dollars in the United States." Uncle Victor had spent much time in America. He and Peter's father had a brother in Minnesota, and Victor had visited there. More often than not he spoke of dollars, rather than of the Norwegian coin, the krone.

Peter made a move into the room and it was then they saw him.

"Peter," his father spoke harshly. "Go back to bed. And close the door."

"Wait a minute, Lars," Uncle Victor addressed his older brother. "Peter's nearly thirteen. It's Peter and the ones his age who can save our gold. I see it now. Why didn't we think of it before? We've spent the night considering everything from reindeer sleds to tri-motor planes. And here we have the answer right under our noses — the children."

They looked at Uncle Victor in surprise. But he only stepped up and put his arm around Peter's shoulders. He drew Peter toward the fire and threw a coat over his pajamas.

"How many children in Riswyk School, Peter? Forty?"

424

"There're nearer fifty, Uncle Victor."

"How many do you suppose are over ten?"

"Oh, Uncle Victor, I don't know. Maybe half. You mean girls too?"

"Of course I mean girls too." He spoke hurriedly. "Now, Peter, when I was a boy we thought nothing of a sled trip to the Snake. It's nine miles but we were young and tough. Not soft like you. We thought nothing of a trip like that."

"We go to the Snake too," Peter retorted, glaring. He never knew when Uncle Victor was teasing him.

"Of course you wouldn't start at Riswyk. There'd be two or three miles before you started. That makes, maybe twelve miles. Think you could do it or would you be crying for Mama all the time?"

"Uncle Victor, I don't know what you're talking about. But I know that Michael and I and lots of others have been on sled trips that lasted a week. And we didn't cry for our mamas, either."

"You're all right, youngster, you'll do!" Uncle Victor gave Peter a terrible thump on the back.

CHAPTER THREE

When Peter went back to bed, he was far too excited to sleep.

What was Uncle Victor planning?

It was some dangerous scheme, whatever it was; and somehow, he, Peter, was in it too.

It was a way to save thirteen tons of gold bullion for Norway. That was all he could understand. But how he was going to do it was more than he could hope to know.

The next day he tried to find out what had brought Uncle Victor back from Olso so suddenly. But neither his father nor his mother would tell.

On the way to school Peter and Lovisa saw an unusual sight in the town square. Uncle Victor and a crowd of men were building a wooden shed right beside the statue of King Haakon.

"Why, hello, Uncle Victor." Lovisa had not seen her uncle as Peter had, the night before. "What are you doing?"

"Air raid shelters," he explained.

"Are the Germans coming, Uncle Victor? Or would it be the Russians, like in Finland?"

"Hardly either, Lovisa. Certainly not the Germans. Way up here in the Arctic Circle's too far even for them."

"Then it must be the Russians."

"No, Lovisa. It's not the Russians."

"Then why are you building air raid shelters if it's not the Russians and it's too far for the Germans?"

Uncle Victor had to smile at what he called the relentless logic of childhood. "It's always well to be prepared," he answered. "If you're prepared it won't matter if they do come."

At school that day, it was hard to put one's mind on lessons. All the children knew of the air raid shelters and wanted to talk of nothing else. There was a feeling of restlessness that no one could explain away.

Mr. Anders, the schoolmaster, tried to comfort his pupils. He said that air raid shelters were found in every country, but here they were only a precaution.

"Norway's safe from war," he said. "Our country's

426

been at peace for over a hundred years. We've no quarrel with anyone and no one has a quarrel with us."

There was a knock on the classroom door. Uncle Victor came in. He was a great favorite with all the children. He whispered a few words to Mr. Anders and then spoke to the class.

"Now that we're building bomb shelters, we ought to have an air raid drill," he said. "We want to teach everyone to go in orderly fashion to the shelters and not be crowding the doorways."

"Just like a fire drill," Mr. Anders said.

"Just like a fire drill," Uncle Victor repeated. "In a fire drill you have your leaders and lieutenants. So with an air raid drill. Now besides the boys and girls of this school learning to take care of themselves and not be a worry to their parents, there are other things they can do for their country. For that reason I'm going to help you form a club."

If he had promised to sail his boat to the moon he could not have had a quieter audience.

"You want to know what kind of club? Well, for lack of a better name we'll call it the Defense Club. You must obey your president in everything. You must do all he asks and must never question him. For your president I am going to appoint Peter Lundstrom."

CHAPTER FOUR

"Get up, Peter. Put your clothes on." His father was shaking him.

The lights were lit. The clock on the mantle showed it was after midnight.

"Dress warmly too. We're going out."

"Out? Out where?" Peter found it hard to understand why he would be going out after midnight.

"Come on. Dress quickly. I'll tell you as we go."

"Have the Germans come then?" he asked.

"No, of course not. It was only that idea of Uncle Victor's," Father replied.

"Peter, will you hurry? We've just had word that the time is getting very short."

They strapped on their skis at the door in the light from the house.

"Are any of the others from school coming? Will Michael be there?"

"No, Peter. Only you."

"Why is that, Father?"

"You were appointed head of the Defense Club so it will be up to you to lead the others where we're going. That's why I'm taking you tonight."

Peter's face was grave if there had been anyone to see it in the dark of the deserted town.

"So I want you to watch where you're going and remember how to get back if you have to. Later tonight you'll be taken to a certain part of the woods. I want you to know just where it is and how to get there without me or anyone else showing you."

"Yes, Father. I'll watch. I think I can remember."

"I know you can, Peter. You've spent a lot of your life in the woods. I'm counting on your woods sense to help."

They were now outside the town. The trail led north to Rabbit Mountain. In the dark Peter could see little of the

428

track on which his skis slipped. But the hard tread told him it was a well-traveled path.

"What did Uncle Victor mean about us going on our sleds to the Snake?" It was his first real chance to ask his father about the thing that was uppermost in his thoughts.

"Well, it's like this, Peter. There is a good deal of gold in Norway, more than we'd like to have fall into the hands of an enemy, especially one that might use it to make war on us. So we've decided to guard it with our lives. It isn't the gold itself so much. It's the fact that it may be used to bring death to the very people to whom it belongs."

"You're afraid of a German invasion, Father?"

"Well, that's the tale that Victor brought back from Oslo. When you came home and said he had returned, I knew that only one thing would bring him back at this time and that was that his country was in danger. But I didn't want you to know about it then. Today, however, other things have happened — foreign mine layers have been sighted off our coast. There is little use trying to hide from something that may have to be faced."

"They're building air raid shelters all over the south," Peter said.

"Yes, and they're taking other precautions too. All this week a treasury official has been at the bank. He believes that the best way to safeguard our people is to put our wealth beyond the reach of those who would use it to do us harm. Other countries have been sending their gold to the United States for safe keeping. That's what we want to do too, if it can be managed."

Peter could hardly believe this was real life and that it was he and his father who were talking and not two characters in a book.

"There may not be time to safeguard all the gold in the Bank of Norway this way," Mr. Lundstrom spoke confidentially. "To do so involves a good deal of care. Each of the places where the gold can be hidden has to be inspected by trusted people in the government. The treasury official came here first of all and had a long list of other places to visit. But even if he doesn't get to the other towns, good care will be taken of the rest of the money because it's a staggering sum, bullion worth hundreds of millions of kroner."

"And Uncle Victor will take it on his boat?" Peter asked.

"What we have here — if we can get it to the boat in time."

"So we are supposed to take it down the mountain on our sleds?"

"If there is an enemy in our country and there is no other way to get it out. You children would never be suspected, but the men wouldn't be allowed to load so much as a pound."

"But why don't you send it away before the enemy comes?"

"Because the British and French are mining our coasts, laying miles and miles of explosives in the sea. A ship that would stray in their direction would be blown to bits. So Uncle Victor has to wait until he can find out something about their location. Why, it would be suicide to sail until he does! That's why we have to hide the gold in the cave."

"Cave?" Peter blinked. "What cave?"

CHAPTER FIVE

Peter and his father reached a level stretch. Their trail paralleled a railroad siding that ended abruptly in the woods.

At one end of the track was a boxcar and on both sides of it were men and sleds. Peter could see only dark outlines against the snow for no light was showing. But when he got close he saw that a lantern was lit, its beams carefully shielded by the backs of the men.

One of the backs belonged to Uncle Victor.

"Hi, Lars," he greeted his brother cheerfully. "So you've brought Peter! Good!"

"He can help," his father said.

"He can go with Olsen. He's ready to leave. You can help him pull his sled, Peter."

His father turned to him. "Watch where Ole is taking you, Peter. That's the place you'll want to remember."

"Yes, Father." Peter gave a tug to the rope of the sled. It didn't move.

"It's heavy!"

"Heavy! I should say it is." Ole took up the rope. "It's a hundred and seventy thousand kroner. Your Uncle Victor would say forty thousand dollars."

Peter didn't care what Uncle Victor would say. "One hundred seventy thousand kroner in that sack!" He couldn't believe it.

They followed the railroad siding in the direction he and his father had come. Then they took a trail that led downhill for a distance. After a time they came to a dense part of the woods.

"Father said we were going to a cave," Peter asked Ole, "what cave?"

"Wait. You'll see."

Peter was mindful of his father's words to watch where he went and be able to return without help. Now he found he was recognizing landmark after landmark. Here was the rock they called The Ship when they played. There was the tree that was rotted through. Here he was in the woods he had known since babyhood, but in all his life he'd never heard of a cave there.

"We must be going a long ways off," he said. "I never heard of a cave anywhere near."

Ole grinned. "I guess you didn't," he said. "It's one we made ourselves."

432

They came to a high wall of snow. There they stopped. Ole led him past the wall and around its end. Now Peter could think of no part of the forest like this, where a wall stood as high as a man. And yet all the things near it were familiar — The Ship and the tree.

Then he guessed that the wall, like the cave, had been built by the men. When they drew the sled around it, he found himself blinking in the lights of lanterns and flashlights.

He was in a cave, indeed. In it were a dozen men and there was room for many more.

"You made it?" Peter was staggered.

"Not all," Ole explained. "Behind those stacks is a wall of stone that slopes so you could stand under it in a heavy rain and not get wet."

"I know. Thor's Rock. But it used to be open on every side."

"We closed it in with blocks of ice."

The men in the cave greeted Ole and Peter. Peter knew them all. There were Helga's father and Nanson, the sail maker, and Dr. Aker and Mr. Anders, the schoolmaster, among them. Three of the others rushed forward to remove the heavy brown sack from Ole's sled. Peter saw them rip it open and noted with surprise that it contained a number of smaller packages, each the size and shape of a building brick. These were counted carefully and listed on a paper Mr. Anders carried.

"Seventy-two, seventy-three, seventy-four," Dr. Aker was counting aloud. Later the doctor reached "thirteen hundred."

"Thirteen hundred of those bricks?" Peter asked Ole.

"Yes, and each of them contains eighteen and a half pounds of gold bullion — over twenty thousand kroner."

"Here comes the rest of it," someone said as Uncle Victor and Peter's father came in together. "Every last pound's been removed."

CHAPTER SIX

The next night saw Norway blacked out from one end to the other. Over a thousand miles and not a light. Windows were draped in black and people were cautioned not to allow so much as a candle ray to show outside their houses.

That was the night of April eighth.

Peter would have liked to go out to see what Riswyk

434

looked like without a light anywhere. But that was impossible. Even though there was not yet a war, his father was leaving that night to join the regiment to which his class in military college belonged.

"You're the man of the house, Peter," his father told him. "You must look after your mother and the little ones."

Peter had expected to do this without being told.

"What about the gold?" he asked his father.

"Uncle Victor will tell you what to do. You may not need to do anything at all. There may be no trouble after all."

Some of the men of Riswyk had already left town. Nanson, the sail maker, had gone and Michael Berg's father and many more. Mr. Anders, the schoolmaster, too. With him away, that day had been a holiday as would be the morrow and every other day. But what was the good of a holiday like that? No one wanted to play.

After supper his father seemed to be waiting for some message. It never came. He kept taking his watch out to see the time although there were clocks everywhere you could look. His train did not go until midnight and the sleigh to take him to the station would not come for hours yet.

When the hour finally came for Mr. Lundstrom to leave, they all tried to be cheerful. Peter's mother even started to make a little joke. Old Per Garson shuffled in for the bags and then the door closed and blotted out Peter's father in the black of the outside.

Mrs. Lundstrom turned to Peter in a flood of tears. He tried to comfort her but there was little he could say.

Four hours after that, German parachute troops landed

in Norway, and through all the ports clear into the Arctic Circle, soldiers and marines pored out of merchant ships in the harbors. There were even grey-clad Nazi soldiers on the beach at Riswyk Fiord. It was Uncle Victor who brought the news in the morning.

"On your sleds, children," he directed. "There's not a day to lose."

CHAPTER SEVEN

"Aren't you in danger, Uncle Victor?" Peter asked. "Couldn't they take you prisoner?"

They were in the living room of Peter's home. Mrs. Lundstrom had taken Lovisa and Bunny and had gone to get some of the older children who were to help.

"Per Garson's on the watch. He'll tell me if anyone comes and I'll slip out the back and down the slope. They'll be good skiers to catch me."

"But they could shoot."

Uncle Victor only shrugged.

"Do you know where the British and French have laid their mines?" Peter hoped the answer would be yes. Otherwise what would be the use of taking the gold out of the cave if Uncle Victor couldn't sail away with it?

"Only partly."

"Well, why do we take the gold down the mountain if you can't sail away? I should think it'd be safer where it is."

"Peter, it's not right you should question anyone in authority," his uncle spoke irritably. "But I'll tell you why it's important for you children to be seen on your sleds today. In the future, however, you're not to question."

436

"Yes, Uncle Victor," Peter spoke meekly.

"Peter," his uncle continued, "The reason you must be on your sleds today near the fiord is to accustom the Germans to seeing you there. If they see you today and every day, they won't suspect anything unusual. But if, all at once, you started going in the direction of the Snake, they'd be stupid geese not to know something was going on."

Peter hadn't thought of that. How smart Uncle Victor was!

Victor Lundstrom thought he heard a noise. But it was not the heavy tread of marching men but the light quick steps of children, those who were to be seen on their sleds around the town or down at the Snake. Today, only four of them would take gold to the Snake but after that there would be many more. Mrs. Lundstrom had gone first for Michael and Helga; here they were, and Lovisa was with them.

"Now we can get started," Uncle Victor spoke. "Listen carefully while I tell you what you're to do. I may have to leave any minute so pay attention. If there's anything I miss, Fru Lundstrom or Per Garson will tell you."

There wasn't a sound from any of the four.

"What I'm going to say is of the gravest importance. On you, to an extent, depends the welfare of your country. If you do what you're told and do it right, you'll be helping countless Norwegians — not only the soldiers in the army but the people at home."

Eyes were bright at this mention of a chance to help their country.

"Peter will take you to a place where we've hidden

thirteen tons of gold bullion — money, you know, that's not been made into coins. Now, you are to take the bullion from its hiding place to the Snake where it will be loaded on my boat and taken to America to be kept safe for Norway.

"Peter will take you to the hiding place. After that it's up to you. You'll have to find your own way back there later. What is more, you'll have to show the other children. So watch how you get there. Now in Riswyk School there are thirty-eight pupils, we think, old enough for this. These will divide into teams of nine, a captain and a squad of eight."

"That leaves two over," Peter spoke.

"Right," his uncle answered. "You and Michael will each have ten. Your mother has made up the teams. You four are captains and you must take the ones assigned to you, and no quarreling. And if any differences arise, Peter's the one to settle them. You must do as he says. Of course, your teams will split up on the way. You'll go in twos and threes. For if they counted nine and ten each time, they'd know something was up."

He stopped for a minute and then went on. "It's getting late and I've something very important to tell you. And that is, under no circumstances must you speak one word to a stranger. Not a syllable. Not so much as yes or no or good-day. Understand?"

The four of them nodded.

"Now today Peter will take you to the cave where we hid the gold. Per Garson will go along to load each sled. You'll each be given seventy-five pounds of bullion, packed in flat bricks and each of you will take four bricks. These

438

you'll sit on or lie on when you ride 'belly-grinder.'

"When you get to the Snake this afternoon you're to look for a place where there are two fallen trees. They are pretty well buried under the snow, but you'll find them because you're Norwegians. You know such things. Between these trees you're to bury your bricks in the snow. Over the top of each pile you'll build a snowman. When I come out at night with Rolls, my mate, I'll only have to find the snowmen.

"Now about the return trip. You start back up the mountain to the Holm's farm where you'll spend the night. They have room for dozens. The girls will stay in the house and the boys in the barn. You will get a warm supper and breakfast next day. Then you'll come back here. But it won't matter if you are late because you are to rest that day and start back to the Snake the next day. The way we've planned it is for two teams to go one day and the two others the next. That will give you a day to rest up, or almost a day."

Per Garson stuck his head in the door.

"Jan from the sailyard comes," he said. "He thinks the Germans are starting up the mountain."

Uncle Victor jumped up.

He slipped out of the room and through the kitchen to the outside. They could hear the whiz of his skis on the hard snow.

CHAPTER EIGHT

"Well, what are we waiting for?" Michael asked. "You know the way to this cave or whatever it is." He turned to Peter.

"Right." Peter jumped up. "We're supposed to be seen near the beach today so we'll have to get started.

"We'd better be off to the cave for our loads. It's just us today. Tomorrow or the next day we will take the others."

"Beat you to the sleds," Helga spoke.

There was a scramble for the door. On the way, buttons were done up and zippers made magic silver seams down the fronts of windbreakers that had been loosened when the children came indoors.

"Per Garson," Peter remembered. "He's to be at the cave to load the sleds."

He ran to the kitchen to look for him. He was not there. Peter opened the kitchen door. Outside on the snow he saw a strange sight.

Per Garson was racing madly around and around on skis. Old and bent, he was nevertheless skiing with the grace of an Olympic entrant. He swooped and sailed. He would loop and then would take off in a jump. Peter thought he had lost his senses. Then he saw there was a design in the crazy pattern he was making in the snow.

"He's covering Uncle Victor's tracks," he guessed. For Per had already been down the slope and had made cat steps all the way down to the hollow at its base.

"We're going now, Per Garson," he called.

"Ja, I go too." He made a mad leap and landed exactly at Peter's side. "I see you by the woods. You know how to go? Sure?"

Peter had not the least doubt where to go. He told Per Garson so.

They all knew the way to Thor's Rock, so Peter found he wasn't much needed as a guide. Never mind. After they

440

got there he'd have to show them how to go around the wall of snow into the cave.

They trudged through the woods taking all possible short cuts. When they got to Thor's Rock and the place where the cave had been, Peter got the surprise of his life.

There was no cave.

CHAPTER NINE

Peter was sure he had not been mistaken. But here was Thor's Rock and there was no cave anywhere that he could see.

There had been a high wall of snow in front of it, he remembered. But look as he would, all he could see were young pines.

"Ole said it was where the rock curved so you could stand in a heavy rain and not get wet. That's here," he told the others. But for all they searched they could find neither wall nor cave.

It was Lovisa who spied Per Garson's brown face framed in the branches of a young fir.

"You said you could get here without help," he teased Peter when they came close. "It's here all the time."

"There weren't any trees the other night." Peter felt ashamed. He had been so sure he knew just where to find the cave but he had to be shown after all.

"These we fixed to make it seem more real," Per Garson explained. When Peter looked again he saw that a strip of evergreens made a narrow corridor in front of the wall.

"You made it since the night I was here — since the night before last?"

"Ja. Ole and some others. They came yesterday and finished before the blackout."

Peter was still unbelieving. But sure enough, behind the trees was the wall of snow and back of that the cave.

Per Garson led them around shrubbery to the entrance. He went at once to the end where a stack of brown bricks rose up like a garden wall.

"Gold," Peter whispered to Michael.

"That? Gold?" Peter agreed with Michael that it was hard to believe that each of those brown bricks was money enough to buy an airplane.

Per Garson began lifting down the bricks.

He laid four of them, side by side, on Peter's sled. Then he went to a pile of rough brown sacks like potato sacks. He carried one of these to Peter's sled. He folded it twice and laid it over the rectangle of bricks.

"Next the rope." He produced a new clothesline and with it began lashing the sack and bricks to the sled. Over and over went the rope. Then he drew out a long knife and cut the clothesline.

"Now I show you how to untie the rope," Per Garson announced. "When you get to the Snake you first look for a pair of trees that are fallen and covered with snow. They're 'bout two hundred feet apart. Be sure you find them for that's the place your uncle thinks is safest. Now you untie the knots. And so. And so!

"Can you do it? Try." He laced the bricks onto the sled again and Peter tried to untie them. He was clumsy at first. Instead of openings he made knots. But after a time

442

he learned how to untie the rope.

When it came Helga's turn she gave one quick pull and the rope was dangling from her hand.

"Good. You learn things fast," Per Garson praised.

Each of them had to prove he knew how to unload the sleds.

"All right, then. Off with you. You bring back the ropes and sacks. These we need again," Per Garson instructed. "For your pockets, here." He handed each a flat parcel. "Your lunch. For supper you go to Holms' farm where you'll get plenty good hot meal."

He led the way to the opening. "Now I think it's time you go."

CHAPTER TEN

"Come on, Michael. Race you to the lookout." Peter wiped his mouth on the back of his mitten.

The lookout was where Peter and Michael, Helga and Lovisa had seen Uncle Victor the day he had so strangely returned to Norway. But now, when the four companions reached that point, it was not to be the scene of a snow battle and all the fun that went with it. Instead there were solemnness and silence, and Lovisa's blue eyes were round with fright.

A German freighter was at anchor in the fiord. Steaming up, she might be about to sail. On the beach that lay between the Atlantic Ocean and Riswyk Fiord, there were hundreds of grey-clad soldiers and there were others on the narrow strip of land between the big fiord and the small one they called the Snake. They were unloading enormous supplies because the snow was covered with bales, boxes, crates, and drums. Rifles were stacked in neat rows, and up and down the beach in front of the fishing pier, sentries were goose-stepping while their companions worked.

"Whew!" Peter drew off his cap to wipe his forehead.

And now Lovisa was not the only one to be afraid. Fear looked out of all eyes.

It was Helga who made them brave again.

"I'm not afraid of any goose step!" She shook her curls from under her hood.

"Come on, then." Peter straightened his shoulders. He drew his sled away from the others. "Let's go."

"Look!" Michael could not take his eyes off the beach. "Soldiers marching right up our sled track. How'll we get down?"

"We'll have to meet them sometime," Helga said. "It might as well be now as later."

"Right," Peter answered. "Uncle Victor said they were to see us today on our sleds. If we sail right into them they'll see us for sure."

He fell face down on his sled. With a shove he began the descent to the beach.

"Maybe they're not coming all the way," Peter told himself. "Maybe they'll turn aside."

But when he rounded the slope's last bend he had no such hope. Directly in front was a company of grey-clad, goose-stepping soldiers.

Peter had no way to stop himself and now he found he was headed right into the middle of them. He let out a war whoop, a warning he was coming. But the Germans were directly in his path. He didn't see how he could avoid knocking them down like ten pins.

Down he flew, faster, faster.

At one hundred yards he swerved toward the bank to avoid knocking down a whole row of men.

A voice was barking a command in German and the company took three steps to the side and out of Peter's path.

His swerve drove him into the bank and stopped him.

He raised his eyes from the snow. He was looking into the smiling face of a German infantry captain.

"I turn my men aside." He spoke in Norwegian. "It is not right that we spoil your sledding. When I was a boy I liked nothing better than sledding."

CHAPTER ELEVEN

The blood rushed out of Peter's head. He was certainly dizzy. He closed his eyes. When he opened them again, he was looking up the slope at the heels of the last row of German goose-steppers.

Michael and the girls joined him on the bank.

"Well, what do you know about that?" Michael was open-eyed with wonder.

There were more German soldiers to pass before they could make the bend into the farther fiord they called the Snake. To these they would likewise have to come close.

Nearest were the sentries that patrolled between the stacked rifles and the road down from the mountains. The sled would pass within a few feet of where they walked.

"If Uncle Victor wants them to see us today, he gets what he wants," Lovisa pointed out. "They'd have to be blind to miss us."

"Uncle Victor didn't know it would be as bad as this," Peter grumbled. "He didn't say they'd be marching on the road."

On their sleds again, and the last mile before they would turn the bend by the cliff that hid the entrance to the Snake.

The sentries were taking their stiff-kneed walks beside the rifles. The other Germans went on with their work of

446

unloading the supplies. Nobody so much as looked at the children on their sleds.

When Peter went directly in front of the first sentry, he saw only a blank face. There was not so much as a look to show if he was pleased or displeased.

Beyond the sentry Peter saw some soldiers dragging a heavy tarpaulin over the snow. One of them looked in his direction. Under the round cap and fringe of yellow hair he saw the bluest eyes he had ever seen in his life. They seemed to say that he, too, would like to be sled riding.

Peter breathed a sigh of relief and dug his heels into the snow for a fresh start.

The cliff that hid the Snake was just ahead. Beyond it they would be safe from curious eyes. There only remained to find the two fallen trees and to bury the gold and build the snowmen.

In the Snake, Peter stopped to get his breath. His sled was terribly, terribly heavy.

The others were close on his heels. They, too, seemed tired. Even Helga crept along, dragging her crushing load of gold.

"But where's Uncle Victor's boat?" Peter searched both sides of the stream with his eyes. There was no boat on the black water.

"The trees!" Lovisa's eyes fell on the flat stretch that was closed in at two ends by long ridges of snow.

"Here's one of them." She poked her arm to the elbow into the crusted white. Then she ran through the deep untrodden stretch. "And here," she called, "is the other."

The four of them began burrowing in the snow. Four

pits were made and into each went the brown-covered bricks. Then four snowmen rose over the bricks. Each stood guard over a mound of gold worth more than eighty thousand kroner — twenty thousand dollars. So, between the trees, eighty thousand dollars in gold bullion lay buried in the snow.

"We've done it!" Peter exulted. "We passed them and they never guessed."

"We did it! We did it!" Lovisa thumped Helga on the back and then threw her arms around Peter.

And now none of them was tired.

CHAPTER TWELVE

Peter would have liked to tell Uncle Victor about the events of that day. But Uncle Victor and his boat were nowhere to be seen.

It was strange, for Peter knew the *Cleng Peerson* was somewhere in the Snake. But look where he would, all he could see was the black rushing water, the bobbing ice cakes and the snow that covered ground and trees alike.

It was getting late. They had to get to the Holms' farm before the blackout. It was three miles up the road from the beach. They'd have to hurry.

It was twilight by the time the little band turned into the farmyard.

At the farm kitchen Michael pounded on the door.

"Who is it?" a frightened voice called out.

When Michael gave their names, there was a scuffle inside. They had to be recognized before the door would be opened.

"But come in, come in," the farmwife called. And Peter thought that for all the sadness of that terrible day, there was still a cheerfulness about the good brown face. That they had succeeded in carrying the gold past the Nazi sentries seemed to bring hope for Norway.

"You had no trouble?" Her husband came out of a dim corner.

Their supper was even now being dished into great earthenware bowls. Peter thought he had never smelled anything so good.

"First they eat, Papa. Then they talk." Fru Holm and her servant bustled back and forth between the fire and the table. "Draw up now and eat, you brave children. You must be famished."

The children fell upon the food like puppies around a basin of milk. It disappeared like snow when brought into the house. Fru Holm and Marie, the servant, were kept busy walking back and forth between the table and the stove refilling the bowls.

"So you got through all right?" The rough old farmer could not wait to hear their story.

Peter drew a long sigh of satisfaction. Never before had he felt so content. The warm food sent a glow to every part of his body.

"We fooled them, all right," he boasted. "They even turned out of our way. The captain said they didn't want to spoil our sledding."

They told him all that had happened, even to Lovisa's finding the fallen trees.

"But Uncle Victor's boat! It's not there." Peter was serious.

"You find the trees but not the boat," Herr Holm chided. "That's because your uncle wishes it so."

Herr Holm would have kept the children talking all night if his wife had let him.

"To bed with them. Their eyes are buttoned with sleep."

Peter remembered being led from the house to the barn but was aware of nothing else. The next thing he knew it was morning.

"Wake up, my little soldiers," the farmer was saying. "Hours ago I came by and did my milking and you heard not a sound."

Peter was grumpy at being aroused.

"But would you sleep till noon?" Herr Holm asked in surprise. "You have work to do."

Peter murmured, "Why do we have to be in such a hurry? We can get past those sentries any time."

"Ja, if the snow holds," Herr Holm spoke anxiously.

In alarm Peter jumped up.

"IF THE SNOW HOLDS!"

CHAPTER THIRTEEN

All that week and all the next there was a steady stream of children and sleds down the mountains. And every sled carried gold, sometimes as much as would equal twenty thousand dollars.

For the first time in the history of Riswyk, no one wanted to see spring come. Warm weather would bring the end of the snow and stop the sled trips. That far in the north snow lasted well into May, sometimes late May. But

450

the thaws could come any time now and, indeed, were looked for since winter had set in so early.

"If the snow holds" was the one thought in all the town. Could it stay long enough to get the whole thirteen tons of bullion to the Snake?

Three weeks of hard, hard sledding for the children and what was the result? Back in the cave Per Garson looked ruefully at the big stacks of bricks that remained. Why, they seemed hardly to have made a hole in them!

"How much more?" Peter kept asking him.

Well, he was no Mr. Anders, the schoolmaster. But as well as he could count, it would take another three weeks, maybe longer, to empty the cave.

At home Per Garson complained of his bones aching.

"I don't need any almanac to tell me when there'll be a change in the weather," he said.

"A change in the weather!" Peter's voice sounded high and excited. "What sort of change?"

But Per Garson only shook his grey head and said nothing.

After supper Per went out to bring in the kindling. He threw a big log on the fire. The curtains were drawn for the blackout. Their dark heavy folds showed not the tiniest brightness, not even a glint of reflection from the fire. The northern day had lengthened. It should have been twilight. So the darkness outside was all the more forbidding.

Peter went to the kitchen to get a drink of water. Per was busy locking the house for the night. When he had finished, he came back to the kitchen and carefully shielding the light so it would not be seen outside, peered through the window. But there was nothing to be found out about this blackness. He stepped out of doors.

Peter followed him. He sensed more trouble or sorrow in the old man. Per Garson shoved out his hand. Clearly Per Garson had no intention of including the younger master in what was going on in his busy mind.

But when next he spoke, Peter found out what he wanted to know. He only spoke one word but that word spelled catastrophe.

"Rain," he said.

CHAPTER FOURTEEN

Rain. But that couldn't be.

The children couldn't go down to the Snake with their bricks of gold if the rain melted the snow and spoiled their sled track.

"It could be snow," Peter told Per Garson.

"No. Rain," the servant said flatly. "See for yourself."

But Peter had no need to stretch out his hand for the raindrops. They were on his hair and in his face. The rain had begun to fall steadily.

When Peter went back to the living room, the rain was pounding against the windows. Lovisa was putting Bunny to bed. She always told him a story before he went to sleep. Ordinarily the sound of her voice, and sometimes his, would be heard in the living room. But tonight the storm shut out everything but itself.

The rain kept drumming down. When Lovisa came in to say good night, it seemed less heavy. There was a new noise outside.

The wind seemed to have caught up with its sleep and

to have shaken off the stupor that had held it all day. Now it blew a loud roar. It tried to get into the house that had been well sealed against the northern winter. The only entrance was by the chimney and down that it came with a shower of sparks that blew out on a rug. Peter was kept busy stamping them out.

Per Garson came in to bank the fire before he would go to bed. Instead of his slow shuffling gait, there was a new sprightliness to him.

"Ja, my bones. They tell me when there'll be a change in the weather. The rain turns to snow, my shoulder says. By midnight, all will be as you've never seen it, something you've not seen in your time." He spoke happily but there was just a trace of scorn in his tone. It was scorn for all who had not lived as many years as he. "Tomorrow you will see something you know nothing about. For this late in April — a blizzard!"

Per Garson was right.

The next morning the world was a raging white fury.

The Lundstrom house rocked through the night as the storm battered and pounded and pummeled. The wind seeped in through the tight fitting double windows. It entered through cracks and crevices that no one knew existed. It seemed to force its way through openings that had been puttied and sealed with the greatest care. It tossed ancient ashes of the many fireplaces into little whirlpools of dust in all the rooms. By morning the kitchen had a spread of gritty black dirt over its usually spotless boards.

There was no question of going to the Snake or anywhere else. For three days the people of Riswyk kept

453

to their homes. The postman seemed to be a person of the past. No one knew what had become of him. On the third day of the blizzard, Dr. Aker started out to see one of his sick. But the way he walked backward in the wind and battled to keep his coat from being blown off, and dug his sealskin earmuffs into the collar of his coat, was enough to make people turn back to their own fires with a feeling of thankfulness that they didn't have to go out.

But what of the Germans? How were they standing this storm, the like of which only the very old could remember?

Well, what of the Germans? Nothing could be done for them anyway. And since nobody had invited them to come up to the Arctic Circle to share a Norway blizzard, they would have to manage the best they could. Their buildings were erected hurriedly and without the many inventive devices the Norwegians used to secure their own homes against the cold.

"If their barracks blow over, they'll be good and mad," Lovisa chuckled. She was enjoying being snowbound, as was every member of the Lundstrom household, including four-year-old Bunny, who had missed his brother and sister on their trips away from home.

CHAPTER FIFTEEN

Throughout Riswyk was a flurry of snow-shoveling the day the blizzard subsided. It commenced from almost the earliest light.

On the way to the cave, Peter found the snow knee-deep in places. He would sink into it but his light sled rode on top or would drop but a few inches below the crest. His team had the rare pleasure of making fresh footprints in the white world of the forest.

Only the animals had preceded them, for Per Garson's skis cut across the hills where feet and sleds could not follow. So the new snow showed only the stars of small animal paws and now and then a round spot where a rabbit may have sat on his haunches.

After a time Peter saw ski marks and noted that several pairs of snow shoes had traveled into the forest that morning.

He had an uneasy feeling. The ski trail was not Per Garson's for he would have come from an entirely different direction. Near the cave he picked up another trail that seemed to come in a great loop from behind the evergreens at the cave entrance. Then, farther on, the loop sent off a shoot the way a branch grows out of a tree.

Peter was cautious about approaching the cave. He was not going to walk into a trap. When he first came on the ski trail he warned his team to silence. So the ten of them moved over the snow as quietly as possible. Near the cave he lined his boys and girls behind a thick clump of bushes that the new snow had made into a solid blot of white. Leaving them to guard his sled he quietly followed the trail into the cave.

He would not have been surprised to see grey-green Nazi uniforms inside. But instead, there was only Per Garson wiping his forehead on his sleeve.

Peter's stealthy approach was not lost on old Per.

"So you was frightened, eh? You think to come on the Germans? I should have told you it was only us."

"There are snowshoe trails too."

"Na, na. Not to worry about them. Miles and Ole made them. One hour more, then there'll be trails all ways you can look, of snowshoes, of skis, and of just plain feet. No one could find the way here by following the marks you boys and girls make with your boots and sleds."

"Well, I didn't know," Peter said. "I knew you had come across the valley but I didn't think one pair of skis could make so many trails. And I didn't know about the snowshoes."

"I make the many ski trails myself. I make more when

456

you go off." Per drew out a blue bandana handkerchief and wiped his running eyes. "You thought the Germans knew already about the cave? Not yet, but we must be careful or they'll learn."

"So you and Ole and Miles are making a lot of trails so they can't follow?" Peter had to admire the forethought behind this.

"And why not? Without them, what could be easier than to know everything. As plain as the noses on their faces would be the way. From all the houses come footprints and sled marks. They all go to one place, to the woods. So, if you're a German what do you do? You follow the tracks and they lead you to a cave that is no cave at all, only what was put here by someone with something to hide. Well, what is there to hide? Nothing but these brown bricks. And what are these bricks for? They're not to build a wall. One doesn't wrap such bricks in brown covers. And they're not for the fire. It takes only a minute to slit open the covers. And what do you find? Why just plain gold, gold enough to pave a street!

"Where's your sled?" he asked sharply.

Peter replied with a scurry through the door.

"It's all right, kids," he called. "Come on, and bring my sled."

The storm hadn't destroyed the German barracks. This the children could see when they reached the lookout.

Beaten by the wind and lashed by the sea, they still stood trim beside the fishing pier. One of the Nazi warehouses had suffered some damage for a crew of workers was busy repairing its roof. The big fiord had been on a rampage because there was wreckage along its

457

shore. But whether it was German or Norse property that had been carried away, the children couldn't tell.

"The Nazis didn't know what to make of the storm," Helga decided when her team reached the point where the beach lay spread before her. Peter's team was already there. His boys and girls had lunched and were about to start down the mountain to the Snake. "They didn't know whether they'd be drowned like the people in the Flood in the Bible," she said. "They wouldn't have had time to build an ark."

In any event, being housebound for three days hadn't improved the Commandant's disposition. Peter could see that from where he was watching. The head officer was striding up and down before the barracks. Hands behind his back, he would now and again lift a leather riding crop to shake it at someone who displeased him. Even up at the lookout they could hear the snarl of his voice.

"He's telling them they are stupid as Norwegians." Helga had studied a little German and was translating for her team. "He says that the people of this country have better sense than they, for they build their houses for the crazy wild weather in this part of the world."

"He must think we have blizzards like this all the time," Peter cut in.

Helga went on. "He says that if he'd been there when the barracks were started, they wouldn't have had all this trouble."

"I guess the storm did them more damage than we know," Peter concluded as he gathered his team together for the final push to the Snake.

458

Down on the beach Peter had his first brush with the Commandant.

"Big boy like you, playing with a sled!" he taunted. "In Germany you'd be one of Hitler's Youth. You'd learn to march. You'd be on your way to being a soldier!"

"Don't want to learn to march. Don't want to be a soldier like you," Peter said under his breath.

"I could use a boy like you," the Commandant went on. "To polish my boots and bring me shaving water. What about it, boy? Would you like to come live here in the barracks?"

Peter, of course, made no reply. The Commandant strode over and stood directly above him. Seated on his sled he began to be afraid the officer would yank him up by his coat.

"Speak, boy. Are you dumb?"

But Peter had no word to say. He was too frightened to speak, even if it were not forbidden.

"Dumb stupid cattle, you Norwegians." The Commandant turned on his heel. "You deserve to lose your country. You're too brainless to defend it. But we'll put an end to this sled riding. There's no sense in a whole country growing up in ignorance. On Monday you go back to school."

CHAPTER SIXTEEN

Peter chuckled to himself.

The Commandant didn't know that Mr. Anders, the schoolmaster, had joined the Norwegian Army, had gone away to fight.

There would be no school, no matter what the Commandant ordered.

But that was reckoning without that resolute individual. There would be school if a German officer had to teach it, the grown folks had been told. When they first heard of the new order they sent a committee to tell the Commandant about Mr. Anders, and such was his reply.

When Peter came back from the Holm's farm the next day he saw German soldiers posting notices throughout the town.

One of the soldiers was the blue-eyed private Peter had noticed the first day the Germans had come to Norway. He looked wistful then, and today seemed sadder than ever. It was as if he hated sending the children back to their books.

"Hello," he said shyly in Peter's own language. But, of course, Peter could not reply. And seeing him close, Peter thought he looked younger than the others. He would be twenty or twenty-one at the most, Peter fancied.

To the children the German uniform was a common enough sight. But among the grown folks it caused consternation. In truth, the Germans had stayed by themselves on the beach near their barracks and only in rare instances had come up the mountain to the town.

But if their appearance caused a commotion among the townspeople of Riswyk, they did not show it. They chose to act as if they did not know the Germans were there. The German soldiers stared frankly, but the Norwegians walked along the streets with their heads in the air. They finished their errands hurriedly and went to their homes and stayed there. Then the minute the soldiers marched out of town they began coming out of their houses.

They gathered around the notices to study the new orders. There was a little procession to the pastry shop, the *konditeri*. Peter saw his mother coming out of their house. He stacked his sled against the wall and ran to join her.

"The notice, Mother. You've read it? It says school must open on Monday."

"Yes, I know." Mrs. Lundstrom quickened her steps.

Inside the *konditeri*, a little knot of people had already gathered. They had come to discuss this latest order. But there was no need for anyone to say aloud the question that was first in their thoughts.

With school reopened, how are we going to get the gold to the Snake?

Mrs. Lundstrom felt they should be careful about discussing it and warned the others to caution. The soldiers had barely left the town. They might return.

"I'll take a dozen of your raisin cookies, Fru Flack," she said. "*And do be careful,*" she was saying when the door actually did open and in came a Nazi recruit, "that you wrap them carefully," she finished lamely.

The soldier was the blue-eyed private who had said "hello" to Peter. He only wanted a *smorsbord*. He chose one of the open egg and herring sandwiches and asked for a cup of coffee. Then he took a seat at one of the tables by the wall, his back to the women at the counter. Fru Flack brought him his order.

He began to eat his *smorsbord* slowly at first and then more rapidly. With his entrance, the many busy tongues

461

were stilled. Not a single syllable had been spoken the entire time he was there. When his own words died away there was a complete silence. As if he realized that all eyes were on his back, he ate his sandwich and tried to drink the steaming coffee. But it was too hot. After a couple of mouthfuls he pushed aside the cup, rose and took his leave.

"You see?" Mrs. Lundstrom stretched out her hands. "I don't want to spoil your day's sales, Fru Flack, but I think it would be better if we talked about this in our homes."

Peter picked up the box of pastries his mother had bought and followed her out of the door. But she did not go home as she had advised the others to do. She walked along the diagonal of the town square to its opposite side and beyond to the home of Dr. Aker.

She lifted the brass knocker. Marta, the housekeeper, smiled in welcome. Yes, the doctor was home. Would Fru Lundstrom and Peter come in?

They entered the doctor's study, cheerful with its chintz-covered furniture and shining hearth brasses. Dr. Aker gave them a cordial welcome.

Mrs. Lundstrom dropped into a deep chair the doctor drew up for her. Peter sat down beside her on a stool.

"And how are you, Doctor?" she asked as he fussed with the fire.

"Never better, Fru Lundstrom. I think the blizzard did a lot of good to my old bones. I tell you I feel spry."

"Is there any sickness in the town, Doctor?" Mrs. Lundstrom asked.

"I must say, Fru Lundstrom, Riswyk has never had a healthier winter. I think the long cold is beneficial. It seems to have killed the germs."

"But I saw you going out during the blizzard. I thought someone must be very sick to get you out on such a day."

"It was only to see Granny Gohla. The poor soul gets pretty lonesome living by herself. She's always so glad for company. So I make it a point of seeing her twice a week. It was my day to go and I didn't want to disappoint her."

Peter's mother returned to the subject of illnesses but the doctor disclaimed any for the town. "I tell you, Fru Lundstrom, a doctor has a hard time getting along in Riswyk. A healthier community you won't find anywhere on earth."

"You've been out today, Doctor? You read the notice?"

463

"Yes, I read it when I went for my walk. A good thing too, I thought. It's best to keep the people busy, especially the children."

"But, Doctor Aker, going back to school will stop —" Peter began.

"Peter!" his mother silenced him. But there was something in Dr. Aker's face that told them he understood what Peter started to say.

"I'd quite forgotten about that," he said. "I'd forgotten what reopening the school will mean. After school is too late, I suppose."

The wood cracked in the fireplace.

"Wait a minute, Fru Lundstrom, you were asking about the sick. Now I'm not sure I told you the whole truth. You see, we doctors don't like to alarm the townsfolk but in the winter one can always expect some sickness."

"And widespread sickness amounts to an epidemic," Mrs. Lundstrom added.

"And during an epidemic one always closes the school," Dr. Aker finished.

An epidemic! Yes, if they had to make one.

CHAPTER SEVENTEEN

A new disease found its way into Riswyk.

It attacked only the smallest children, the ones who had not yet started to school.

They were covered with red spots from head to foot.

But the disease differed from the better-known rashes like diphtheria and scarlet fever. The patient had no high temperature. His appetite could be just as good as before the rash. Indeed, Dr. Aker did not insist that the children

464

stop eating. He only said they must stay indoors while covered with the red spots.

"What is this new disease?" the people asked each other. Dr. Aker told them a name of many syllables. They could never remember it so they called it the plague.

"German measles" was Peter's name for it and with reason. He had been in Dr. Aker's study when he packed his bag before going to visit Bunny, the first of his patients. Peter had seen him put in a bottle of red disinfectant that he used for cuts and bruises. Cotton on the end of a toothpick made a good paint brush. Bunny Lundstrom had as thick a coat of spots as the leopard of his Noah's ark.

Bunny was told he was quarantined. He had no idea what that meant until his mother explained that Peter and Lovisa would go live at Helga Thomsen's house while Bunny had those spots. So quarantined meant that Peter and Lovisa had to go away from home, he decided.

The three-year-old Dal twins were sick too. And Ole's two-year-old son, Little Ole. But as none of these had big brothers or sisters, Peter and Lovisa had the distinction of being the only ones turned out of their homes while the disease raged.

School? Well school was out of the question during an epidemic. Dr. Aker went to the Commandant to explain why his order could not be carried out. Some of the children, he told, were dangerously ill. It might be fatal for the whole town, for the Germans themselves, if the disease was not checked at once. To open the school would be a sure way to spread it.

On his return from the beach, Dr. Aker found Mrs.

Lundstrom and Peter waiting in his office for news of his interview with the Commandant and of how the doctor found himself trapped by making his plague so unusual.

" 'How long will this disease last?' the Commandant asked me. But I could not tell. 'It's a new thing with us,' I said, 'a disease I've never treated before. It could run nine days like measles or thirty days like scarlet fever. But we're taking every precaution. We're isolating and disinfecting.'

"When I said it could spread to the troops on the beach I thought he looked white. He sent for the German army doctor, a civil enough fellow named Metzger. This Metzger began asking me a long list of questions. Were the tongues coated? Was there undue perspiration? Was there a high fever? He seemed surprised with my answers and none too well satisfied. Then he nearly had me when he proposed something I hadn't thought about at all.

" 'I'll take a look at one of your cases, Doctor. I'll go back with you when you go,' he said to me.

"Well, he had me there," Dr. Aker went on. "It was the last thing I expected. It hadn't occurred to me that an army doctor would be called in for civilian illness, and if so, that he would insist on seeing for himself. One look by him and the epidemic would be over. Those spots might deceive an ordinary person but they'd never fool a doctor."

"Yes, and that would arouse suspicion," Mrs. Lundstrom said. "Maybe they don't suspect us of anything yet. But if they learn we have a reason for keeping the school closed, they'll begin to ask what it is and possibly find out."

466

Peter was open-eyed as the doctor went on with his story.

"Well, I had to think fast," he said. "I couldn't behave as if I didn't want him for that would surely make them inquire why he couldn't see one of the patients. So I said, 'There's nothing I would like better, Doctor. I'm distressed at how quickly this sickness spreads. I'll appreciate another opinion. For it seems to travel like wildfire. I'm not sure but what it could spread to your whole camp here.'

"I thought the Commandant drew away from me when I started to tell of the disease. He acted as if I could give it to him just by being there. But now I saw him sort of jump. But Dr. Metzger didn't seem afraid. 'If it's as fast a thing as that, I would indeed like to see one of your cases,' he said.

"The Commandant, however, had a different idea. My words about how it might travel to the whole camp had struck home. He made a sign to the doctor. They went into a little room nearby. I could hear only a buzz of talk and now and again some words I could understand. Dr. Metzger was trying to win his permission to visit Riswyk and see the new rash for himself but the other was firm.

" 'Our men were up there, yesterday,' I overheard the Commandant say. 'You'll have all you can do to see they don't come down with this disease.' He said some other things I didn't hear but I caught some words to the effect that they were living in a heathenish, outlandish place where a blizzard could blow up out of a calm, and that the diseases were probably as freakish and unexpected as the weather. The best course for them to follow was to

467

have as little as possible to do with the people. When they came back to me, the doctor spoke.

" 'It will not be necessary for me to see any of your patients,' he said. 'Continue with the treatment you've begun and keep a careful quarantine.' Then he gave me a long list of orders about sanitation, and burning waste, and so on. When he finished, the Commandant said, 'Remember, if this disease spreads to our army, you'll be held accountable.'

"I could give him my word that none of his soldiers would take the disease."

Mrs. Lundstrom and Peter had to laugh. Nothing but the red disinfectant and the cotton-tipped toothpicks could spread Bunny's strange disease.

"He waved his hand at me to tell me I was dismissed," Dr. Aker went on. " 'I've taken the liberty of closing the school,' I told him. 'I've also ordered all healthy children to stay outdoors whenever possible. There's nothing like fresh air to check an epidemic,' I said."

So the children's task could go on in spite of all that had happened to prevent it.

Bunny recovered and Lovisa and Peter were allowed to go back to their home. So it was a short-lived disease, the townsfolk decided. Like three-day measles. But there were enough new cases to keep the school closed.

So the gold kept spilling down the mountains, thousands and thousands of kroners of bullion every day.

Two teams would go out one morning and two teams the following day. On every sled was more gold than any of the children had ever seen before.

One day Helga's team got the start on Peter's. When he

468

reached the Snake her team was already there. She seemed buried in her own thoughts. When Peter approached she hardly answered his wave of greeting.

When he began unloading his sled she came over beside him and dropped on her knees in the snow. "Peter," she whispered, "I'm frightened. I heard something."

"Heard something? What?"

"Listen," she warned, still in whispers. "There it is again. It's even louder here than over by my snowman."

"I don't hear anything."

"Look! Something moved in the bushes!" She pointed to the far side of the fiord.

They ran in the direction she pointed. They pushed through the snow-hung brush but were stopped by the black water at their feet. They were unable to cross the angry rushing stream to the far side where the snow made a thick screen over the heavier shrubbery.

"If we could only get over, we could see the prints in the snow."

"Are we being watched?" Peter asked.

"I don't know. For the last week I've felt eyes on me every time I've turned around."

CHAPTER EIGHTEEN

Uncle Victor would have to be warned if someone were spying at the Snake. But Peter had no way of finding him. If his boat were hidden by camouflage, covered by trees and snow to make it hard to see, it might also be concealed by one of the bends of the twisted stream.

It would be useless to search for the *Cleng*, he knew.

Besides, it would be downright dangerous. If they were being watched it would give the whole thing away.

So all he could do was to get back to Riswyk and tell his mother or Per Garson. Maybe they knew some way to get in touch with Uncle Victor.

From the other side of the Snake, Peter could have climbed a woods trail that saved many miles on the road. But he had no way to cross. Nor could he leave his team. It was up to him to see that they were all brought back to Riswyk the following day.

For four weeks now, they'd been taking gold down the mountains under the very noses of the Germans. Except for trying to reopen the school the Germans had made no attempt to stop them. Perhaps they knew all along what they were doing.

If only he could talk to Uncle Victor! If only he knew that the bricks were taken aboard the *Cleng Peerson* every night! But they must be. For every time he returned to the Snake the snow soldiers were lying on the ground.

"Come on, everyone." Peter was impatient at his lagging team. "We'll be caught if we don't hurry."

The Germans had issued a new order, a curfew. No one could be out after sunset.

Following the blizzard, the Germans had adopted the custom of the country. They had taken to skiing. Some were clumsy and the children, who could ski almost as soon as they could walk, roared with laughter at their struggles. There was one fat lieutenant who spent most of his time on the seat of his pants, they said.

"Lieutenant Sit-Down," they called him to themselves.

"Of course some of them can ski," Peter had to admit. "How do you think they got into our country?" he asked Lovisa. "A lot of them came weeks ago by train in disguise. They brought their skis and pretended they'd come for the winter sports. Then they learned all about us and our defenses. They showed the way to the ones who came by parachutes and those who pretended to be sailors on the freight boats."

Tonight, they would have to run for it to be at the Holms' farm before sunset. Peter increased his pace and urged his team to hasten theirs.

They were passing the place where Peter would have come out on the road if he could have crossed the fiord and taken the short-cut up the rocks. The trail went straight up for a time. When it reached a crest it dipped down again to meet the road below.

The wind had blown the dry snow off the branches of some of the pines. They looked black against the white of the forest.

Out of the dark pines just ahead shot a German soldier on skis.

CHAPTER NINETEEN

So that was what Helga heard and saw at the Snake — this Nazi soldier!

There could be no mistake. The trail he had taken could have come only from the Snake.

From where he was Peter could not see the soldier's face. But the cut of his uniform was unmistakable and against its grey were the markings of his service corps.

So they'd been spied on after all. Peter forgot to be afraid. He was only angry — angry and sorry.

Uncle Victor would certainly have to be warned. But how? To find him at night would be impossible when Peter couldn't even find him in the daytime.

Perhaps Herr Holm could help him. Maybe he could find Uncle Victor's boat. Or he could hitch up his sleigh and go to Riswyk and ask Peter's mother or Per Garson. But would he dare risk disobeying the curfew? He could get shot if he were caught. It said so on the notice on the school door.

The Holms had serious faces when Peter told of seeing the Nazi soldier on skis.

"We're all in on this," Herr Holm said. "If we're being trapped, I'm the first to face the firing squad. Night after night I harbor you children."

But Peter thought he didn't seem much afraid.

"Your mother'll certainly have to be told," he decided.

472

"The teams of Lovisa and Michael will be starting out in the morning. We cannot let them be caught and the gold taken."

"We could head them off when they pass here," Fru Holm suggested.

"But where could we hide the gold? It wouldn't be safe here and there's no use having them haul it all that distance just to cart it back. No, I'll have to talk it over with Fru Lundstrom. I'll go tonight."

"Tonight? But you can't. There's the curfew." His wife spoke sharply.

"I must. There's no other way. Fru Lundstrom'll know what to do."

"But you could be shot."

"They'll have to catch me first. A sheet for me, Mama, and off I go."

Over his heavy outdoor clothes he draped a sheet. It fell in folds from his shoulders to his feet.

"Now a towel for the head." This he twisted into a turban. "Now do you think they'll know me from the snow?"

They went outside with him while he strapped on his skis. "Lucky they're down on the beach, not up here. If I'm fortunate I won't meet any Germans."

"They could be in the woods, Papa." The good farmwife was anxious.

"Then I'll hide." He took up his ski poles. "Well, I'm off to tell your mother about this spy," he addressed Peter. "She'll surely know some way to get in touch with your uncle."

The next morning when Peter awoke he was alone in

the barn. The others had gone long before, Fru Holm told him.

"Papa brought word from your mother you're to stay here until she comes. We did not call you because you seemed so tired and she won't be here till afternoon."

"Why am I to wait for Mother?" he asked.

"She's going to look for your Uncle Victor. You're to go along in case we need to get in touch with him again. Papa and your mama and Per Garson thought it best for you to go."

So he would have to go back to the Snake that very day and maybe face the Commandant who wanted to make him his servant. Well, it didn't matter. Herr Holm was safe and Uncle Victor would be warned. That was all that counted.

It was one o'clock when a bobsled turned into the farmyard. Pulling it was Peter's mother and on it sat Bunny and two other small children. Bunny smiled all over to see his brother in this strange place.

"Peter," his mother greeted him, "I'm glad you had a nice long rest."

"But how are you going to find Uncle Victor?" he asked.

"I have a chart of the Snake right here," she tapped her pocket. "The *Cleng Peerson*'s marked with a cross. Uncle Victor left it in case we needed to know."

"You'll have to walk when you reach the beach," Peter warned. "I don't know if these little fellows can all walk that distance."

"Then I'll pull them. I meant to, anyway. For the looks of it, Peter. Tomorrow and the next day Mrs. Berg and

474

Mrs. Olsen and some of the others are going to go down and take the babies.''

Peter understood. Anything to throw the Germans off the scent. For unless the spies already knew everything, no one would look for anything out of order from a woman with a sled load of children.

"We can carry a little gold too," his mother said. "Every bit counts and this snow isn't going to last forever."

CHAPTER TWENTY

Peter transferred the gold from the bobsled to his own sled. He gave his mother a start for he knew he could overtake her whenever he wished.

Mrs. Lundstrom sat on the bobsled and steered it skillfully. But with the children on it, she didn't dare take the long stretches with the speed Peter could have made.

Down on the beach he was angry to find his mother the object of much curiosity.

Soldiers were filing into the open space before the barracks. Their drill master made them stand at attention while she pulled the long sled past their lines. The drill master froze in stiff salute.

Peter wanted to tie his sled to the long one to help his mother pull the children over the level stretch but she told him to go ahead.

"It's the looks of the thing, Peter," she whispered.

He was glad he had gone on when, a minute later, he heard the voice of the Commandant. Peter knew he was addressing his mother but he dared not turn around to look. He'd been lucky to escape as lightly as he had, the day the officer stopped him and asked if he would like to be his servant.

"Good morning, good lady. You've a fine day for your sled ride." Peter knew his precise Norwegian accent.

His mother made no answer.

"If you like, I'll have one of my men pull that sled," he spoke politely.

Still his mother was silent. Then from up the beach Peter could see Lieutenant Sit-Down coming toward him and toward the Commandant. He had a paper in his hand. He paid no attention to Peter but went rapidly toward the chief officer. He must have handed the paper to the Commandant for there was silence as if the latter were reading a message.

Peter dug into the snow as hard as he could. He was afraid the Commandant might recognize his back.

He reached the cliff that hid the Snake. From there he watched his mother pulling hard on the rope of the bobsled. It seemed to him that she would never arrive at the wall that would hide her from the eyes of those hundreds of Germans. She had to turn into the valley before Peter dared give her a hand on the rope.

"But the snow soldiers are all knocked down," she noted. "That means that Victor and Rolls came out last night and loaded the gold you children brought yesterday. Could you and Helga possibly be mistaken?"

"Helga's nearly always right," Peter spoke ruefully. "If Helga says she's seen anything, you can be pretty sure she has.

"Anyway, I saw a soldier on skis just before we turned

476

into Holms' farm last night. He would have had to come from here. There's nowhere else he could have come from."

"In any event we'll have to tell Uncle Victor so he can be on guard. Now the thing to do is to find the boat." Mrs. Lundstrom drew from her pocket a drawing of the Snake with the *Cleng Peerson* marked with a cross.

"But that's right here," she said. "Here are the two fallen trees."

But although it was clearly marked on the drawing, there was nothing of it to be seen. Not a spar, not a boom, not a foot of the mast. Only the everlasting snow, the pines and the jutting cliffs that made pincers around the black rushing stream and its narrow borders of land.

Peter and his mother walked to the very edge of the water. In the little wooded strip they saw a strange new kind of vegetation. The forest seemed to dance. Pines they thought rooted in the bank, now seemed to have no roots at all but were bobbing up and down with the rush of the current.

And now that they were in a part of the valley where something was amiss, they could see other strange sights. Through the thick brush on the bank they could just about make out the *Cleng Peerson*. But what a strange *Cleng Peerson*. Pines were growing right out of her hull. Her mast was a towering evergreen. The branches thickened at the crow's nest and then tapered to a stately point.

"A pretty good job of camouflage, don't you think?" a voice spoke softly at their side. Both of them jumped in fright.

477

CHAPTER TWENTY-ONE

It was Uncle Victor who had spoken. It took some minutes for Mrs. Lundstrom and Peter to recover from their astonishment. When they did they realized that they were being shown up a fir-screened gangplank. At its head stood Rolls, the mate, with a hand to help them alight on the dancing deck.

"But you're not the ones to be surprised," Victor was saying. "What about me? I was expecting the two teams as usual. Instead I find only you two and Bunny and his friends."

The *Cleng Peerson* was a fishing smack of fifty tons. She had been built long before Uncle Victor's time for the herring industry. She carried a sloop rig and could set a course and square sail. But Uncle Victor had installed a thirteen-horsepower engine. So the *Cleng* had no need to wait for a wind but could travel under her own force at all times.

It was all so cheery and bright aboard the ship. In the cabin Peter could see his face reflected in a dozen different surfaces. Leather bunks along two sides served as seats in the daytime. A large round table centered the cabin. It was fastened to the deck and above it hung a lamp on a chain. About the only other thing of importance was a large map of Europe as it was in the nineteen thirties. The map was draped with the red field and white-bordered blue cross of the flag of Norway.

"And what is the news of Lars?" Victor asked about his brother.

"There's little to tell," Mrs. Lundstrom said sadly. "His regiment got to Trondheim and that's about all we know." Then Mrs. Lundstrom explained the purpose of their visit.

"We didn't come to make a social call," she said. "I don't dare leave Bunny and the others very long. They may get tired and wander away. We came to warn you that someone may be watching you. Helga Thomsen said she heard something and saw someone move down here yesterday. Then Peter saw a German soldier on skis come out of the trail from here that cuts the road near Holms'."

Uncle Victor looked grave. "It could have been Rolls or me that Helga saw. We've been watching every move these youngsters make. They haven't come once that one or the other of us hasn't stood guard."

"Yes, we thought as much," Mrs. Lundstrom said. "We talked of that last night when Herr Holm brought the news. I wouldn't have given it a thought if Peter hadn't seen the soldier on skis come out of the trail."

"You could tell from the snow prints," Peter suggested.

"Yes, we could. After a distance. But it's pretty well trampled around here with Rolls and me going out night after night to bring the gold aboard. But one of us will go up the trail tonight and see," his uncle answered.

"But the curfew?"

Uncle Victor only laughed.

"There's no such thing as being too cautious about spies," Uncle Victor said after a time. "But if anyone had been here in the daylight, surely Rolls or I would have seen him. Of course, I did take forty winks yesterday afternoon when the childen were here. You see, when the two of us dig up and carry on board almost a thousand pounds of gold, it's pretty late and we're tired. We've things to do in the morning to get ready to sail. So we have to catch up on our sleep when we can. But Rolls was around, weren't you, old fellow?"

"Yes, I was. But when I saw Peter I knew everything'd be all right. I came back just long enough to . . . ."

"Then someone could have been around and neither you nor I would have known."

"Is there much more gold to load?" Victor asked his sister-in-law after a pause.

"No. You have nearly all of it. Per Garson's been checking. The last of next week will finish it. And it won't be six weeks until Tuesday. We've been lucky, Victor. Think, if the thaws had come earlier."

"Well, you can't get it down here too soon to suit me. This business of hanging around isn't exactly safe."

"You mean you're ready to sail?" Peter asked. "As soon as the gold's loaded you can go to America?"

"That's right, son. That's exactly what I mean."

CHAPTER TWENTY-TWO

"There's nothing to do but what we've been doing," Victor Lundstrom decided. "We'll have to chance that this spy, or whatever he is, is still mystified and wants to learn more about us before he tells on us. He probably doesn't know that the bricks are gold bars because not one of them has been touched. So the best we can do is to get the rest of it here and let me get away while there's still a chance."

They agreed they had no choice in the matter.

480

"Yes, we've started it," Mrs. Lundstrom said. "The only thing to do now is to finish it."

The visitors dared stay no longer aboard the *Cleng* because of the little children.

"This is good-by, Victor." Mrs. Lundstrom kissed her brother-in-law. "God bless and keep you always. You've undertaken a mighty task."

"Not at all," he said. "I'm the lucky one. I'm going to get out of this while the rest of you have to stay and face it. Rolls and I have it easy. It's Lars and the ones who have gone to fight who are the brave ones."

Again Peter had to precede his mother along the beach past the German camp. He waited for her up on the road beyond the bend where he could not be seen from below. When at length she reached him, he tied his sled to the end of the bobsled and together they pulled up the steep hillside.

At the Holm farm there was a flurry of excitement. That much was evident the minute they turned in from the road. Fru Holm wanted to tell them something. But she was silent until the small children had eaten their bread and milk and were tucked into bed.

"There's something strange going on," she waved a wooden cooking spoon. "But first — " She went to the door and looked out. Then she bolted it and came over to where they sat beside the fire.

"Today, just before you came, I saw a German soldier in my woods. He was wearing skis. But why would he be skiing about my place? I ask myself. He comes cautiously as if he's looking for something. I watch and he comes close to my barn. Then he slides himself along with his

481

poles and pulls himself up the runway into my barn. INTO MY BARN, I tell you!

"I think I will call out to him, 'Get out of my barn, you loafer.' But then I think, No, that's bad. It might make him angry and he would turn me over to the officers. So I say to myself, I'll say nothing till I've talked with Fru Lundstrom."

"Then what happened?" Mrs. Lundstrom asked.

"I just waited and waited. By and by he came out and started back the way he'd come."

None of them knew what to make of Fru Holm's visitor. Peter tried to find out what the soldier on skis looked like. He was anxious to know if he was the same soldier he had seen himself the day before. But he remembered he had seen nothing of that one but his back. So he could hardly compare the two.

The next day, and for some days after that, Mrs. Berg and a number of the other women joined the children in their trips. They would take the bobsled and on each was a small pile of gold and over the gold sat the smallest children.

The next week the pile of bricks in the cave was nearly down to the ground. There were less than a hundred to be sledded to the Snake.

Nothing further was seen of the German soldier on skis. Peter was always on the watch. But not once did he see the grey-green uniform.

Late one afternoon he was unloading his sled in the Snake. He untied his rope and removed the sack covering and placed the bricks in the hole he had made in the snow.

482

He took two handfuls of snow and began to make his snowman. He patted it hard. As he reached for more, something made him look up. It was just the merest noise — soft like breathing.

He looked into a pair of blue, blue eyes. Their owner was wearing the dull-colored uniform of a German infantry soldier.

CHAPTER TWENTY-THREE

So it was all over.

They'd been discovered.

The Nazis knew what they were doing and had come to stop them.

Peter knelt in the snow, trembling. The blue eyes under the fringe of fair hair were familiar. Even in his fright Peter knew he had seen this private before. He'd seen him the very first day they'd passed the Nazi sentries. He had been helping unload the supplies. He was the one who had seemed to want to go sled riding too. More. He was the soldier who came to the *konditeri*.

Then Peter had another surprise. The brush behind the soldier parted and Uncle Victor sprang out. He grabbed the soldier's arms and pinned them behind him and before he could make an outcry he had a gag over his mouth.

Behind Uncle Victor came Rolls, the mate. Then the men turned back into the brush towards the *Cleng Peerson*.

It all happened so fast that none but Peter saw. Not even Helga, a few feet away, knew what took place. She was hard at work on her snowman.

"Helga, take my team back with yours," Peter asked. "I want to see Uncle Victor."

Peter had no idea whether or not his uncle would allow him aboard the boat. But he was going to find out. So he hurried through the brush to the side of the water.

From below the deck came strange sounds. Not to lose any of the excitement, Peter almost fell down the companionway in his haste.

Uncle Victor and Rolls had untied the prisoner's arms and had taken the gag from his mouth.

Then the captive soldier drew off his round army cap and threw it on the floor and tramped on it. He beat it with his feet, up and down. Then he tore at the insignia on his collar and tried to rip it off. All the while he was making hideous faces.

"What is it, man? Speak. Your mouth is no longer tied," Uncle Victor commanded sharply.

Then came a torrent of words, Norwegian and some other tongue Peter did not recognize.

"I'm no German even if I do wear the uniform. I'm a

Pole. They took me and made me serve them, and the deceit is theirs, not mine."

"But what are you doing with a German army of occupation?" Uncle Victor asked.

"I tell you it is not my fault. It's theirs. I'm no more to blame than, than — than that boy there."

He pointed at Peter and now Uncle Victor and Rolls saw him too. But Uncle Victor made no move toward Peter. He gave him a glance that seemed to say, It's all right. At your age I wouldn't have missed it, either.

"I want to go to the United States," the Pole went on. "If you'll take me on this boat, I'll cook and I'll scrub the decks. I'll sew the sails and carpenter. I'll stand watch. I'll do anything you ask. Only don't leave me here with those merciless machines, those Germans."

"What's he talking like that for?" Uncle Victor turned to Rolls. "What makes him think I'd take a man in a German uniform anywhere? How do I know he's a Pole and hates the Germans? Does he think I'm a baby to take him on his own word?"

Then he turned on the Pole and spoke severely.

"Come, now tell us what you know. How long have you been following these children?"

"If I follow the children, it's only because I'm lonely. It's because I want to be with someone I can like and trust. I will not make friends with the Germans. They don't even speak to me unless I can do them a service." Tears came into his blue eyes.

"Come, now, that's absurd. You have been following these children because you are spying on them. You want to find out what brings them here on their sleds. Then you go tell the Commandant and win a promotion. I know your sly German tricks.''

"No. No. No. I have no sly German tricks. I'm a Pole. I have no love for the Germans. To me, they have done every wrong short of putting me to death. If I follow the children, it's not to do them harm.''

He spoke convincingly. Peter believed he told the truth. Even Uncle Victor seemed inclined to believe him for his next question was put in milder tones.

"But if you wanted to be with the children, why did you not make yourself known when you were here last week?''

"I was on the other side of the fiord. I could not cross over.''

"But what were you doing in Holms' barn?'' Peter asked. "For it was you, of course.''

"If one is lonesome, even cows can be companions.''

Uncle Victor turned away.

Peter spoke again. He was sorry for the captive, believed his story. But with so much at stake they couldn't afford to take chances.

"But it was you who were in the *konditeri* the day you posted the notices about going back to school. Why is it you can have so much liberty and the others have to go back to the barracks?''

"They don't have to go. It's by choice. When they found the Norwegians were ignoring them they decided they would stay together entirely. And then when the epidemic came they were frightened.''

Uncle Victor cleared his throat. If he was going to say something, the Polish boy didn't give him a chance.

"But won't you take me with you to America, for surely

486

that is where you are going?" He looked about the cabin. "From the other side of the fiord, I saw the boat in its clever disguise and I knew you'd be sailing soon for that country. I'll be no trouble if you take me. And when I get there I've a place to go. I have a married sister in Pittsburgh."

"But that's utter nonsense," Uncle Victor protested. And his voice was again loud and angry. "Even if I didn't think this some sly Nazi trick, how could I land you there? They wouldn't let you in without a passport."

CHAPTER TWENTY-FOUR

Uncle Victor wanted to know how his prisoner came to be wearing a German army uniform and this is the story the Polish boy told:

"My name is Jan Lasek. My home is in Cracow, near the German border. I was born the year of the Armistice, 1918, when Poland declared her independence.

"Until last summer I was a student of languages at the University of Cracow. Always I wanted to go to America where I could practice my English and study it further. But there were six in our family and to spare the money was out of the question. My sister went to Pittsburgh to marry one of our countrymen. My grandmother was already living there. When grandmother died she left me some money. The legacy was in a bank in Pittsburgh and it was easier if I'd go there to get it. So I was to have a year of study in America, after all.

"All last summer when there were signs of trouble my father would say, 'Jan, you go to America.' But I had a job tutoring, and was making money, and so I waited until just before the University of Pittsburgh would open. I waited too long.

"The last week in August I went to Gdynia to take the boat to America. I had my ticket and my passport. But when I turned them in to go aboard a strange thing happened. Two men wearing police uniforms came up and took me by the shoulders.

" 'You're to come with us,' they said.

"I had to go along. There was nothing else to do. But instead of taking me where someone would tell me what was wanted of me, they threw me into a dark basement and there I stayed for two days and nights without so much as a crust of bread or a drop of water.

"In the meantime the Germans crossed into Poland and bombed, I think, twenty-three cities. But this I learned later. Then I knew only what I could guess from what had troubled my father, and from the sound of the bombs dropping all around.

"After two days they remembered about me and brought me food and water. I inquired what had happened and they told me that Germany and Poland were at war. I asked about my ticket and passport and they only shrugged.

" 'The boat left on schedule,' they said, 'Jan Lasek was aboard.'

"Little by little I began to understand. They had wanted my passport for someone else. So I was locked up, and that other is masquerading in the United States doing I don't know what harm. The men who arrested me were not Polish but German secret police in uniforms they brought with them from their own country. For in the

488

house where I was kept prisoner, I saw every kind of uniform or costume you could think of.

"One of the people in the house wore the black dress and inverted collar of a cleric. Here is one who will help me, I thought. This man of God will advise me in my troubles. One day when I had a chance, I spoke to him. 'I'm being kept here against my will,' I said. 'Will you help me to get back to my own people?'

"He laughed to put me to shame. 'So you think I make a convincing looking clergyman?' he said. 'But you flatter me.' When next I saw him he was wearing the uniform of a German Gestapo.

"But he did not hold my question against me. I thought he seemed to like me for he spoke to me often which was more than the rest of them did. One time I saw him packing a valise preparatory to going away. But first he had to unpack it. He took out the uniform of a streetcar conductor.

" 'This is what I wore when I first came to Poland two years ago.' He held up the cap for me to read the letters of its insignia and then he showed me the coat and trousers. From one of the pockets he drew out a book of streetcar tickets.

" 'I learned more about Poland in one year of riding the Warsaw tramcars than most people will know in a lifetime. And I found my knowledge very useful.'

" 'Spies!' I said, entirely without regard of what he would do to me. But it didn't make him angry. He only shrugged his shoulders.

" 'Call us that, if you like. We describe ourselves as patriots.'

489

" 'Patriots? Yes, you can call yourselves that if you mean coming into a peaceful country and getting control of it by lies, sneakiness, bribery, and corruption.'

" 'But that's the highest form of patriotic duty to one's own country,' he said, and I'll say this much for him. He was speaking the truth as he knew it.

"One of these disguises was given me. It was the uniform of a German army private. I had to put it on or I'd be shot.

" 'But what do you want of me?' I asked the woman who kept the house.

" 'Our Fuehrer needs your passport for work of his own in America,' she said.

" 'But why must I wear a German uniform?' I asked.

" 'We needed someone who knew languages — not one or two but many foreign tongues. Your papers say you are a student of languages. So you will be an interpreter for the army.'

" 'Never,' I said. 'My country's at war with Germany and I'll do nothing to help an enemy.'

" 'Don't worry,' she said. 'In a short time there'll be no war. Poland will have surrendered.'

"One day I was taken out of that house and with a body of German guardsmen I was put on a train and sent south to my own city of Cracow.

"I was in Cracow for months after that. You can imagine my shame when one of the few old neighbors that were left saw me in a Nazi uniform.

"My father was dead. He was shot when he went to the assistance of an old priest who was dragged off the altar at mass. My mother was not there. They said she got to

490

Rumania and took my little brother and sister. Two of my brothers died defending our city. My home I saw. There are hardly two bricks standing on top of each other.

"Now you know why I am not spying on you to tell the Germans and win a promotion. You know why I've watched your children because, if you belong to a country that has been invaded as mine has, then you are drawn in sympathy to people that have similarly suffered. You know now why I must get to America."

CHAPTER TWENTY-FIVE

"Well, what are we going to do with him?" Uncle Victor asked when Jan Lasek had finished his story. They had put him in the hold while they discussed the problem.

"We daren't turn him loose, that's certain," Rolls replied. "We can't take the risk that he won't tell the Commandant."

"His story sounds true enough," Uncle Victor decided. "I can well believe what he's told us. We know about the disguises ourselves, about men who came to Norway dressed as sports lovers but who turned out to be secret police. But I think it's dangerous to let him go. Whether he meant to or not, he could accidentally say something that would put the Germans on our trail."

"But what shall we do with him?"

"He'll have to be kept in the hold. We can't stand guard over him. I've a crew coming on tomorrow, but even so I cannot spare a man just to watch him."

Rolls was laying the table for supper. Since it was so late, Peter was to spend the night aboard the *Cleng*, and there was no place on earth he would rather be. His mother would not miss him that night for he was supposed to be at the Holms' farm.

"Couldn't you take him with you to America, Uncle Victor?" Peter pleaded. "It seems a shame he can't go."

"But I *can't* take him without a passport. That's all there is to that," his uncle said shortly.

"It would be a terrible thing to go that distance and be turned back at the end," Rolls explained.

"I could sign him on as a sailor," Uncle Victor answered. "But he'd be interned because I'm not planning to return. I'm afraid that would be pretty hard on him after all he's gone through."

"You could land him somewhere along the coast where the fighting is going on," Rolls suggested. "There are Poles with the British army."

"Too dangerous," his captain replied. "Once I get out of this fiord, I'm going to stay out to sea. Overnight the Germans have been capturing our towns. I might run into an enemy occupation. Once I get past, I'm going to stay past."

The Polish boy had been frightened when they told him they would have to lock him up for the night.

"Nothing will harm you," Uncle Victor said. "You won't have to go back to the barracks. We're hiding and you can hide with us."

They had to wait for the long twilight to fade to bring in the gold that the children had buried that day. They didn't dare carry a light.

"You see now why I had you build the snowmen?" Uncle Victor asked Peter. "We just have to feel our way.

So all we do is to feel for a snowman, and under him is the gold."

With three of them at work it wasn't long before they had the bullion aboard the *Cleng*.

"Fifty-one bricks," Rolls grunted in satisfaction.

"And each brick is worth five thousand United States dollars," Uncle Victor spoke cheerfully. "That's two hundred and fifty-five thousand dollars we collected from these snowmen. And quite a lot of money."

"Uncle Victor, that's just about all the gold in the cave. One day more'll bring it all out. This morning I asked Per Garson how much was left and he said a hundred bricks. Well, here are fifty-one of them right here."

"That's what I've been hoping. As soon as this Polish boy is missed, the Germans will start searching for him. They may come here. Even with the camouflage, it's dangerous if they get too close. If I had my crew, I think I would sail tonight. Although I'd have to leave the rest of the gold, I'd do it to be safe."

Before he turned in that night Rolls quizzed Jan Lasek about when he would be missed at the camp.

Jan said he *might* be missed that night, but they couldn't help noting his absence at roll call in the morning.

When Rolls told his chief, Peter thought his uncle looked solemn.

"Then the search may start tonight." He went to the porthole to look through a slit in the fir branches.

"You don't expect them here already?" Peter asked.

"No, I want to see if there's any sign of my sailors. They'll come at night."

"But the curfew, Uncle Victor?"

"It'd be a lot safer for them at night. But don't worry. Hans Torp and Sten and Dino are resourceful fellows. They'll manage. I told them to be here no later than tomorrow, and they'll be here."

There were voices out of the night beyond the portholes. From the direction of the beach came calls. Crowded at the peepholes in the fir branches, the three in the cabin waited. The voices grew louder. Outside in the snow were several squads of Germans.

"So the search has started," Victor spoke softly. "And they're even looking here. Whew! What a narrow squeak! If they'd come an hour earlier, they would have found us out there with the gold!"

CHAPTER TWENTY-SIX

It had taken the Germans until taps to miss the Polish recruit.

Then the hunt for him had started. Nearer and nearer to the *Cleng Peerson* came the searching party. But Uncle Victor was calm.

"If you couldn't find the boat in the daytime, knowing it was here, they're not going to find it at night," he comforted Peter. "So let's not worry about their finding us. I'm only hoping that Torp and the other two don't pick this time to come aboard."

Uncle Victor, Rolls, and Peter continued to crowd at the peepholes in the fir branches over the ports. After a time they saw the Germans turn back toward the cliff and the beach.

"If they search the woods, they can't help coming on the ski trail of our friend here." Uncle Victor meant Jan Lasek. "That'll lead them here by the back way and you can be sure they'll do some close searching."

The next morning the Snake was quiet as always. The Germans evidently had not yet found the ski trail, and Uncle Victor hoped to be at sea before they did. Just before dawn, Hans Torp and the two other sailors came aboard. They took turns watching for the enemy's approach, but the morning wore away and they neither saw nor heard anything. The last of the gold would be brought down that afternoon. When it was dark the *Cleng* could sail.

It was going to rain, Peter noted with satisfaction. It wouldn't matter now. The gold had been saved.

Lovisa's and Michael's teams came to the Snake that day. Peter went out to join them. He longed to remain in the Snake to see Uncle Victor set sail. But for the safety of them all and for the accomplishment of all they had set out to do, he made no protest when Uncle Victor said he must go back to town.

"Oh, Peter! We did it! We did it!" Lovisa threw her arms around him. "Every last brick's out of the cave. It's all down here. We fooled those old goose-steppers!"

"What about the soldier that's missing?" Peter wanted to know at once. "Was there a search for him in town last night?"

"Was there? Well, you should have been at home! In the middle of the night they pounded on the door. Per Garson went to open it. They almost knocked him down pushing past him. They started searching the house. They looked in closets, even with Mother's dresses. They woke up Bunny and he started hollering. Mother told them she didn't know what they were looking for but if they'd tell her she'd know how to help them. But they just went on poking behind curtains. Do they think we'd hide one of their men?"

Lovisa went on, "There's a notice on the school door. It said that anyone with information about this missing soldier must report at once to the Commandant, and if anyone is found to know something and *hasn't* told, he'll be punished with death. Ugh, these Germans!"

496

"Whew!" Peter whistled.

"Mother's afraid for the Holms," Lovisa went on. "She thinks the missing man might be hiding around their barn and she's going down this afternoon to warn them to get him out. For she said if they did find anyone there it'd be pretty hard to make the Nazis understand the Holms didn't want him. She'll be there when we get back."

Peter nodded. "Let's get these bricks down and get out of here."

Lovisa turned back to her sled and Peter, watching her, saw her stiffen in fright.

"Look, Peter," she whispered.

Into the Snake filed a company of German soldiers and an officer.

"They've come to search," Lovisa said.

"They did that last night. I guess they've come to look again."

"Peter, what'll we do? They'll see us with the gold."

"Right," he snapped into action. "The kids'll have to hurry. Get your bricks in the snow. Quick, team," he lowered his voice. "Here come the Germans."

Like squirrels burying nuts, the children burrowed in the snow. It flew in all directions.

"Not so deep," Peter directed. "Just lay the bricks down and start the snowmen. Faster. They're coming."

Mittened hands had unloaded the sleds. Now the snow was being patted into hard lumps. The children were well-practiced after so many months of winter. Soon was standing a fine army of snowmen.

"All right, Lovisa, let them come," Peter dropped on his knees in the snow and began another figure. It was easier to do that than to stand waiting for the Germans. In all the weeks they'd been coming to the Snake, this would be the first time the Germans had come there at the same time.

It was Lieutenant Sit-Down who led the company into the Snake. They came plodding through the snow to the level space between the two trees and here the ground was dotted with children and snowmen.

"There's no one here but these youngsters," he told the sergeant. "There's no use to ask them if they saw anyone for they won't answer. I think we might as well go back."

The sergeant drew up stiffly. "Pardon, Herr Lieutenant," he said, "the Commandant comes."

CHAPTER TWENTY-SEVEN

Near the cliff Peter could see the bulky figure of the Commandant, the head of the German forces at Riswyk. He was picking his way up the valley. They wanted to get up and start for home but they didn't dare move.

The Commandant came puffing along. He seemed to have trouble lifting his feet in the deep snow. In his hand he carried a light little cane, a swagger stick.

He plodded along until he came to the children.

"If he'd only go on," Peter growled to himself. But he didn't dare look up to see. His hands were busy with the snow. His head was hot and his mouth dry and there was a buzzing in his ears.

"We're searching for a German infantryman," the Commandant announced to the children. "Have any of you seen a man in these woods?"

Of course, there was no answer. He turned aside to whisper a few words to the Lieutenant Sit-Down. Then he spoke to the children in a loud voice:

"I said we are looking for a German infantryman. It's very important for you children to tell if you've seen one."

Still the children said nothing.

"I've a good mind to give you children a lesson in manners," his voice was angry. "When you're spoken to, it's only right that you should answer. Has no one taught you that? Now then. Yes or no? Have you seen a German infantry soldier in this fiord?"

The children acted as if they had not heard him. Lovisa sat back on her heels to admire her handiwork. But Peter, for all he tried to be cool, felt a terrible thumping in his chest.

The Commandant strode across the snow and stood above Lovisa.

"Little girl, tell me, did you or did you not see a German infantryman?" he screamed in anger. "Answer me."

Lovisa only turned her big blue eyes up at him. Not so much as a nod did she give him.

"Don't you know I can make you talk? Don't you realize that we Germans can make anyone do our will? We've only to command to be obeyed."

The Commandant's eye fell. "Bah, you Norwegians!" With his stick he slashed off the snowman's head. It was as if he would do the same to Lovisa's. Then he raised the stick and cut the snowman neatly in two. The upper part rolled beside the head. Only the haunches remained.

"Down you go," he shouted in his rage. "Just the way all people go who stand in our Fuehrer's way. The way

Norway goes. And Holland and Belgium and France and England and all countries that oppose the German will."

Lovisa was near to tears, Peter could tell. But she winked them back.

"So, little girl, let this be a lesson." The high officer was still in a rage. "Unless you want yourself and all who belong to you to go rolling over like that — and that — and that —"

He began kicking the stump of Lovisa's snowman. The snow flew out in a shower. With each kick, Peter winced. For the Commandant's foot could only be a few inches from her two bricks.

The high officer had evidently decided to give Lovisa a thorough lesson for he lifted his foot for another kick. Like a football player he stood back to swing at what was left of the snow figure.

In another minute he'll stub his toe against the bricks, Peter thought.

Then he gathered up a handful of snow. He rolled it into a hard ball. Then he stood back and took aim.

It landed exactly on the Commandant's right ear as Peter meant it should.

Then Peter took to his heels and ran for the woods.

CHAPTER TWENTY-EIGHT

"There he goes! After him!"

Peter had little chance to escape. Lieutenant Sit-Down and almost his whole company were chasing him.

But Peter knew these woods and the foreigners did not. He hoped to cross the Snake above where it was narrower

500

and take the ski trail up the mountain. In the forest above he had a good chance to hide.

But he was cut off before he could get upstream far enough to cross. The Germans spread out in a circle and blocked all points. Peter felt like a rabbit facing a pack of hounds.

Rough arms were around him and he fell to the ground. There was a tussle, and Peter all but succeeded in throwing off his captor. But the others came up and he was one against many, a boy surrounded by men.

There was nothing to do but submit. They dragged him to his feet. He fell in step with them. They were marching him off to their barracks.

But the snowball trick had worked!

He had succeeded in distracting the Commandant.

When Peter was led back to the place between the two fallen trees, he saw the Commandant was leaving. The snowmen were still standing and the children were filing out of the Snake.

How much of this had Uncle Victor seen? he wondered. No doubt every bit of it.

But could he do anything to help him?

A soldier marched on his right and one on his left. Ahead and behind were others. When they reached the sentries, these sprang up, their rifles on their shoulders. So they were quite a little company when they turned into the barracks they had built before the fishing wharf.

The heavy boots of the Nazis clumped in rhythm over the wooden boards of the barracks floor. Thump, thump, thump, thump, down a long hallway they pounded. Then they stopped. Peter was shoved into a box of a room no bigger than a clothes closet. A key was turned in the door. Then the thump, thump, thump of the soldiers as they left him alone in the twilight.

He stumbled against something like a low shelf. It was supposed to be his bed, he guessed. There was a window at one end of the tiny room. It was barred. Through it he could see the beach, snow-covered to the very edge of the black lapping water. Through the snow the sentry stepped, up and down, up and down, his legs swinging straight out from his hips like those of a toy soldier wound with a key. Rain began to fall, softly at first, then increasing with each passing minute.

What were they going to do with him, Peter wondered. Would he be tried at a court martial?

Up past the window stepped the sentry. Then he

turned and followed his own footprints back in the direction he had come.

Was it a serious offense to snowball a high German officer? Peter believed it was. It had something to do with order and respect for authority. Well, he didn't care how serious it was. They could shoot him if they liked. He was glad he had thrown the snowball.

But still, he was horribly afraid. Jan's story of Poland kept coming back. When he thought of Jan his mouth was hot and dry again. For whether or not he was in serious trouble for having snowballed the Commandant, he knew he would be if it were known he'd seen the escaped Pole. Lovisa said there was a notice on the school door saying that anyone who was found to know something about him and not telling would be punished by death.

By death.

After a time a soldier came to the door. He brought Peter a deep dish of stew and some dark bread.

The soldier spoke to him. "I come back to get your dish. Then I will take you to the Commandant," he said in German.

Peter couldn't eat. He tried to but it was no use.

Later there were footsteps in the hall. A key turned in the lock. The time was up. The soldier had come to take him to the Commandant. He stepped into the cell. Even in the dim light Peter could tell it was not the same soldier.

CHAPTER TWENTY-NINE

The soldier came inside and shut the door and leaned against it.

Peter looked hard at him. He could see so little from the streak of light from the window. But there was something familiar.

The soldier was Jan Lasek, the Pole. But, no. That couldn't be. Jan was on Uncle Victor's boat in the Snake. Peter had seen him there that day.

"Shhhh," Jan put his finger to his lips. From his tunic pocket he dug a scrap of paper. It was a note from Uncle Victor. Holding it up to the window Peter read:

"Jan Lasek is risking his liberty and perhaps his life for you. Follow him at all costs, wherever he goes. On that depends your safety and his."

There was no signature but Peter knew well his uncle's bold handwriting. He nodded to show he understood.

Jan kept listening for a sound. What was he waiting for,

504

Peter dared not ask. From afar Peter could make out a kind of din, a rattle like knives and forks, pans and mugs. When the rattle became much louder Jan seemed satisfied. He looked out of the door. He stepped outside and closed it.

When he came back into the cell there was high excitement in his whisper.

"Come now," he said, "quickly!"

They were out in the hall. Jan stopped to turn the key in the lock outside the door where Peter had been kept prisoner. Into his pocket went the key.

And now Peter could hear the tramp, tramp, tramp, of boots. It came from a distant end of the barracks but it grew noisier with each step.

"We'll have to run," Jan whispered.

All the time the sound of the marching soldiers came closer. They seemed to be coming down a hall that would meet the corridor at right angles. And now Peter could hear nothing because of sound in his own ears. He wanted to run in the opposite direction. Why go this way? he wondered. We'll only run into them.

The marching men must be nearing the corner. But Jan only kept going faster toward them. Uncle Victor said he was to follow Jan at all costs. So behind him ran the breathless, frightened Peter.

And now, on the right, Peter saw a door. Through it Jan pulled him. There was just time to close it softly. The Germans were turning the corner as Peter could tell by the sound of their steps on the other side of the door.

Peter fell into the wet snow of the beach. They were outside the barracks and, for the moment, safe.

Jan flattened himself against the wall of the building and Peter stood up beside him. The shadow of the barracks hid them. The rain was loud on the crusted snow.

"We're lucky the sentry was going up the beach, not down," Jan whispered. "Otherwise he'd have seen the light when we opened the door."

Peter felt a throbbing in his ears. He tried not to pant but his breath was loud. Against the snow they could see a dark figure. It was the sentry returning. He walked up to a point on a line with the door, the very door over which he stood guard. He was not ten feet away from where Jan and Peter were flattened against the wall.

Slap, slap, slap, his heavy leather mittens thumped his shoulders. He changed his rifle from one side to the other and changed it back again. Then he turned and began goose-stepping back in the direction he had come.

Jan tugged at Peter's sleeve. It was now or never, he seemed to say.

Peter was not prepared for what happened next. Jan led him down the beach to the very edge of the fiord and then right into the water itself.

The cold water bit his body. The breath left him. He didn't think he could stand another minute of it. He wanted to run back to the beach but Jan kept wading out and Peter, remembering the warning in the note, found himself following him.

It seemed forever, these few minutes they waded in the water. And now Jan was swimming and Peter found himself doing the same. But you couldn't swim in that close-to-frozen water. You had no strength. Peter felt the

506

breath going out of him. Then there was a numbness over him. He closed his eyes.

He must be dreaming for nothing like this could happen in real life. A hand reached out and grabbed his arm and he was pulled into a boat. A heavy coat was put over him and a pair of arms were cradling him.

Rolls, Uncle Victor's mate, was holding him. There was another sodden mass on the bottom of the boat. It was Jan Lasek.

The boat, he knew, was the *Cleng Peerson*'s lifeboat. Strong arms were pulling it toward the fishing smack.

CHAPTER THIRTY

Peter was dry and warm in Uncle Victor's cabin. The coast of Norway was somewhere out in the blackness. The Atlantic rolled and the *Cleng Peerson* pitched and Peter was jounced up and down with the wash of the waves.

So Peter was going to America!

He was going to see New York and go to Pittsburgh with Jan Lasek and then travel to Minnesota where his uncle was a professor in St. Olaf's College in Northfield.

Uncle Victor could arrange it, he said.

"You can be admitted as a minor in my custody. Our minister in Washington will do that much for us. He'll be only too glad to do something in return for all this gold."

"But what about Jan Lasek?" Peter asked. "How can he go without a passport?"

"But he *has* a passport — the one that was stolen. There'll be a record of it in Washington and they'll be grateful for the information about the one who is masquerading in his name. They won't be long finding him."

Peter was overjoyed with this good news for Jan. Since he had risked his life for him, there was no reward too high.

"It wasn't as easy for Jan as it looks, Peter. He ran a grave risk. Of course, he knew the routine of the camp. He knew that at supper hour the barracks would be deserted, except for the mess hall. And he knew about the side door and the sentry. But he was still in danger of being caught himself. If one little thing had gone wrong, he would have been caught."

"He had his uniform too," Peter mused. "One German uniform looks pretty much like another."

Then a thought struck him. "But how did he get the key to open the cell door?" he wanted to know.

"The keys are kept on a panel in the guard room. The room was empty while the guard was at mess. All Jan had to do was to slip in and take the key marked "das Gefangnis."

His uncle went on. "All that part was easy. The only hard part was getting him to the barracks without his being seen on the way there. For he was being looked for everywhere. So we didn't dare have him go by foot from the Snake to the beach and barracks."

"It was Rolls who solved it for us," his uncle went on. "He suggested that, since the roads were being watched, we make a landing by water. The *Cleng* was pretty well covered by camouflage so she could be moved to the mouth of the Snake where it meets the big fiord. We were lucky it was a bad night. The rain and mist shortens the day. When it got dark Rolls and Hans Torp and Sten lowered the lifeboat and rowed him right up to the fishing pier. But they couldn't wait for him because it was too dangerous. They had to get back to the cover of the *Cleng*. That's why you had to swim so far."

"But how did Jan get past the sentries into the barracks?"

"Just the way you got out. He waited for one to come up, turn and start back. The minute his back was turned, he stepped inside the door. It isn't bolted till taps and Jan knew that. The sentry was there to guard that very door but there are ways to get past sentries if you can think of those ways."

"Wasn't Jan afraid he'd be caught when he got inside the barracks?"

"Of course. Terribly. But he had to risk it."

"He did it for me?"

"For you and because I said I'd take him to America if he got you out."

"We heard the soldiers marching in the hallway. Were they coming to get me?"

"Whether they were or not, you and Jan would have been in a pretty tight place if you'd run into them."

Peter fell back in the bunk. "So I'm to go to America. But what about Mother and Lovisa and Bunny?"

"Peter, I know you think it high-handed of me to be taking you this long distance without so much as asking if you wanted to go. But there was nothing else to do. When I got you on board, there was nothing to do with you but to take you along. We daren't turn back with all this gold."

Peter thought about the night his father had gone away, the night of the first blackout. And of all the things that had happened since.

"It's a shame, Peter, for you to be leaving without so much as saying good-by to your family and Helga and Michael and Per Garson and the others. But your mother

510

was glad when I told her what we were going to try to do. You know she had gone to the Holms to warn them that the missing Nazi might be in their barn. When Lovisa got to the farm with the news of what happened to you she strapped on her skis and took the back trail through the woods to the Snake.

" 'Take him to America by all means,' she said. 'I want him to grow up in a country where people are free.' "

There was a clatter of steps in the companionway. Rolls came into the cabin.

"Submarine off sta'board," he said.

Uncle Victor jumped to his feet in alarm. Then he saw the sheepish grin on Rolls's face.

"But it's a British sub," he spoke lamely. "The *Cleng*'s doing five knots in this sea," he added.

"She ought to ride well," Uncle Victor answered. "She's got a cargo of gold."

Key to Pronunciation

Letter Symbol for a Sound	Key Word and Its Respelling	Letter Symbol for a Sound	Key Word and Its Respelling
a	pat (PAT)	oo	boot, rule (ROOL)
ah	far (FAHR)	or	for (FOR)
ai	air (AIR)	ow	power (POW-ər)
aw	jaw (JAW)	u	put, book (BUK)
ay	pay (PAY)	uh	cut (KUHT)
e	pet (PET)	ch	church (CHERCH)
ee	bee (BEE)	hw	when (HWEN)
ehr	berry (BEHR-ee)	ks	mix (MIKS)
er	term (TERM)	kw	quick (KWIK)
i	pit (PIT)	ng	thing (THING)
igh	sigh (SIGH)		finger (FING-gər)
ihr	pier (PIHR)	sh	shoe (SHOO)
o	pot (POT)	ss	case (KAYSS)
oh	oh, boat (BOHT)	th	thing (THING)
oi	oil (OIL)	th	this (THIS)
		zh	pleasure (PLEZH-ər)

y used in place of (igh) before two consonant letters as in child (CHYLD)

ə represents the sound for any vowel spelling when a syllable is sounded very weakly, as in the first syllable of about, or the last syllables of item, gallop, or focus, or the middle syllable of charity.

Glossary

a•ban•don (ə-BAN-dən) *verb*. 1. To desert; leave or withdraw from completely: The passengers *abandoned* the sinking ship. 2. To give up or discontinue: The search for the plane was *abandoned* after two weeks. **abandoned, abandoning.** —*noun*. Recklessness; lack of care.

a•blaze (ə-BLAYZ) *adjective*. 1. On fire: The leaves were set *ablaze* by the match. 2. Glowing brilliantly.

ab•sent (AB-sənt) *adjective*. 1. Not present; away. 2. Lacking. —(ab-SENT) *verb*. To keep oneself away: He *absented* himself from the meeting because he was ill. **absented, absenting.**

ab•sent•ly (AB-sənt-lee) *adverb*. In an absent-minded manner.

ab•sorb (ab-SORB) *verb*. 1. To draw in; soak up (a liquid): The sponge *absorbed* the spilled water. 2. To take in without reflecting or rebounding: Drapes help to *absorb* sound in a room. 3. To hold the attention of; interest greatly. **absorbed, absorbing.**

ac•tiv•i•ty (ak-TIV-ə-tee) *noun*. 1. The state of working or acting; the state of being active: The students were in a state of great *activity* preparing for the school fair. 2. Action in a special area of interest: Of Sue's after-school *activities*, skating was her favorite. **activities.**

512

ad•duc•tor (ad-DUHK-tər) *noun*. A muscle that draws two parts, as of a body, together.

ad•join (ə-JOIN) *verb*. To be next to or close to: Our garage *adjoins* our house. **adjoined, adjoining.**

ad•just•ment (ə-JUHST-mənt) *noun*. A change or an alteration: The store made an *adjustment* on the bill after Mother pointed out an error.

ad•mi•ra•tion (ad-mə-RAY-shən) *noun*. High regard or respect, often with feelings of wonder or delight: Our class showed its *admiration* for the astronauts by writing essays in their honor.

aer•o•dy•nam•ics (air-oh-digh-NAM-iks) *noun*. (Plural in form but used with a singular verb.) A branch of physics dealing with forces exerted by air in motion on flying and windblown objects.

af•fec•tion•ate (ə-FEK-shən-it) *adjective*. Showing or having warm feelings of fondness or love: At his graduation Paul received an *affectionate* hug from his sister. **—affectionately** *adverb*.

ag•gres•sive (ə-GRESS-iv) *adjective*. 1. Hostile; ready to start a fight or argument. 2. Bold or assertive.

ag•o•ny (AG-ə-nee) *noun*. Extreme suffering of body or mind. **agonies.**

al•ter (AWL-tər) *verb*. To change or make different in some way. **altered, altering.**

al•ter•nate (AWL-tər-nayt) *verb*. To switch from one to another; take turns. **alternated, alternating.** —(AWL-ter-nit) *adjective*. 1. Coming in turns, rotating. 2. Substitute: If I can't have pie, my *alternate* choice is cake. **—alternately** *adverb*.

al•ti•tude (AL-tə-tood or AL-tə-tyood) *noun*. The height from sea level to any point in space above.

al•um root. (AL-əm ROOT) *noun*. Name given to several plants having a particular medical effect.

am•a•teur (AM-ə-chər) *noun*. 1. A person who uses his talent or skill for fun and not to make money. 2. An athlete who has never received money for playing.

am•ble (AM-bəl) *verb*. To walk leisurely; to stroll. **ambled, ambling.**

an•i•mate (AN-ə-mayt) *verb*. 1. To bring to life, to put life into. 2. To make appear to move: Story characters are often *animated* in cartoons. **animated, animating.**

an•nounce•ment (ə-NOWNSS-mənt) *noun*. 1. A public or formal message or notice: The *announcement* of the school closing on Thursday was made over the public address system. 2. The act of announcing.

an•tic (AN-tik) *noun*. (Usually plural) A playful or silly act: The baby loved the *antics* of the kitten.

an•tic•i•pa•tion (an-tiss-ə-PAY-shən) *noun*. Expectation, act of looking forward to: I brought an umbrella in *anticipation* of a rainstorm.

an•vil (AN-vil) *noun*. A heavy block on which metal is molded: Blacksmiths shape horseshoes on anvils.

ap•pa•ra•tus (ap-ə-RAY-təss or ap-ə-RAT-əss) *noun*. Equipment or tools for a certain job. **apparatus** or **apparatuses.**

ar•ba•lest (AHR-bə-list) *noun*. A type of speargun used by divers for catching fish.

ar•mi•stice (AHR-mə-stiss) *noun*. A halt in a war or a military action by a pact between the hostile parties: a truce.

as•so•ci•a•tion (ə-soh-see-AY-shən or ə-soh-shee-AY-shən) *noun*. 1. A group united for a special purpose: Freda belongs to an *association* dedicated to helping the poor. 2. A relationship between things or ideas.

a•sun•der (ə-SUN-dər) *adverb* or *adjective.* 1. Into many pieces or parts: Spot knocked the vase *asunder.* 2. Separated; far apart: The leaves were scattered *asunder.*

at•mos•phere (AT-mə-sfihr) *noun.* 1. The layer of air that surrounds the earth. 2. The influence, feeling, or mood experienced in a particular place or situation: An *atmosphere* of joy filled the school picnic. 3. The air in a particular place: The *atmosphere* was damp along the waterfront.

at•ten•dant (ə-TEN-dənt) *noun.* A person who waits on or takes care of (something): The *attendant* at the gas station checked our engine.

au•di•ble (AW-də-bəl) *adjective.* Loud enough or able to be heard: The music is not loud, but it is *audible.* —**audibly** *adverb.*

a•vi•a•tion (ay-vee-AY-shən) *noun.* The study or science of aircraft.

a•vi•a•tor (AY-vee-ay-tər) *noun.* The man who flies a plane, a pilot.

awe•struck (AW-struhk) *adjective.* Filled with awe or admiration; speechless.

bad•ger (BAJ-ər) *noun.* A short-legged, furry animal that lives in a burrow, or hole, dug in the ground.

balk (BAWK) *verb.* To stop; refuse to continue; to block; to boycott: Roger *balked* at taking piano and violin lessons. **balked, balking.** —*noun.* 1. Something that stops, blocks, or hinders. 2. A fake pitch in baseball, usually an illegal move.

bal•lot (BAL-ət) *noun.* 1. A piece of paper on which a person votes, or a list of names with places to check off a vote: Mark your *ballot* for the candidate of your choice. 2. The system of voting by ballot. —*verb.* To vote by means of ballots. **balloted, balloting.**

bar•ren (BA-rən) *adjective.* 1. Not fertile; bare: No plants would grow in the *barren* desert area. 2. Not able to have children or produce offspring.

bar•ter (BAHR-tər) *verb.* To trade or exchange one thing for another: Peter *bartered* his frog for Jack's penknife. **bartered, bartering.**

bask *verb.* 1. To expose oneself to comfortable warmth. 2. To enjoy or find satisfaction in, as popularity or success: The pupil *basked* in the glory of his perfect history test. **basked, basking.**

bath•y•sphere (BATH-i-sfihr) *noun.* A sturdy steel sphere in which people can be lowered into the ocean for underwater exploration.

bear (BAIR) *verb.* 1. To hold; to support: This bridge can *bear* the weight of the truck. 2. To carry: The workman will *bear* his tools to the shed. 3. To endure; to withstand: Some animals cannot *bear* very cold weather.

bear•ing (BAIR-ing) *noun.* 1. A way of conducting oneself in manner and posture: The old gentleman is a person of noble *bearing.* 2. (Usually plural) Direction or location in terms of other places: The hunter lost his *bearings* in the woods.

ben•e•fit (BEN-ə-fit) *noun.* 1. Anything that is of help or advantage: Aunt Mae enjoyed the *benefit* of a good education. 2. A performance, as of a play or concert, that raises money for a special cause. —*verb*. 1. To receive help; to profit. 2. To give help; improve. **benefited, benefiting.**

be•seech (bi-SEECH) *verb*. To plead with; beg for. **besought** or **beseeched, beseeching.**

be•tray (bi-TRAY) *verb*. 1. To be disloyal or unfaithful to: The boy *betrayed* his friend by telling his secret. 2. To turn over to an enemy: The traitor *betrayed* the fort to the enemy. **betrayed, betraying.**

bick•er (BIK-ər) *verb*. To quarrel; argue, especially about minor details. **bickered, bickering.**

bid•ding (BID-ing) *noun*. An order; command: I will not follow his *bidding*.

bil•low (BIL-oh) *verb*. To fill, to bulge: The wind *billowed* the sails. **billowed, billowing.** —*noun*. 1. A large wave: The wind created *billows* which made the boat rock. 2. A moving mass that sweeps like a wave: *Billows* of smoke came from the chimney.

bi•o•sphere (BIGH-ə-sfihr) *noun*. The section of the earth, waters, and atmosphere that supports living things, whether plants, worms, animals, fish, or birds.

bi•plane (BIGH-playn) *noun*. An aircraft that has two pairs of wings, one mounted over the other.

bleak (BLEEK) *adjective*. 1. Bare and lonely: The seashore is *bleak* in February. 2. Cold; chilling: A *bleak* wind made hiking unpleasant. 3. Depressing; cheerless. **bleaker, bleakest.** —**bleakly** *adverb*.

blood•let•ting (BLUHD-let-ing) *noun*. An ancient means of curing certain diseases by taking blood from the patient.

boot *noun*. 1. A shoe made for heavy wear or protection, at least ankle high but usually higher. 2. (Plural) Rubbers or outside shoes. 3. A trunk or chest in which things are stored. —*verb*. 1.

To kick or stomp. 2. To get rid of: The farmer *booted* out the vicious dog. **booted, booting.**

bor•der (BOR-dər) *noun*. 1. The edge or rim of anything: Grass grows to the *border* of the pond.

2. The line which separates political divisions or private property: We were stopped for inspection when we crossed the *border* of Mexico. 3. A decorative edging: There was a *border* of lace on the hem of Jane's dress.

brac•ing (BRAY-sing) *adjective*. Giving strength or freshness: a *bracing* wind.

brack•et (BRAK-it) *noun*. An L-shaped support made of metal, wood, or stone: John made bookshelves by nailing *brackets* on the wall and placing boards on them. —*verb*. To support with a bracket. **bracketed, bracketing.**

bract (BRAKT) *noun*. A leaf or group of leaves that grows on the base or stem of a plant. —**bracted** *adjective*.

break•wa•ter (BRAYK-waw-tər) *noun*. A wall or other barrier that protects a shore from the full force of the waves.

bril•liant (BRIL-yənt) *adjective*. 1. Shiny, bright, glowing: The stars were *brilliant* last night. 2. Having great intelligence or talent. —**brilliantly** *adverb*.

bul•le•tin (BUL-ət-n) *noun*. 1. A short account of the latest news: A *bulletin* on TV announced the end of the war. 2. A brief paper or magazine regularly issued by an organization.

bus•tle (BUHSS-l) *verb*. To work or hurry busily or noisily; to hustle. **bustled, bustling.**

cal•cu•late (KAL-kyə-layt) *verb*. 1. To use mathematics to arrive at an answer or result. 2. To figure out or estimate: Mother *calculated* she had enough food for two extra guests. **calculated, calculating. —calculation** (kal-kyə-LAY-shən) *noun*.

cal•i•co (KAL-i-koh) *noun*. A coarse cloth, usually printed in bright colors. **calicoes** or **calicos. —***adjective*. Spotted: a *calico* cat.

cam•ou•flage (KAM-ə-flahzh) *noun*. Disguise used to hide something, generally by making it look like its surroundings. —*verb*.  To disguise in order to conceal. **camouflaged, camouflaging**.

cam•paign (kam-PAYN) *noun*. 1. A series of military actions aimed at a special target. 2. Any series of actions organized for a specific purpose: a political *campaign*. —*verb*. To take part in a *campaign*. **campaigned, campaigning**.

can•di•date (KAN-də-dayt) *noun*. A person who runs or is considered for an office or position.

car•riage (KA-rij) *noun*. 1. A vehicle for carrying people, usually drawn by a horse. 2. Posture; bearing; a way of holding oneself erect.

car•tridge (KAHR-trij) *noun*. 1. A small cylinder or case that contains gunpowder and usually a bullet or pellets. 2. Any small container, especially one inserted into a mechanical device: a *cartridge* of film. —**cartridged** *adjective*. Having a *cartridge*.

case•ment (KAYSS-mənt) *noun*. A window or window frame that opens on hinges.

cask (KASK) *noun*. A barrel, made in various sizes and used especially for holding liquids.

ca•su•al (KAZH-oo-əl) *adjective*. 1. Not careful or serious; careless. 2. Infor-

mal, relaxed; easygoing. —**casually** *adverb*.

cat•a•pult (KAT-ə-puhlt) *noun*. 1. A machine used in ancient warfare for hurling boulders, stones, or arrows. 2. A powerful machine used to launch planes from the deck of an aircraft carrier or other ship. —*verb*. To hurl as though from a catapult. **catapulted, catapulting**.

cen•sus (SEN-səss) *noun*. A survey made to count the number of people or things living in an area and to gather information about them. **censuses**.

cer•e•mo•ni•al (sehr-ə-MOH-nee-əl) *adjective*. Of or related to ceremony; formal; stately. —**ceremonially** *adverb*.

cer•e•mo•ny (SEHR-ə-moh-nee) *noun*. 1. A formal occasion or a ritual, or the observances required by such a ritual. 2. Formal behavior; a polite manner of acting. **ceremonies. —ceremonious** (sehr-ə-MOH-nee-əs) *adjective*.

chaise (SHAYZ) *noun*. A light, open carriage, usually with a folding top.

char (CHAHR) *verb*. 1. To change to charcoal by burning. 2. To burn to a cinder: The bark on the tree was *charred* by the forest fire. **charred, charring**.

check•point (CHEK-point) *noun*. A place of inspection on a road or border.

chem•is•try (KEM-iss-tree) *noun*. The science concerned with the make-up of substances, their characteristics, and the processes by which substances combine or are changed.

choke (CHOHK) *verb*. 1. To keep from breathing by blocking or squeezing the windpipe or throat; strangle. 2. To block or clog: Leaves *choked* the drainpipe. **choked, choking. —***noun*. A device that regulates the flow of air to a gasoline engine.

516

cho•rus (KOR-əss) *noun.* A group or organization of singers, a choir. **choruses.** —*verb.* To sing or recite as a part of a group. **chorused, chorusing.**

cinch (SINCH) *noun.* 1. A strap that holds a pack or saddle in place. 2. (Slang) Something that is easy to do, or a person sure or able to do something. **cinches.** —*verb.* 1. To strap on. 2. (Slang) To make sure of; get a firm hold on; *cinch* the victory. **cinched, cinching.**

cli•max (KLIGH-maks) *noun.* The point of greatest interest, importance, or excitement: the *climax* of the program. **climaxes.** —*verb.* 1. To reach the point of greatest interest. 2. To bring to an end: A visit to the Grand Canyon *climaxed* our vacation. **climaxed, climaxing.**

clod (KLOD) *noun.* A lump of dirt or earth.

clut•ter (KLUHT-ər) *noun.* A messy, untidy state. —*verb.* To create disorder. **cluttered, cluttering.**

coach (KOHCH) *noun.* 1. A large, enclosed carriage; a stagecoach. 2. A passenger car on a train. 3. A bus. 4. A person who teaches or trains others, especially in athletics. **coaches.** —*verb.* To teach or train in some special skill or procedure. **coached, coaching.**

com•bus•tion en•gine. (kəm-BUHSS-chən EN-jən) *noun.* Motor that operates by the burning of some kind of fuel like gas or oil.

com•pete (kəm-PEET) *verb.* To take part in a contest; strive or vie: The runners *competed* against one another. **competed, competing.** —**competitor** (kəm-PET-ə-tər) *noun.*

con•cen•trate (KON-sən-trayt) *verb.* 1. To fix one's attention upon something: Mary turned off the radio so she could *concentrate* on her homework. 2. To focus, or draw toward one center. 3. To make more powerful: The company *concentrated* the soap powder so that it could clean very soiled clothing. **concentrated, concentrating.**

con•cen•tra•tion (kon-sən-TRAY-shən) *noun.* 1. Undivided attention: To understand the instructions requires *concentration.* 2. The act or process of concentrating.

cone (KOHN) *noun.* A three-dimensional figure that rises to a point at one end from a rounded base at the other.

con•fi•dent (KON-fə-dənt) *adjective.* 1. Sure; certain: Jack is *confident* that he will get a good grade in mathematics. 2. Having faith in one's own abilities. —**confidently** *adverb.*

con•front (kən-FRUHNT) *verb.* 1. To meet face to face; to encounter. 2. To face with defiance or hostility. **confronted, confronting.**

con•scious (KON-shəss) *adjective.* 1. In a state of being awake or able to think and feel. 2. Aware; having knowledge of. 3. Deliberate; intentional; with determination: a *conscious* effort. —**consciously** *adverb.*

con•sid•er•a•ble (kən-SID-ər-ə-bəl) *adjective.* 1. Important; significant. 2. Large; great; much. —**considerably** *adverb.*

con•spic•u•ous (kən-SPIK-yoo-əss) *adjective.* 1. Standing out; obvious. 2. Remarkable; worthy of attention. —**conspicuously** *adverb.*

con•ster•na•tion (kon-stər-NAY-shən) *noun.* Great amazement or alarm.

con•trap•tion (kən-TRAP-shən) *noun.* Contrivance, gadget: John's *contraption* was designed to feed the cat at 11 o'clock each morning.

con•triv•ance (kən-TRIGH-vənss) *noun.* A gadget or a device: A pencil sharpener is a useful *contrivance.*

con•trive (kən-TRIGHV) *verb.* 1. To invent or design. 2. To plot or scheme, often for evil purposes. **contrived, contriving.**

cor•du•roy (KOR-də-roi) *noun.* A heavy, ribbed cotton cloth.

corps (KOR) *noun.* 1. A group of persons organized for a special purpose: The police organized a *corps* of volunteers to search for the missing child. 2. A special unit in the armed forces: the Signal *Corps.* **—corps** (KORZ) *plural.*

coun•sel (KOWN-sl) *noun.* 1. Advice or opinion: My father gave me good *counsel* when he suggested I start my homework early. 2. The act of exchanging ideas or opinions. **—verb.** 1. To give advice. 2. To recommend that something be done. **counseled** or **counselled, counseling** or **counselling.**

count•less (KOWNT-liss) *adjective.* More than anyone can or will count; innumerable.

cou•ple (KUHP-əl) *noun.* 1. Two together; a pair: Form a line in *couples.* 2. A man and woman who are married, engaged, or dating. **—verb.** 1. To join together: The train crew *coupled* the engine to the freight cars. 2. To pair off; match up. **coupled, coupling.**

cra•dle (KRAYD-l) *noun.* 1. A small bed, most often on rockers, for a baby. 2. The place or location where something  (a plan, idea, movement) is started and kept alive: Faneuil Hall in Boston is called the "*cradle* of American liberty." **—verb.** 1. To rock or put in a cradle or cradlelike device. 2. To hold or rock in one's arms; shelter. **cradled, cradling.**

crag•gy (KRAG-ee) *adjective.* Rough; uneven: He had a difficult time getting over the *craggy* ground.

cre•a•tive (kree-AY-tiv) *adjective.* 1. Having the power to make or create. 2. Coming from imagination or original thought: *creative* writing. **—creatively** *adverb.* **—creativity** (kree-ay-TIV-at-ee) *noun.*

crest (KREST) *noun.* The top or head of anything: the *crest* of a wave. **—verb.** To come to a head or form a crest. **crested, cresting.**

crim•son (KRIMZ-n) *noun* and *adjective.* A bright shade of red.

crit•i•cal (KRIT-i-kəl) *adjective.* 1. Referring to a time of crisis, danger, or peril: The Revolution was a *critical* period in American history. 2. Likely to give harsh or rash judgments, as a *critical* person. 3. Referring to skilled judgment: The doctor gave a *critical* opinion. **—critically** *adverb.*

crock (KROK) *noun.* A pot, jar, or other container made of baked clay.

cu•ri•ous (KYUR-ee-əss) *adjective.* 1. Desiring to know or learn: Jane is *curious* about wild horses. 2. Odd; peculiar. **—curiously** *adverb.*

cur•rent (KER-ənt) *noun.* 1. A steady flow: The river *current* carried Jo's hat downstream. 2. Electricity flowing through a wire.

curt•sy (KERT-see) *noun*. A woman's greeting or sign of respect made by bending the knees and bowing the body. **curtsies.** —*verb*. To make a curtsy. **curtsied, curtsying**

cus•tom-made (KUHSS-təm-mayd) *adjective*. Made to order; made specially for an individual customer.

cut (KUHT) *verb*. 1. To make an opening in; remove or separate into parts: Father *cut* into the watermelon. 2. To make shorter or trim. 3. To take the shortest way: Jim *cut* across the grass. 4. To make less in amount or price. **cut, cutting.** —*noun*. 1. A place that has been sliced into: There was a *cut* on Bill's arm. 2. A snub or remark meant to hurt. 3. Part of a hill or mountain that has been removed for a railroad or highway.

dash•board (DASH-bord) *noun*. The instrument panel in a car or truck.

debt (DET) *noun*. Something owed: I owe Joan 50 cents; I must pay the *debt*.

de•cap•i•tate (di-KAP-ə-tayt) *verb*. To cut off the head of. **decapitated, decapitating.**

dec•o•ra•tion (dek-ə-RAY-shən) *noun*. 1. Something used to decorate or adorn: Christmas *decorations*. 2. The action of decorating. 3. A medal; an award.

def•i•nite (DEF-ə-nit) *adjective*. 1. Certain, without doubt: The trip is *definite*; we will leave today. 2. Exact, accurate: Howard told us that 2:15 was the *definite* arrival time of his plane. —**definitely** *adverb*.

del•i•cate (DEL-i-kit) *adjective*. 1. Beautifully fine, light, or airy: The bride wore a dress of *delicate* white lace. 2. Broken easily; fragile: Eggs are *delicate*. —**delicately** *adverb*.

de•liv•er•ance (di-LIV-ər-ənss) *noun*. A delivering or a being delivered; rescue: The parting of the Red Sea aided in the *deliverance* of the children of Israel.

de•mure (di-MYOOR) *adjective*. 1. Proper, soft-spoken, shy: a *demure* young lady. 2. Pretending to be shy or modest. **demurer, demurest.** —**demurely** *adverb*.

dense (DENSS) *adjective*. Thick, crowded: The child became lost in the *dense* forest. **denser, densest.** —**densely** *adverb*.

de•pose (di-POHZ) *verb*. To dethrone (a king); remove (a high official) from a position. **deposed, deposing.**

de•pot (DEE-poh) *noun*. A bus or train station.

der•e•lict (DEHR-ə-likt) *adjective*. Having been deserted: *derelict* ship. —*noun*. Someone or something that has been forsaken or abandoned.

de•ri•sive (di-RIGH-siv) *adjective*. Scornful, mocking: His *derisive* laughter when the girl sang off-key was unkind. —**derisively** *adverb*.

de•scend (di-SEND) *verb*. 1. To move downward: The rain *descended* upon us. 2. To decline or slope downward. **descended, descending.**

des•ti•na•tion (dess-tə-NAY-shən) *noun*. The place to which someone or something is going: Mars may be the *destination* of future space travelers.

de•struc•tion (di-STRUHK-shən) *noun*.
1. Complete ruin, condition of being
destroyed: Each year, fire causes
much *destruction* of our forests. 2.
The act of ruining or destroying.
—destructive *adjective*. **—de-
structively** *adverb*.

de•tail (di-TAYL or DEE-tayl) *noun*. 1.
One small part of a whole: Getting
paper plates was one *detail* we overlooked in planning the school picnic.
2. Many or all of the small parts of
something: Mary's ability to concentrate on *detail* makes her a good
planner.

dic•tate (DIK-tayt) *verb*. 1. To say or
read something aloud so that another
person can write it down word for
word. 2. To command or order: My
conscience *dictates* that I tell the truth.
dictated, dictating.

di•lap•i•dat•ed   (di-LAP-ə-day-tid)
adjective. Run-down, worn-out: Jim
bought a *dilapidated* car that he
planned to use for parts.

dis•may (diss-MAY) *verb*. To alarm or
cause fear. **dismayed, dismaying.**
—noun. Loss of courage, a troubled
feeling.

dis•mem•ber (diss-MEM-bər) *verb*. To
cut off or separate the limbs, members, or parts of. **dismembered, dis-
membering.**

dis•tend (diss-TEND) *verb*. To become
larger or cause to become larger;
swell: The croaking frog *distends* its
body when it is frightened. **distended,
distending.**

dis•tinct (diss-TINGKT) *adjective*. 1. Not
alike, different. 2. Clear, sharp, definite: The blue jay has *distinct* markings. **—distinctly** *adverb*.

dis•tinc•tion (diss-TINGK-shən) *noun*. 1.
A way in which things differ: Sometimes it is hard to find a *distinction*
between truth and untruth. 2. The act
of finding a difference or keeping

separate: Our school welcomes all
races without *distinction*. 3. Importance, fine character: The judge is a
man of *distinction*.

dis•tin•guish (diss-TING-gwish) *verb*.
To be able to tell the difference; recognize: He can *distinguish* the real
from the counterfeit. **distinguished,
distinguishing.**

dole•ful (DOHL-fəl) *adjective*. Sorrowful,
unhappy. **—dolefully** *adverb*.

down•grade (DOWN-grayd) *noun*. A
slope, a drop in the land. **—verb**. To
point out only the bad things. **down-
graded, downgrading.**

dra•ma (DRAH-mə or DRAM-ə) *noun*. 1.
A story or poem written to be acted
out on a stage; a play. 2. An exciting
or moving experience in real life.

dras•tic (DRASS-tik) *adjective*. Serious,
extreme. **—drastically** *adverb*.

drear•y (DRIHR-ee) *adjective*. Dull, sad,
gloomy. **drearier, dreariest.**
—drearily *adverb*.

du•bi•ous (DOO-bee-əss or DYOO-bee-
əss) *adjective*. Doubtful, uncertain, or
undecided. **—dubiously** *adverb*.

du•ra•ble (DUR-ə-bəl or DYUR-ə-bəl)
adjective. Lasting, even with much
use: Babies grow out of clothes so
quickly they do not need anything
durable. **—durability** (dur-ə-BIL-ə-tee)
noun. **—durably** *adverb*.

e•clipse (ih-KLIPS)
noun. 1. The hid-
ing or blocking of
one heavenly
body by another.
2. A blocking or
dimming of light.
—verb. 1. To
darken or con-
ceal: The moon
eclipsed the sun.

2. To completely outdo (others) so that they seem in the shade: The baseball star *eclipses* the other players. **eclipsed, eclipsing.**

e•col•o•gist (ih-KOL-ə-jist) *noun*. A scientist who studies the relationship of living things to each other and to their surroundings.

edge (EJ) *noun*. The place where something begins or ends: The *edge* of the blanket was torn. —*verb*. 1. To put a border on: Father *edged* the lawn with flowers. 2. To move sideways: Jim *edged* his way through the hole in the fence. **edged, edging.**

ef•fect (ə-FEKT) *noun*. 1. A result: The *effect* of so much rain was a flood. 2. The act of making a particular impression: talked merely for *effect*.

e•lec•tion (ih-LEK-shən or ee-LEK-shən) *noun*. 1. Choosing between two or more people, usually by vote: The *election* was close; Pat won by only two votes. 2. The act or process of voting: Student Council *elections* are held every year.

e•lude (ih-LOOD) *verb*. 1. To escape or avoid by clever means. 2. To puzzle; be beyond (one's) understanding. **eluded, eluding.**

em•brace (em-BRAYSS) *verb*. 1. To hug or hold in the arms. 2. To take up eagerly: Mother *embraced* the fight against pollution. 3. To include: The school recreation program *embraces* many different activities. **embraced, embracing.** —*noun*. A hug.

e•merge (ih-MERJ) *verb*. 1. To come out. 2. To become known: The story of his narrow escape *emerged* several days later. **emerged, emerging.**

en•crust (en-KRUHST) *verb*. To cover with a layer: The bottom of the boat was *encrusted* with barnacles. **encrusted, encrusting.**

en•dan•ger (en-DAYN-jer) *verb*. To put in peril or danger: The blinding fog *endangered* the lives of the passengers. **endangered, endangering.**

en•list (en-LIST) *verb*. 1. To join: Joe *enlisted* in the Navy after finishing college. 2. To get the support or help of: Mother *enlisted* her neighbor to help in moving the furniture. **enlisted, enlisting.**

en•tire•ty (en-TIGHR-tee) *noun*. The state of being entire or complete; whole.

en•try•way (EN-tree-way) *noun*. A hallway or vestibule through which one enters a building or house.

en•vy (EN-vee) *verb*. To be jealous of: Sally *envied* her brother because he had new ice skates. **envied, envying.** —*noun*. Jealousy.

ep•i•sode (EP-ə-sohd) *noun*. One or more of a series of happenings; part of a long series of events or of a long story: The argument was the only unpleasant *episode* of the entire vacation.

e•qua•tion (ee-KWAY-zhən) *noun*. (Math) A mathematical expression of equality between two amounts: $5 - 1 = 4$ is an *equation*.

e•rect (ih-REKT) *verb*. To build. **erected, erecting.** —*adjective*. Straight: The soldier stood *erect* before the reviewing officers. —**erectly** *adverb*.

es•pe•cial (eh-SPESH-əl or ih-SPESH-əl) *adjective*. 1. Special; unusual. 2. Particular: Pay *especial* attention to the way he holds his guitar. —**especially** *adverb*.

es•sen•tial (ə-SEN-shəl) *adjective*. Basic; absolutely necessary. —*noun*. A necessary element: Water is an *essential* of life. —**essentially** *adverb*.

es•ti•mate (ESS-tə-mayt) *verb*. To make a guess of size, age, value, or the like based on some facts or knowledge: I *estimate* his age as six or seven because his two front teeth are missing. **estimated, estimating.** —(ESS-tə-mit) *noun.* A guess based on some knowledge: The repairman gave Dad an *estimate* of the cost of fixing our dishwasher.

e•ter•ni•ty (ih-TER-nə-tee) *noun.* 1. Never-ending time. 2. Time that seems never-ending: The time before recess seemed an *eternity.* 3. Time after death. **eternities.**

ex•clu•sive (eks-KLOO-siv) *adjective.* 1. Tending to exclude or shut out. 2. Not shared with anyone else: Mrs. Park gave me the *exclusive* right to the job of mowing her lawn. **—exclusively** *adverb.*

ex•hi•bi•tion (ek-sə-BISH-ən) *noun.* 1. A public display. 2. A fair, usually lasting several days, at which machinery, hobbies, paintings, or the like are shown.

ex•hil•a•rate (eg-ZIL-ə-rayt) *verb.* To enliven; make happy or excited. **exhilarated, exhilarating. —exhilaration** (eg-zil-ə-RAY-shən) *noun.*

ex•panse (ek-SPANSS) *noun.* A widely spread out area: Most deserts are vast *expanses* of sand.

fa•mil•iar (fə-MIL-yər) *adjective.* 1. Well-known; common; met with or seen every day. 2. Having great knowledge of; understanding thoroughly: Please be *familiar* with chapter three; I will test you on it Friday. **—familiarly** *adverb.*

fam•ine (FAM-ən) *noun.* 1. A shortage of food; a period of widespread hunger. 2. An extreme lack or great shortage of anything.

fence•row (FENSS-roh) *noun.* Land at the base of a fence where brush is allowed to grow, providing shelter and food to small wild animals.

fer•ret (FEHR-it) *noun.* A yellowish-brown weasel of the western part of North America that hunts prairie dogs.

fi•na•le (fi-NAL-ee) *noun.* The last part of a performance, especially of a musical composition.

fi•nals (FIGH-nəlz) *noun.* The last in a series of competitions: Our team is going to play in the *finals* of the basketball tournament.

flail (FLAYL) *noun.* A device used for threshing consisting of a swinging short stick attached to a long wooden handle. —*verb.* 1. To hit with a flail or as if with a flail: Sam *flailed* at the snake with a stick. 2. To wave (something) about like a flail. **flailed, flailing.**

flank (FLANGK) *noun.* 1. The side of a human or four-legged animal between the ribs and the hip. 2. Either side of a military formation: The left *flank* of the army bore the brunt of the attack. —*verb.* 1. To be at the side of: A meadow *flanked* the house. 2. To go around the side of (an army). **flanked, flanking.**

floun•der (FLOWN-dər) *verb.* To struggle in a clumsy way; lose balance or control. **floundered, floundering.**

flout (FLOWT) *verb.* To scorn, insult, or scoff at; ignore or treat with disrespect. **flouted, flouting.**

fly•wheel (FLIGH-hweel) *noun.* A heavy wheel that steadies the speed of a machine.

folk•lore (FOHK-lor) *noun.* The customs, beliefs, and rituals long observed by the common people.

for•mer (FOR-mər) *adjective.* Past, at a previous time: Our principal is a *former* teacher. —*noun.* The first of two: When the choice is play or work, I prefer the *former.* **—formerly** *adverb.*

522

frame•work (FRAYM-werk) *noun*. 1. A structure of joined parts. 2. An outline; a plan for organization: A constitution is usually the *framework* for a government.

fric•tion tape. (FRIK-shən TAYP) *noun*. A strip or band of fabric or plastic having the quality of sticking to: He put *friction tape* on the handle of his baseball bat for a better grip.

frig•id (FRIJ-id) *adjective*. Extremely cold. **—frigidly** *adverb*.

frond *noun*. A large leaf, divided into many tiny sections, found in ferns and some palm trees.

fu•ri•ous (FYUR-ee-əss) *adjective*. 1. Very angry; enraged. 2. Wild, violent. **—furiously** *adverb*.

fu•ry (FYUR-ee) *noun*. 1. Extreme anger; rage. 2. Violent action: The *fury* of the storm caused great damage. **furies.**

fu•se•lage (FYOO-sə-lahzh) *noun*. The body of an airplane to which the wings and tail are attached.

gape (GAYP) *verb*. 1. To open the mouth wide. 2. To stare or gaze with the mouth open. 3. To become wide open. **gaped, gaping.**

gauge (GAYJ) *noun*. 1. A standard measuring scale. 2. An instrument for measuring amounts: a gas *gauge*. —*verb*. 1. To measure, determine exactly: He *gauged* the amount of steam that escaped. 2. To judge or make an evaluation: I cannot *gauge* whether John is telling the truth or not. **gauged, gauging.**

gawk *verb*. To stare in a stupid way. **gawked, gawking.**

gin•ger•ly (JIN-jər-lee) *adverb*. Very carefully or cautiously.

glare (GLAIR) *noun*. 1. An angry stare. 2. A strong, blinding light. —*verb*. 1. To give an angry look. 2. To shine with a blinding quality: The car lights *glared* in the hikers' eyes. **glared, glaring.**

gov•er•nor•ship (GUHV-ər-nər-ship) *noun*. 1. State of being governor, an elected official who heads a political unit. 2. Someone's term as governor: His *governorship* was marked by tax reform.

gra•cious (GRAY-shəss) *adjective*. Kind, having good manners and breeding: "If a man be *gracious* and courteous to strangers, it shows he is a citizen of the world." (Bacon). **—graciously** *adverb*. **—graciousness** *noun*.

grasp *verb*. 1. To hold tightly with the fingers. 2. To understand: Can you *grasp* the meaning of the poem? **grasped, grasping.** —*noun*. 1. The ability to reach and hold: The book on the top shelf was beyond his *grasp*. 2. Understanding; knowledge: He had a good *grasp* of mathematics.

grat•i•fi•ca•tion (grat-ə-fi-KAY-shən) *noun*. Pleasure, satisfaction.

gru•el (GROO-əl) *noun*. A thin porridge made by boiling oatmeal or other meal in water or milk.

gul•ly (GUHL-ee) *noun*. A deep ditch made by running water after heavy rains. **gullies.**

gun•ny sack. (GUHN-ee sak) *noun*. Sack or bag of strong, coarse fabric made of jute.

gym•na•si•um (jim-NAY-zee-əm) *noun*. A large room or building especially equipped for exercise and athletic games or performances.

hab•it•a•ble (HAB-ə-tə-bəl) *adjective*. Good enough to live in: Early people found caves *habitable*. **—habitably** *adverb*.

hab•i•tat (HAB-ə-tat) *noun*. 1. The kind of place or environment in which a plant or animal is found in nature. 2. The place where a person or thing is likely to be found.

hack•le (HAK-l) *noun*. 1. One of the long, slender feathers on the neck of a rooster. 2. (Plural) Hairs on the back of a dog's neck that can become erect.

half-dazed (HAF-DAYZD) *adjective*. Being in a confused or semi-conscious condition.

hap•haz•ard (hap-HAZ-ərd) *adjective*. Happening by chance or accident; not planned. **—haphazardly** *adverb*.

har•mon•ic (hahr-MAHN-ik) *adjective*. 1. Getting along well together. 2. Going well together in appearance or sound.

har•mo•ni•um (hahr-MOH-nee-əm) *noun*. A small antique organ which produces music by forcing air from bellows through metallic reeds.

hay•mow (HAY-mow) *noun*. The part of a barn in which hay is stored.

heed *verb*. To take notice of, pay attention to. **heeded, heeding.** **—noun.** Attention; careful listening.

her•e•tic (HEHR-ə-tik) *noun*. One who holds a view contrary to established belief in religion, politics, or science, or to other accepted standards.

her•o•ine (HEHR-oh-in) *noun*. 1. A girl or woman who shows courage or is admired for her outstanding achievements. 2. The main female character in a poem, story, or play.

hes•i•tate (HEZ-ə-tayt) *verb*. 1. To hold back because of fear; pause because of indecision: "He who *hesitates* is sometimes saved." (James Thurber). 2. To feel reluctant or unwilling. 3. To speak with pauses in between words.

hesitated, hesitating. **—hesitation** (hez-ə-TAY-shən) *noun*.

host (HOHST) *noun*. 1. A man who invites and entertains guests. 2. An army: The enemy *host* descended on the city. 3. A large number. 4. An animal or plant on which another animal or plant relies for the support of its own life: A dog is often a *host* for many fleas. **—verb.** (Informal) To act as a host. **hosted, hosting.**

house•bro•ken (HOWSS-broh-kən) *adjective*. Trained to have clean habits for living indoors.

hov•er (HUHV-ər or HOV-ər) *verb*. 1. To remain in or near one place in the air: The helicopter *hovered* over the scene of the accident. 2. To remain near one place; linger. 3. To be in a wavering or uncertain condition: The injured driver *hovered* between life and death. **hovered, hovering.**

hus•tle (HUHSS-l) *verb*. 1. To work or play with energy and zest. 2. To hurry or rush. 3. To move or be moved roughly; push or shove. **hustled, hustling. —noun.** Energy; spirit.

i•den•ti•fy (igh-DEN-tə-figh) *verb*. 1. To establish (who someone is): The sentry asked the man to *identify* himself. 2. To recognize. **identified, identifying.**

ig•no•rant (IG-nər-ənt) *adjective*. Lacking knowledge. **—ignorance** *noun*. **—ignorantly** *adverb*.

im•i•tate (IM-ə-tayt) *verb*. 1. To copy the actions or speech of another. 2. To look like: The markings on one kind of butterfly *imitate* a dead leaf. **imitated, imitating.**

im•mac•u•late (ih-MAK-yə-lit) *adjective*. 1. Clean, spotless. 2. Pure, having no faults. **—immaculately** *adverb*.

im•mo•bil•ize (ih-MOH-bə-lighz) *verb*. To stop or prevent movement of. **immobilized, immobilizing.**

im•mor•tal•i•ty (im-or-TAL-ə-tee) *noun*. 1. The state of living forever. 2. Lasting fame.

im•pas•sive (im-PASS-iv) *adjective*. Without feeling; showing no emotion. **—impassively** *adverb*.

im•pe•tus (IM-pə-təss) *noun*. 1. The energy of motion; momentum: The ball rolled down the hill under its own *impetus*. 2. A motivating or rousing force; stimulation. **impetuses.**

in•cline (in-KLIGHN) *verb*. 1. To bend; slope; slant. 2. To tend; be likely or willing: Cindy *inclines* to giggle too much. **inclined, inclining.**

in•dus•try (IN-duhss-tree) *noun*. 1. All manufacturers, workers, products; business: the *industry* of the nation. 2. A specific manufacturing group: the auto *industry*. 3. Steadiness; close attention. **industries.**

in•ev•i•ta•ble (in-EV-ə-tə-bəl) *adjective*. Not to be avoided; sure to happen: No matter how long summer seems, the start of school is *inevitable*. *—noun*. Something that is sure to come about: "There is no good in arguing with the *inevitable*." (J. R. Lowell). **—inevitably** *adverb*.

in•fect (in-FEKT) *verb*. 1. To spread disease germs; cause to be sick. 2. To bring on a particular mood in: Her enthusiasm *infected* the crowd. **infected, infecting. —infection** (in-FEK-shən) *noun*.

in•flate (in-FLAYT) *verb*. 1. To blow up or fill with air, as a balloon. 2. To cause a feeling of importance: *inflate* with pride. 3. To enlarge or expand beyond normal: *inflate* prices. **inflated, inflating. —inflation** (in-FLAY-shən) *noun*.

in•ge•nu•i•ty (in-jə-NOO-ə-tee or in-jə-NYOO-ə-tee) *noun*. Great skill in inventing things, making up reasons; planning or designing; cleverness. **ingenuities.**

in•hab•i•tant (in-HAB-ə-tənt) *noun*. A person or animal that lives in a particular place; a resident.

in•step (IN-step) *noun*. The arched part of the foot between the ankle and the toes.

in•tact (in-TAKT) *adjective*. 1. Whole; all together: The table game is *intact*; not one piece is missing. 2. Not damaged.

in•te•ri•or (in-TIHR-ee-ər) *noun*. 1. Inner space, the inside. 2. The center part of a land area, as of an island, country, or continent. *—adjective*. 1. Located inside. 2. Removed from the edges or from the shore; inland.

in•ter•view (IN-tər-vyoo) *verb*. To meet with someone for the purpose of obtaining information: The employer *interviewed* several people who applied for the job. **interviewed, interviewing. —noun.**
1. A meeting between persons for the purpose of obtaining information. 2. A writing or recording containing information gathered at an interview.

in•tri•cate (IN-trə-kit) *adjective*. 1. Very complicated: It took the students an hour to solve the *intricate* problem. 2. Having very many details or parts: The inside of a radio contains an *intricate* system of wires and other parts. **—intricately** *adverb*.

525

in•trigue (in-TREEG) *verb*. 1. To interest; greatly arouse the curiosity of: The child was *intrigued* by the music box. 2. To plot or plan secretly: The spies *intrigued* against the foreign government. **intrigued, intriguing.** —*noun*. (IN-treeg or in-TREEG) Secret plotting or planning.

ir•reg•u•lar (ih-REG-yə-lər) *adjective*. 1. Not in the usual order or way. 2. Not according to rule. 3. Varying from time to time. 4. Not straight or even: The hemline was *irregular*. **—irregularly** *adverb*. **—irregularity** (ih-reg-yə-LAR-ə-tee) *noun*.

ir•ri•tate (IHR-ə-tayt) *verb*. 1. To annoy or anger: Phil *irritates* people by slamming doors. 2. To make sore. **irritated, irritating. —irritation** (ihr-ə-TAY-shən) *noun*.

is•sue (ISH-oo) *noun*. 1. A single edition of a publication: the June *issue* of a magazine. 2. The point of a discussion or argument: The *issue* was whether Jane would be allowed to go to the party. —*verb*. 1. To publish: They *issued* the magazine monthly. 2. To come or go out: Steam *issues* from the kettle. **issued, issuing.**

jaun•ty (JAWN-tee or JAHN-tee) *adjective*. Joyful, carefree. **jauntier, jauntiest. —jauntily** *adverb*.

khak•i (KAK-kee or KAH-kee) *noun*. 1. Heavy dull-olive cloth used for soldiers' uniforms. 2. (Also *adjective*) A dull color of olive mixed with yellow and brown tones.

knick•ers (NIK-ərz) *noun*. (Plural in form and use) Short, loose-fitting trousers gathered at the knee.

 ←

la•dle (LAYD-l) *noun*. A spoon with a long handle and large bowl, used for serving soups and other liquids. —*verb*. To dish out with a ladle. **ladled, ladling.**

lapse (LAPS) *verb*. 1. To decline; fall into a lower or worse condition or position: The patient *lapsed* into a coma. 2. To become useless or ineffective. **lapsed, lapsing.**

launch (LAWNCH or LAHNCH) *verb*. 1. To fire, send off with force or power: *launch* a rocket. 2. To put into the water for the first time: *launch* a ship. 3. To begin something: The track team *launched* a drive for funds. **launched, launching.** —*noun*. 1. The act of launching (a rocket). 2. An open motorboat. **launches.**

lav•ish (LAV-ish) *adjective*. Overly generous, extravagant. —*verb*. To give or spend freely. **lavished, lavishing. —lavishly** *adverb*.

lean-to (LEEN-too) *noun*. 1. A small shed, with one sloped roof, that is attached to a larger building. 2. A rough shelter made from branches or other covering slanted against supporting poles.

le•vi•a•than (lə-VIGH-ə-thən) *noun*. 1. A huge sea animal. 2. Any great and powerful person or thing.

lim•pet (LIM-pit) *noun*. A saltwater shelled animal that attaches itself to rocks.

lit•ter (LIT-ər) *noun*. 1. Scattered objects, especially paper, cans, bottles, and other rubbish that has been carelessly discarded. 2. A stretcher for carrying the sick and injured. —*verb*. To throw away trash carelessly. **littered, littering.**

loin•cloth (LOIN-kloth) *noun*. A piece of clothing worn around the hips, generally by primitive people in warm climates.

long•house (LAWNG-HOWSS) *noun.* A large, rectangular dwelling of certain North American Indians, especially the Iroquois.

lure (LUR) *noun.* 1. Something that attracts or tempts: the *lure* of outdoors on the first warm day of spring. 2. A device used as bait for fish. —*verb.* To attract with bait; tempt. **lured, luring.**

lush (LUHSH) *adjective.* 1. Having heavy green growth. 2. Luxuriant: *lush* carpets. **lusher, lushest.**

lust•y (LUHSS-tee) *adjective.* Full of vigor and strength. **lustier, lustiest.** —**lustily** *adverb.*

lute (LOOT) *noun.* A stringed instrument played by plucking with the fingers.

mag•ne•to (mag-NEE-toh) *noun.* A small electric generator which uses a magnetic field to produce an electric current.

ma•lig•nant (mə-LIG-nənt) *adjective.* 1. Causing sickness or death. 2. Very evil or hateful. —**malignancy** (mə-LIG-nən-see) *noun.*

ma•lin•ger (mə-LING-gər) *verb.* To pretend sickness in order to avoid something unpleasant. **malingered, malingering.**

ma•neu•ver (mə-NOO-vər or mə-NYOO-vər) Also **manoeuver** *noun.* 1. A planned and directed movement of troops and military equipment, as in battle or a training exercise. 2. A carefully planned trick or action. —*verb.* 1. To carry out some plan or action, as a military operation. 2. To plan carefully; to scheme: The ambitious student *maneuvered* to win the class election. **maneuvered, maneuvering.**

ma•nip•u•late (mə-NIP-yə-layt) *verb.* 1. To handle or operate skillfully. 2. To manage or control, especially in an unfair manner: The selfish student *manipulated* his classmates so that they did his work for him. **manipulated, manipulating.** —**manipulation** (mə-nip-yə-LAY-shən) *noun.*

man•na (MAN-ə) *noun.* Substance sent by God as food for the children of Israel while they were in the wilderness.

man•tel•piece (MANT-l-peess) Also **mantel** *noun.* The trim over or on either side of a fireplace, especially a shelf over a fireplace.

man•u•al (MAN-yoo-əl) *noun.* A book or booklet that gives instructions or explains how to use something: The *manual* for our automobile explains how to change a flat tire. —*adjective.* Done with or related to the hands: *manual* labor. —**manually** *adverb.*

mar•tyr (MAHR-tər) *noun.* 1. A person who chooses to die or suffer for a cause. 2. A person who pretends to suffer in order to attract attention or sympathy. —*verb.* To cause (a person) to die or suffer because of his beliefs. **martyred, martyring.**

ma•tron (MAY-trən) *noun.* 1. A married woman, especially an older woman. 2. A woman in charge of an institution, as a school or prison.

me•chan•i•cal (mi-KAN-i-kəl) *adjective.* 1. Relating to machinery; made or run by machine: *mechanical* toys. 2. Without liveliness or expression: Jill recited the poem in a *mechanical* way. —**mechanically** *adverb.*

me•chan•ics (mi-KAN-iks) *noun.* (Plural in form but used with a singular verb) 1. The branch of science that studies the action of forces and their effects on matter. 2. The design or operation of a machine: the *mechanics* of a car.

527

med•i•tate (MED-ə-tayt) *verb.* To think deeply (about a subject). **meditated, meditating. —meditation** (med-ə-TAY-shən) *noun.*

meek *adjective.* 1. Patient; gentle and peace-loving. 2. Weak; timid. **meeker, meekest. —meekly** *adverb.*

me•lo•de•on (mə-LOH-dee-ən) *noun.* A small, portable reed organ which uses suction bellows to draw air inward through the reeds.

men•ace (MEN-iss) *verb.* To threaten; endanger. **menaced, menacing. —noun.** 1. A threat, danger, or hazard: Water pollution is a *menace* to our health. 2. A nuisance; a troublesome person.

midst *noun.* The middle; center part. **—in the midst of.** Among; surrounded by; during. **—in our midst.** Among us.

mince (MINSS) *verb.* 1. To cut up into tiny pieces. 2. To walk with small, dainty steps. 3. To behave or speak in an overly polite way. **minced, mincing.**

min•i•mum (MIN-ə-məm) *noun.* The least amount needed, possible, or allowed: We're packing a *minimum* of clothes for the weekend at Grandfather's farm. **—minimums** or **minima** (MIN-ə-mə) *plural.* **—adjective.** As low as possible; of the least allowed: *minimum* wages.

min•is•try (MIN-i-stree) *noun.* 1. The position, duties, and time in office of a minister. 2. Any one group of church or government ministers. **ministries.**

mi•rac•u•lous (mə-RAK-yə-ləss) *adjective.* 1. Of or about a miracle; supernatural. 2. Unexpected and wonderful: a *miraculous* victory. **—miraculously** *adverb.*

mock-up (MOK-uhp) *noun.* A model of something, either smaller or full size, usually for testing or demonstration.

mo•men•tum (moh-MEN-təm) *noun.* The force with which an object moves: The truck lost *momentum* when its engine failed. **—momenta** or **momentums** *plural.*

mon•o•plane (MON-ə-playn) *noun.* An airplane that has a single pair of wings.

mo•not•o•nous (mə-NOT-n-əss) *adjective.* 1. Unchanging; always the same: *monotonous* scenery. 2. Boring, dull, or tiring because of the lack of change: a *monotonous* speech. 3. Said in the same tone; using the same sound: a *monotonous* voice. **— m o n o t o n o u s l y** *adverb.* **—monotony** (mə-NOT-n-ee) *noun.*

mood•y (MOOD-ee) *adjective.* 1. Sad; unhappy; having fits of gloominess. 2. Changing moods often. **moodier, moodiest. —moodily** *adverb.*

Morse code. (MORSS KOHD) A system of relaying messages with telegraph or light by the substitution of dots and dashes for letters and numbers.

mo•sa•ic (moh-ZAY-ik) *noun* and *adjective.* 1. A design or picture made of small pieces of colored glass, stone, tile, wood, etc. 2. Anything that looks like a mosaic.

mu•sette (myoo-ZET) *noun.* A rather large bag to be carried over the shoulder for holding supplies.

mute (MYOOT) *adjective.* 1. Not speaking; silent: The prisoner was *mute* in front of his questioners. 2. Unable to speak: The *mute* boy learned sign language so he could communicate. **—noun.** 1. A person who is unable to talk. 2. A device used on a musical instrument to soften its tone. —*verb*. To soften (the sound or color of something). **muted, muting.** —**mutely** *adverb*.

nav•i•gate (NAV-ə-gayt) *verb*. 1. To plan the position and course of a craft, especially a ship or airplane. 2. To sail or travel on, over, or across. **navigated, navigating.**

non•com•bat•ant (nahn-kəm-BAT-ənt) *noun*. 1. Person in the armed forces who does not carry or use a weapon. 2. A person who is not fighting; having civilian status during wartime.

nov•el•ty (NOV-əl-tee) *noun*. 1. Newness: the *novelty* of moon landings. 2. Anything new, unusual, or strange: Travel was a *novelty* to me. 3. (Plural) Small, inexpensive toys, games, or trinkets. **novelties.**

ob•ject (əb-JEKT) *verb*. 1. (Usually followed by *to*) To dislike; disapprove: She *objects* to her friend's bad conduct. 2. To give as an argument or reason for not liking: We *object* that the bus is late. **objected, objecting.** —(OB-jikt or OB-jekt) *noun*. 1. A real thing; something one can touch and see. 2. A person or thing toward which one directs attention, action, or feeling. 3. Something aimed at; a purpose or goal: The *object* of the sport is to develop your body.

ob•ser•va•tion (ob-zər-VAY-shən) *noun*. 1. The act of seeing; the habit or power of noticing or observing: *observation* of the sky. 2. Being noticed or seen: The girl's tears escaped *observation*.

ob•vi•ous (OB-vee-əss) *adjective*. Clear; easy to notice or understand: *obvious* error. —**obviously** *adverb*.

oc•ca•sion•al (ə-KAY-zhən-l) *adjective*. Happening once in a while. —**occasionally** *adverb*.

oc•cur•rence (ə-KER-ənss) *noun*. 1. An event or happening; something that occurs. 2. The fact of existing or taking place.

of•fi•cial (ə-FISH-əl) *adjective*. 1. Related to an office or position of authority: *official* permission for a holiday. 2. Of an authorized or accepted type: our school's *official* song. —**officially** *adverb*.

op•press (ə-PRESS) *verb*. 1. To rule or put down unfairly. 2. To weigh heavily upon the emotions; depress: Tom was *oppressed* by his failure. **oppressed, oppressing.** —**oppression** (ə-PRESH-ən) *noun*.

out•land•ish (owt-LAN-dish) *adjective*. Ridiculous; strange or unusual; not familiar. —**outlandishly** *adverb*.

o•ver•shad•ow (oh-vər-SHAD-oh) *verb*. To be more significant or important than: The news of the explosion *overshadowed* other news. **overshadowed, overshadowing.**

par•al•lel (PA-rə-lel) *adjective*. 1. Equally distant from each other at all points: *Parallel* lines never cross. 2. Alike, very similar: The twins have led *parallel* lives.

pa•ral•y•sis (pə-RAL-ə-siss) *noun*. 1. The loss of ability to feel and move (a part of the body). 2. Stoppage or helplessness. —**paralyses** (pə-RAL-ə-seez) *plural*.

pa•thet•ic (pə-THET-ik) *adjective*. Moving, sad, pitiful. —**pathetically** *adverb*.

pa•tience (PAY-shənss) *noun*. 1. Perseverance, endurance. 2. Tolerance.

per•plex (pər-PLEKS) *verb*. To puzzle, mystify, confuse. **perplexed, perplexing. —per•plex•i•ty** (pər-PLEK-sə-tee) *noun*.

phe•nom•e•non (fə-NOM-ə-non) *noun*. 1. Any happening that can be detected by the senses and can be scientifically explained. 2. An extraordinary or unusual person, thing, or occurrence. **—phenomena** (fə-NOM-ə-nə) or **phenomenons** (for 2) *plural*.

phi•al (FIGH-əl) *noun*. (Also **vial**) A small narrow glass bottle used to hold liquids.

phys•i•cal (FIZ-i-kəl) *adjective*. 1. Having to do with the body: a *physical* examination. 2. Having to do with things that can be seen, heard, felt, tasted, or smelled: the *physical* world. 3. Natural, or having to do with natural sciences such as physics or biology: a *physical* law. **—physically** *adverb*.

phys•i•cist (FIZ-ə-sist) *noun*. An expert in the field of physics.

pi•az•za (pee-AZ-ə or pee-AHZ-ə) *noun*. 1. An open public square in an Italian city or town. 2. A long porch with columns along one or more sides.

piece•meal (PEESS-meel) *adverb*. 1. A little at a time; bit by bit; by degrees. 2. In pieces or fragments; apart. *—adjective*. Made or done piece by piece: a *piecemeal* job.

pin•ion (PIN-yən) *noun*. 1. The last joint of a bird's wing. 2. A wing. *—verb*. 1. To cut off or tie the pinions of (a bird) to prevent flying. 2. To bind the arms of; bind (to something). **pinioned, pinioning**.

pi•ous (PIGH-əss) *adjective*. Having or showing strong religious feelings.

plan•e•tar•i•um (plan-ə-TAIR-ee-əm) *noun*. 1. A projector that shows, on a domed ceiling, a representation of the heavenly bodies and their movements.

2. A building that contains such a projector. **—planetariums** or **planetaria** (plan-ə-TAIR-ee-ə) *plural*.

plunge (PLUHNJ) *verb*. 1. To dive or rush into: *plunge* into a pool. 2. To thrust or push something quickly into: The cook *plunged* the broccoli into boiling water. 3. To rush forward or downward: The car *plunged* down the steep hill when its brakes failed. **plunged, plunging**. *—noun*. A dive or sudden thrust forward or downward.

pneu•mo•nia (noo-MOHN-yə) *noun*. A disease that involves inflammation of the lungs.

poach•er (POHCH-ər) *noun*. One who hunts or fishes illegally.

pol•y•es•ter (pol-ee-ESS-tər) *noun*. Any of several synthetic resins used in various forms as fibers (as for cloth), adhesives, and plastics.

pome•gran•ate (POM-gran-it) *noun*. 1. An acidic seedy fruit with red pulp and tough rind. 2. The shrub or small tree on which this fruit grows.

port•age (POR-tij or por-TAHZH) *noun*. 1. The moving of a boat or goods overland from one body of water to another. 2. The route taken during such a move. *—verb*. To move a boat or goods in this way. **portaged, portaging**.

pov•er•ty (POV-ər-tee) *noun*. 1. The condition of being poor or in need. 2. A poor quality or small amount or degree: a *poverty* of ideas.

prac•ti•cal (PRAK-ti-kəl) *adjective*. 1. Able to be done or used successfully or without great difficulty. 2. Sensible; knowing what can be done: Jim is not a dreamer; he is very *practical*. 3. Related to actual practice rather than to theory or ideas.

prance (PRANSS) *verb*. 1. To move or spring about on the hind legs. 2. To move or strut in a lively manner. **pranced, prancing.**

prick•le (PRIK-əl) *noun*. 1. A sharp point or thorn. 2. A stinging or tingling feeling. —*verb*. To have a stinging or tingling feeling. **prickled, prickling.** —**prickly** *adjective*.

prim *adjective*. Overly proper or demure. **primmer, primmest.** —**primly** *adverb*.

prin•ci•ple (PRIN-sə-pəl) *noun*. 1. A basic rule or truth; a general law or thought from which others are developed: the *principles* of justice. 2. A rule that guides a person's conduct: His basic *principle* is to be good and kind.

priv•i•lege (PRIV-əl-ij) *noun*. A special right or favor; the right to do a certain thing. —*verb*. To give a special right to. **privileged, privileging.**

pro•fes•sion•al (prə-FESH-ən-l) *adjective*. 1. Referring to, connected with, engaged in, or appropriate for a profession: Telling a client's secrets is not a *professional* act. 2. Doing a particular thing to earn a living: a *professional* golfer. —*noun*. 1. One who earns his living through athletics. 2. One who earns his living at a profession: Doctors are *professionals*. 3. One who is very good or expert in his field. —**professionally** *adverb*.

proj•ect (PROJ-ekt) *noun*. An undertaking or plan: I finished my science *project*. —**pro•ject** (prə-JEKT) *verb*. 1. To point outward; to stick out: The cat's tail *projects* behind her. 2. To plan; foretell or foresee: He *projects* a big increase in the size of our city. 3. To cause to appear on: *project* a filmstrip on a screen. **projected, projecting.**

pro•long (prə-LAWNG) *verb*. To make longer than usual; drag or stretch out: Arguments with the umpire *prolong* the game. **prolonged, prolonging.** —**prolongation** (prə-lawn-GAY-shən) *noun*.

prop•er (PROP-ər) *adjective*. 1. Suitable; appropriate: the *proper* tool. 2. Polite, mannerly, formal. 3. Moral or modest: *proper* behavior. —**properly** *adverb*.

proph•et (PROF-it) *noun*. 1. One who foretells the future, or tries to do so; one who makes predictions. 2. One who speaks or acts as if inspired by God: Moses was a *prophet*. —**pro•phetic** (prə-FET-ik) Also **prophetical** *adjective*. —**prophetically** *adverb*.

pro•por•tion (prə-POR-shən) *noun*. 1. The relation of one person, place, or thing to another as to size, extent, amount, or importance; ratio: The *proportion* of clear days to rainy days in June was three to one. 2. Correct relation: In Harry's drawing the arms and legs are not in *proportion*. 3. Amount or number in relation to the whole: The *proportion* of correct answers was high. —*verb*. To adjust (related things) to make a relationship correct or proper: *Proportion* Ruth's pay to the work she has completed. **proportioned, proportioning.** —**proportional** *adjective*. —**proportionally** *adverb*.

pro•te•in (PROH-teen or PROH-tee-in) *noun*. An organic substance that contains nitrogen and is needed for cell growth in animals and plants: Meat, cheese, eggs, and peas are foods that contain *protein*.

pro•test (prə-TEST, proh-TEST, or PROH-test) *verb*. 1. To oppose or resist with strong statements; to object. 2. To state strongly; declare: The man *protested* his innocence. **protested, protesting.** —(PROH-test) *noun*. An objection; demonstration to express disapproval or opposition: the parents' *protest*.

pro•trude (proh-TROOD) *verb.* To jut or stick out; project: The turtle's head *protruded* from its shell. **protruded, protruding. —protrusion** (proh-TROO-zhən) *noun.*

purse (PERSS) *noun.* 1. A small case or bag for holding money. 2. A woman's pocketbook. —*verb.* To draw together: *purse* one's lips. **pursed, pursing.**

re•buke (ri-BYOOK) *verb.* To scold or reprimand. **rebuked, rebuking.** —*noun.* A scolding or reprimand.

re•claim (ri-KLAYM) *verb.* 1. To turn (wasteland) into an area that can be cultivated. 2. To make (new products) from discards.

re•count *verb.* 1. (REE-KOWNT) To count again. 2. (ri-KOWNT) To give an account of; tell in some detail: He *recounted* what happened on the way to school. **recounted, recounting.** —*noun.* (REE-kownt) A second counting.

re•cruit (ri-KROOT) *noun.* A new member of any group, especially the armed forces. —*verb.* To get new people to join; hire; enlist: The Army needs to *recruit* more nurses. **recruited, recruiting.**

re•frain (ri-FRAYN) *verb.* To keep one-self (from doing): I could not *refrain* from telling the story. **refrained, refraining.**

re•gal (REE-gəl) *adjective.* Referring to or like a king. —**regally** *adverb.*

re•hash (ree-HASH) *verb.* To deal with again; work up (old material) in a new or different form: The question has been *rehashed* over and over again. **rehashed, rehashing.** (REE-hash) *noun.* A rehashing; a putting something old into a new form: His story was just a *rehash* of a report we heard last year. **rehashes.**

re•late (ri-LAYT) *verb.* 1. To tell: *relate* a story. 2. To associate or connect two or more things or people: *relate* smoke with fire. **related, relating.** —**related** *adjective.*

rem•e•dy (REM-ə-dee) *noun.* A cure; medicine or treatment offering relief: Swallowing water is sometimes a *remedy* for hiccups. **remedies.** —*verb.* To cure; correct. **remedied, remedying.**

re•mote (ri-MOHT) *adjective.* Far off in time or place; distant. **remoter; remotest.** —**remotely** *adverb.*

re•pose (ri-POHZ) *noun.* 1. A rest, sleep, or period of relaxation. 2. Calm; peace of mind. —*verb.* 1. To lie at rest. 2. To be supported (in or on something). **reposed, reposing.**

re•sent (ri-ZENT) *verb.* To feel indignation and anger about: Bill *resents* having to dress up for company. **resented, resenting.**

re•sign (ri-ZIGHN) *verb.* 1. To quit; give up one's job or position. 2. To make (oneself) accept: Toni was *resigned* to wearing braces. **resigned, resigning.** —**resignation** (rez-ig-NAY- shən) *noun.*

res•o•lute (REZ-ə-loot) *adjective.* Having a firm purpose; determined. —**resolutely** *adverb.*

res•ur•rec•tion (rez-ə-REK-shən) *noun.* 1. A bringing back to life. 2. A bringing back for a new use. 3. [Capital R] The return to life of Jesus Christ after His death on the cross.

re•triev•er (ri-TREE-vər) *noun.* Any of many breeds of dogs trained to retrieve game.

rev•er•ie (REV-ər-ee) *noun.* A state of pleasant daydreaming.

rift *noun.* 1. A break (in friendship): The argument created a *rift* between the two girls. 2. (Geology) A break in the surface of the earth.

rouse (ROWZ) *verb.* 1. To make excited; arouse: The speaker's accusations *roused* the crowd to anger. 2. To wake up; make active: The alarm clock *roused* me. **roused, rousing.**

rut (RUHT) *noun.* 1. A groove or track, like one made in the ground by a wheel: The wagon left *ruts* in the mud. 2. A regular or routine way of doing or acting, often dull: The old professor is in a *rut;* he teaches the same way year after year. —*verb.* To make grooves or slots in. **rutted, rutting.**

sa•rong (sə-RONG) *noun.* A rectangular piece of cloth, usually of brightly colored material, worn as a skirt by men and women in the East Indies.

saun•ter (SAWN-tər) *verb.* To walk slowly and easily. **sauntered, sauntering.** —*noun.* A slow, easy walk.

scheme (SKEEM) *noun.* 1. A plan of action involving slyness or trickery; a clever plot. 2. An impractical plan or project: wild *schemes* for making money.

sci•en•tif•ic (sigh-ən-TIF-ik) *adjective.* 1. Relating to science: Bill enjoys *scientific* hobbies such as chemistry. 2. Meeting the standards or tests of science: Astronomers say that astrology is not *scientific.* **—scientifically** *adverb.*

scorn (SKORN) *verb.* To look upon with contempt as low and unworthy. **scorned, scorning.** —*noun.* 1. Contempt; disdain. 2. An object of scorn: Benedict Arnold became the *scorn* of all patriots. **—scornful** *adjective.* **—scornfully** *adverb.*

scowl (SKOWL) *verb.* To frown; make an angry or mean look. **scowled, scowling.** —*noun.* An angry or mean look; a frown.

scram•ble (SKRAM-bəl) *verb.* 1. To move quickly by running, crawling, or climbing. 2. To mix together (as eggs) for cooking. 3. To destroy the orderly arrangement of. **scrambled, scrambling.**

scull (SKUHL) *noun.* 1. An oar, especially one moved back and forth at the rear of a boat to move it forward. 2. A light, slender rowboat used for racing. —*verb.* To move a boat forward by a scull or sculls. **sculled, sculling.**

scur•ry (SKER-ee) *verb.* To move quickly; to hurry: The insect *scurried* over the picnic table. **scurried, scurrying.** —*noun.* Hasty movement: We watched the *scurry* of the squirrels when the dog approached.

scur•vy (SKER-vee) *noun.* A disease, brought on by a lack of vitamin C, that causes weakness, bleeding gums, and blemishes on the skin.

se•cure (si-KYUR) *adjective.* 1. Safe; free from doubt or fear. 2. Strong, sturdy: The bridge seems *secure.* 3. Fastened tightly: The barn door is *secure.* —*verb.* 1. To tie down; lock, fasten, or otherwise protect from danger. 2. To get: I wish to *secure* a copy of today's paper. **secured, securing.** **—securely** *adverb.*

seethe (SEETH) *verb.* 1. To boil or have the appearance of boiling. 2. To be very angry or excited. **seethed, seething.**

sem•a•phore (SEM-ə-for) *noun.* A signal system or device using flags, lights, or arms in various positions to send messages.

sen•si•tive (SEN-sə-tiv) *adjective.* 1. Capable of intense feeling; tenderhearted; very aware: Poets are usually *sensitive* people. 2. Easily affected by something: Her throat was *sensitive* to smoke. 3. Easily hurt; touchy: *a sensitive* child. **—sensitively** *adverb.* **—sensitivity** (sen-sə-TIV-ə-tee) *noun.*

sep•a•rate (SEP-ə-rayt) *verb.* 1. To divide by placing a barrier between; be the barrier between. 2. To sort into different groups: Mother *separated* the laundry into five piles. 3. To part; no longer be together. **separated, separating.** —(SEP-ə-rit) *adjective.* 1. Unconnected; not shared; divided. 2. Single; individual. **—separately** *adverb.* **—separation** (sep-ə-RAY-shən) *noun.*

se•rene (si-REEN) *adjective.* 1. Calm; quiet; peaceful. 2. Bright; clear: *serene* as a cloudless sky. **—serenely** *adverb.*

shaft *noun.* 1. A long, thin object or part of an object, such as the handle of a rake. 2. The narrow opening to an underground tunnel or mine. 3. The part of a machine that carries power from one part to another: a drive *shaft.*

shal•low (SHAL-oh) *adjective.* 1. Not deep. 2. Not deep or careful (in thought): *"Shallow* men believe in luck."* (Emerson). **shallower, shallowest.** *—noun.* (Often plural) The shallow part of a body of water: We waded in the *shallows.*

sheen *noun.* Brightness or shininess: New silver coins have a *sheen.*

shin•gle (SHING-gəl) *noun.* 1. A thin piece of wood, asbestos, or slate: *Shingles* are put on in overlapping rows. 2. (Slang) A small signboard outside the office of a doctor, dentist, etc. *—verb.* To put on shingles. **shingled, shingling.**

shirk (SHERK) *verb.* To avoid or leave undone. **shirked, shirking.**

shuf•fle (SHUHF-əl) *verb.* 1. To drag or slide the feet when walking; scuffle. 2. To rearrange the order of, as in mixing cards together. **shuffled, shuffling.** *—noun.* 1. A walk or gait in which the feet drag or slide. 2. A mixing together, as of parts of a game.

sid•ing (SIGH-ding) *noun.* A short section of railroad track, connected by switches to the main track and used for temporary storage of railroad cars.

sig•ni•fy (SIG-nə-figh) *verb.* 1. To mean: What can this sudden darkness *signify?* 2. To make known; express: He *signified* his agreement with a nod. **signified, signifying.**

sin•ew•y (SIN-yoo-ee) *adjective.* Strong, muscular.

sin•gle-hand•ed (sing-gəl-HAN-did) *adjective.* Unassisted; done by one person only. **—single-handedly** *adverb.*

size (SIGHZ) *noun.* 1. The measure, dimensions or bulk (of something): the *size* of a room. 2. Relative dimensions of, as of clothing. *—verb.* 1. To make or arrange by size: The manufacturer *sizes* his dresses with even numbers. 2. To cut or trim to order. **sized, sizing.**

slight *adjective.* 1. Small; little: a *slight* fever. 2. Not very important: The book was of *slight* value. **slighter, slightest.** *—verb.* To snub; be mean to. **slighted, slighting.** *—noun.* A snub. **—slightly** *adverb.*

slosh *verb.* To move or splash (in), as in a liquid: The clothes *slosh* around in the washing machine. **sloshed, sloshing.**

slouch (SLOWCH) *noun.* 1. A stooping or sagging posture. 2. A lazy or incompetent person. **slouches.** *—verb.* To walk, stand, or sit in a stooping way. **slouched, slouching.**

sol•emn (SOL-əm) *adjective.* 1. Very serious: a *solemn* expression on his face. 2. Formal; performed with dignity: a *solemn* procession of graduates. **—solemnly** *adverb.*

sol•id (SOL-id) *adjective*. 1. Firm; hard: Some melons were *solid*, but others were soft. 2. Not hollow. 3. Well-built; without flaws: The shaky old shed was not very *solid*. —*noun*. 1. Something in a solid, rather than a gaseous or liquid, state: Ice is a *solid*. 2. A figure having height, width, and length. **—solidly** *adverb*.

son•net (SON-it) *noun*. A rhymed poem of 14 lines.

spasm (SPAZ-əm) *noun*. A sudden tightening of a muscle or muscles.

spec•i•fi•ca•tion (spess-ə-fi-KAY-shən) *noun*. 1. The act of stating exactly. 2. (Usually plural) A plan that includes details such as measurements and materials: He showed us the *specifications* for his new boat.

spec•i•men (SPESS-ə-mən) *noun*. A sample; an example of a particular thing: butterfly *specimens*.

spir•i•tu•al (SPIHR-i-choo-əl) *adjective*. 1. Referring to the spirit rather than the body or material objects. 2. Holy; concerned with religion. —*noun*. A religious song of black Americans. **—spiritually** *adverb*.

squad (SKWOD) *noun*. 1. A small group of soldiers organized to drill and fight as a unit. 2. A small group organized for some kind of activity: the clean-up *squad*.

squad•ron (SKWOD-rən) *noun*. A group of airplanes, naval ships, or soldiers that operates as a unit.

stalk (STAWK) *verb*. 1. To pursue in a quiet or stealthy manner: The hunters *stalked* the leopard for hours. 2. To walk in an angry or proud manner. **stalked, stalking.**

staunch (STAWNCH or STAHNCH) *adjective*. Loyal; true; firm: a *staunch* friend. **—staunchly** *adverb*.

stiff (STIF) *adjective*. 1. Not easy to bend or move; *stiff* cardboard. 2. Forceful, strong: a *stiff* wind. 3. Hard, difficult, severe: a *stiff* test. 4. Formal or awkward. **stiffer, stiffest. —stiffly** *adverb*.

stop•o•ver (STOP-oh-vər) *noun*. A resting or stopping place on a journey.

stow (STOH) *verb*. To pack or arrange: Bob *stowed* his baseball equipment in the closet. **stowed, stowing.**

stride (STRIGHD) *verb*. To walk or run with long steps. **strode, striding.** —*noun*. 1. A long step; the distance covered in one step. 2. Progress: Science has made great *strides*.

stroll (STROHL) *verb*. To walk slowly. **strolled, strolling.** —*noun*. A slow walk.

strut (STRUHT) *verb*. To walk in a proud way, as if showing off. **strutted, strutting.** —*noun*. 1. A showy way of walking. 2. A piece of supporting framework: *Struts* brace the wings of a light airplane.

stud (STUHD) *noun*. 1. An upright timber that forms part of the framework of a building. 2. A removable clothing button or fastener, often used for decoration. 3. A nail or tack with a head that extends above the surface of the material. —*verb*. To decorate or cover as with studs. **studded, studding.**

stump (STUHMP) *noun*. 1. The part of a tree trunk left standing after the upper part has been cut off. 2. The remaining part of anything. —*verb*. To walk with heavy, clumsy steps. **stumped, stumping.**

sub•due (səb-DOO or səb-DYOO) *verb*. 1. To conquer or overcome. 2. To soften; lower the tone of. **subdued, subduing.**

sun•spot (SUHN-spot) *noun*. Any of the dark spots often seen on the sun when it is viewed through a telescope equipped with a dense filter: *Sunspots are produced by magnetic disturbances in the sun.*

sur•face (SER-fəss) *noun*. 1. The outer layer; the part that is seen: the *surface* of a lake. 2. The appearance rather than the true nature: On the *surface*, the family seemed happy. —*verb*. To come to the top: The submarine *surfaced* near the shore. **surfaced, surfacing.**

sur•plus (SER-pləss) *adjective*. Excess, more than needed or used. —*noun*. An amount left over. **surpluses.**

sur•vey•or (sər-VAY-ər) *noun*. One who looks over the land carefully.

sus•pend (səss-PEND) *verb*. 1. To hang down: The lamp was *suspended* from the ceiling. 2. To bar temporarily from a school, office, or position, as a form of punishment. 3. To stop for a time; delay or postpone: Work was *suspended* because of the storm. **suspended, suspending.**

swi•vel (SWIV-l) *noun*. 1. A fastening that allows the thing fastened to turn round freely upon it. 2. A chain link having two parts, one of which turns freely in the other. 3. Support on which a chair, gun, etc., can turn round. —*verb*. To turn on a swivel. **swiveled** or **swivelled, swiveling** or **swivelling.**

sym•pa•thet•ic (sim-pə-THET-ik) *adjective*. 1. Having or showing sympathy or kindness for others: a *sympathetic* smile. 2. Favorable; approving: The principal is *sympathetic* toward our project. **—sympathetically** *adverb*.

tank•ard (TANG-kərd) *noun*. A large, mug-like cup with a handle and (sometimes) a hinged lid.

tense (TENSS) *adjective*. 1. Tight; taut. 2. Under strain; nervous. 3. Causing or showing strain or worry: a *tense* discussion. **tenser, tensest.** —*verb*. To make tight or tense. **tensed, tensing.**

ter•ri•fy (TEHR-ə-figh) *verb*. To fill with terror; cause to have extreme fear. **terrified, terrifying.**

teth•er (TETH-ər) *noun*. A rope that is tied to an animal to limit the range of its movements. —*verb*. To tie with a rope. **tethered, tethering.**

thread (THRED) *noun*. 1. A thin string of cotton or other fiber. 2. Anything thin or fine like thread: the *threads* of a spider's web. —*verb*. 1. To put thread through the eye of (a needle). 2. To move carefully, as through a crowd, a series of obstacles, or dangers: The boat *threaded* its way between the coral reefs. **threaded, threading.**

thresh•old (THRESH-ohld) *noun*. 1. A doorsill. 2. The beginning: the *threshold* of adventure.

thumb (THUHM) *noun*. The short, thick first digit of the hand. —*verb*. Turn pages of (a book, etc.) rapidly, reading only portions. **thumbed, thumbing.**

thun•der•struck (THUHN-dər-struhk) *adjective*. Stunned with amazement, as if startled by thunder; shocked.

thyme (TIGHM) *noun*. A small plant of the mint family, with fragrant leaves used for seasoning.

tim•id (TIM-id) *adjective*. Without confidence or courage; shy; fearful. **—timidly** *adverb*. **—timidity** (ti-MID-ə-tee) *noun*.

tol•er•ance (TOL-ər-ənss) *noun*. 1. The ability to be fair to those whose views, customs, or actions are different from one's own. 2. (Medicine) The natural or acquired ability to resist the effect of (an element, as a drug).

tor•men•tor (TOR-ment-ər) *noun*. One who torments, causes great suffering of the mind or body.

tra•di•tion (trə-DISH-ən) *noun*. 1. The handing down, usually by word of mouth and example, of beliefs, customs, and opinions, from one generation to the next. 2. A principle or standard used as a guide, or a body of such principles and standards: Our country has a *tradition* of equality for all people. **—traditional** *adjective*. **—traditionally** *adverb*.

trans•con•ti•nen•tal (transs-kon-tə-NEN-tl) *adjective*. Crossing or going from one side of a continent to the other.

tran•som (TRAN-səm) *noun*. A narrow hinged window above another window or a door.

treach•er•ous (TRECH-ər-əss) *adjective*. 1. Not faithful or loyal; not trustworthy. 2. Not reliable; looking safe when it is not: Thin ice can be *treacherous*. **—treacherously** *adverb*.

tren•cher (TRENCH-ər) *noun*. A wooden food dish.

trop•ic (TROP-ik) *noun*. 1. Either of two imaginary lines, the Tropic of Cancer and the Tropic of Capricorn, that circle the globe north and south of the equator. 2. [Often Capital T] (Plural) The very warm area between the Tropic of Cancer and the Tropic of Capricorn. **—tropical** *adjective*.

trough (TRAWF or TROF) *noun*. 1. A long, narrow container in which water or food for animals is placed. 2. A long, narrow space or hollow, as between ridges or waves.

tru•ant (TROO-ənt) *noun*. 1. A student who is absent from school without permission. 2. A person who avoids his work. **—adjective**. Purposely absent; idle. **—truancy** (TROO-ən-see) *noun*.

tu•tor (TOO-tər or TYOO-tər) *verb*. To teach or coach privately. **tutored, tutoring. —noun**. A private teacher.

twit•ter (TWIT-ər) *verb*. 1. To utter a series of quick, light sounds, as those of a bird; chirp. 2. To flutter or tremble excitedly. **twittered, twittering. —noun**. 1. A chirping noise: the *twitter* of swallows. 2. A state of trembling excitement. 3. High-pitched, light laughter or talk.

typ•i•cal (TIP-i-kəl) *adjective*. Characteristic of a certain group or class; of a certain type: Dick is a *typical* athlete; he is strong and competitive. **—typically** *adverb*.

un•a•bashed (uhn-ə-BASHT) *adjective*. Not embarrassed, ashamed, or awed. **—unabashedly** *adverb*.

un•ac•count•a•ble (uhn-ə-KOWN-tə-bəl) *adjective*. 1. Without explanation; mysterious. 2. Not at fault or responsible. **—unaccountably** *adverb*.

un•con•tam•i•nat•ed (uhn-kon-TAM-ə-nayt-əd) *adjective*. Still pure or clean; free from stain, pollution, infection.

un•der•pin•ning (UHN-dər-pin-ing) *noun*. A support, prop.

un•ex•pect•ed (uhn-ik-SPEK-tid) *adjective*. Surprising; arriving or happening without warning: *unexpected* visitors. **—unexpectedly** *adverb*.

un•ion (YOON-yən) *noun*. 1. The joining together of two or more things or groups. 2. The result of such joining: a *union* of states. 3. A group of countries joined under one government: the *Union* of South Africa.

537

u•nique (yoo-NEEK) *adjective.* 1. Unlike any other. 2. Having no equal. —**uniquely** *adverb.*

un•quench•a•ble (uhn-KWEN-chə-bəl) *adjective.* Not able to be filled up or satisfied: His desire for more land was *unquenchable.*

up•surge (UHP-serj) *noun.* A rising upward; rise; upturn. —*verb.* To surge upward. **upsurged, upsurging.**

ut•ter (UHT-ər) *verb.* To say; announce; express: "A thought is often original, though you have *uttered* it a hundred times." (Oliver Wendell Holmes). **uttered, uttering.**—*adjective.* Complete; absolute. —**utterly** *adverb.* —**utterance** (UHT-ər-ənss) *noun.*

val•iant (VAL-yənt) *adjective.* Brave; heroic. —**valiantly** *adverb.*

vault (VAWLT) *verb.* To jump (over), especially with the help of one's hands or a pole: He *vaulted* over the counter. **vaulted, vaulting.** —*noun.* A vigorous jump: The cat reached the wall with one *vault.*

vex•a•tious (veks-AY-shəs) *adjective.* Annoying, bothersome.

vi•cious (VISH-əss) *adjective.* 1. Cruel, mean, evil: a *vicious* crime. 2. Savage: a *vicious* dog. 3. (Informal). Terrible, awful: *vicious* weather. —**viciously** *adverb.* —**viciousness** (VISH-əss-nəss) *noun.*

vic•to•ri•ous (vik-TOR-ee-əss) *adjective.* 1. Winning, conquering: the *victorious* team. 2. Indicating victory or conquest: a *victorious* smile. —**victoriously** *adverb.*

vis•i•bil•i•ty (viz-ə-BIL-ə-tee) *noun.* 1. The condition of being visible or able to be seen. 2. Possibility of seeing: *Visibility* in the morning fog was very poor. 3. The distance that a person is able to see clearly: *Visibility* is more

than 20 miles on a clear day. **visibilities.**

vis•u•al•ize (VIZH-oo-əl-ighz) *verb.* To make a mental picture of; imagine. **visualized, visualizing.**

viv•id (VIV-id) *adjective.* 1. Bright; intense: The noon sky was a *vivid* blue. 2. Clear and lively: The story gave a *vivid* description of the race. —**vividly** *adverb.* —**vividness** (VIV-id-nəss) *noun.*

vol•ume (VOL-yoom or VOL-yəm) *noun.* 1. Capacity or amount of room or space: The *volume* of this bottle is one quart. 2. Any book, but particularly one of a set: *volume* II of an encyclopedia.

wake (WAYK) *verb.* 1. (Often used with *up*) To bring or come to consciousness or awareness, as from sleep; to awaken. 2. To excite or arouse. 3. (Often used with *to*) To bring to one's attention or awareness: The accident *woke* them to the danger. **woke, waked,** or **woken; waking.** —*noun.* 1. A stream of white foamy water left behind a boat or other thing moving through water. 2. Any visible or obvious effect, track, or trail left by something that has passed by.

wash•out (WOSH-owt) *noun.* 1. The wearing away or erosion of something by water, as a road by heavy rains. 2. A hole or ditch left by a wearing away with water. 3. (Informal) A failure.

wean (WEEN) *verb.* 1. To accustom (an infant) to food other than mother's milk. 2. To make (a person) give up an activity or situation. **weaned, weaning.**

wea•sel (WEEZ-l) *noun.* A small, slender mammal with short legs and a long tail.

538

weld *verb.* 1. To join metal items by applying enough heat to make them soft enough to melt or be hammered together. 2. To join. **welded, welding.** —*noun.* 1. The act of welding. 2. The spot where metal parts have been welded.

whet (HWET) *verb.* 1. To make sharp or give a cutting edge to: *whet* a knife. 2. To make stronger or more eager: The smell of dinner cooking *whetted* his appetite. **whetted, whetting.**

whir *also* **whirr** (HWER) *verb.* 1. To make a low purring sound, as of a machine operating smoothly. 2. To move with such a sound. **whirred, whirring.** —*noun.* A low, purring or vibrating sound.

wid•ow (WID-oh) *noun.* A woman whose husband is dead and who has not married again. —*verb.* To cause (someone) to become a widow. **widowed, widowing.**

wing•span (WING-span) *noun.* The distance from the tips of outstretched wings of birds, aircraft, and other winged flying things.

wit *noun.* 1. (Often plural) Knowledge; ability; intelligence: Jack used his *wits* in the emergency. 2. A sense of humor: Frank has a sharp *wit.*

won•der (WUHN-dər) *noun.* 1. A feeling of surprise, fear, and admiration: Pam looked with *wonder* at the giant balloons. 2. Something that causes such a feeling. 3. A feeling of confusion or doubt. —*verb.* 1. To have a feeling of surprise, fear, and admiration. 2. To be curious, confused, or doubtful. **wondered, wondering.**

would-be (WUD-bee) *adjective.* Desiring or professing to be: The creative writing class was full of *would-be* writers.

yield (YEELD) *verb.* To produce or provide; give. **yielded, yielding.** —*noun.* An amount that is yielded or produced: the *yield* of apples from a tree.